והגית בו יומם ולילה...

PRESENTED TO

"CAUGHT BEING GOOD - 1997"

JEWISH EDUCATIONAL CENTER
ELIZABETH, NEW JERSEY

A Midrash and a Maaseh

A Midrash and a Maaseh

An anthology of insights and
commentaries on the weekly Torah reading,
including hundreds of old favorites
and new stories

by

HANOCH TELLER

New York City Publishing Company

Rechov Yehoyariv 4, Arzei Habira, Jerusalem 97354, Israel.
hanoch@ibm.net email

Edited by Marsi Tabak

12 11 10 9 8 7 6 5 4 3 2

Library of Congress Cataloging-in-Publication Data

Teller, Hanoch.
A Midrash and a maaseh / Hanoch Teller
p. cm.
Includes bibliographical references
ISBN 1-881939-08-1 (HC : v. 1).
1. Bible. O.T. Pentateuch--Commentaries. 2. Midrash
3. Exempla, Jewish. I. Title.
BS1225.3.T45 1996
296. 1'9--dc20

96–32620
CIP

Distributed by

FELDHEIM PUBLISHERS
200 Airport Executive Park
Nanuet, NY 10954
FELDHEIM PUBLISHERS
POB 35002, Jerusalem, ISRAEL

J. LEHMANN
Hebrew Booksellers
20 Cambridge Terrace
Gateshead
Tyne & Wear

In loving memory of
a true woman of valor

Lorraine Susan
ליבה שרה בת משה ע"ה

Her beautiful soul radiated warmth
and love to family and friends alike.

Her brief, but inspiring life was a
treasure that we will always cherish.

ת.נ.צ.ב.ה.

IDA ZABLOTSKY
CHARLES AND LILY ZABLOTSKY
TED AND VIVIAN ZABLOTSKY

Also by Hanoch Teller

Once Upon a Soul
Soul Survivors
'Souled!'
The Steipler Gaon
Sunset
Courtrooms of the Mind
Above the Bottom Line
Pichifkes
The Bostoner
Bridges of Steel, Ladders of Gold
"Hey, Taxi!"
The Best of StoryLines
Give Peace a Stance
Welcome to the Real World
13 Years
A Matter of Principal
And from Jerusalem, His Word
О ТОМ, ЧТО НА ДУШЕ
ועמך כולם...

APPROBATION FROM HAGAON HARAV CHAIM KAMIL SHLITA

בס"ד

יום ד' ט' תמוז התשנ"ו

כבוד ידידי רב פעלים לתורה

ולמוסר ולחסד הר"ר חנוך טלר נ"י

שמחתי מאד בהוצאת ספרך לאור

ואכן נאים הדברים היוצאים

מפי עושיהם, ובודאי ומכרי

הנאמנים. שכל חייך הם שרשרת

אחת של הפצת תורה ומעשי

חסד. כה יתן ה' וכה

יוסיף שתגבר חילים

בהפצת תורה ומעשי חסד

בעתירה ובהוקרה

חיים הכהן קמיל

APPROBATION FROM
HAGAON HARAV ELIEZER GINSBURG SHLITA

HARAV ELIEZER GINSBURG — הרב אליעזר גינזבורג

מרא דאתרא, אגודת ישראל סניף זכרון שמואל

ראש חדש תמוז שנת תשנ"ו

לאות הוקרה והכרה לידי"נ אוהבי הנעלה, ה"ה הרב חנוך יונתן טלר שליט"א, שזכה וזיכה את הרבים לעורר ולהלהיב לבבות של אחינו בני ישראל, ולהדליק הנר אלוקים נשמת אדם ע"י חיבוריו הרבים של סיפורים נפלאים, ע"י סגנונו המיוחד נחמד ונעים ומופלא מאוד.

דאמת דברים המפורסמים אינם צריכים לראיה, וחיבוריו הקודמים מלאים תועלות לאלו המבקשים לעלות ממדרגה למדרגה באמונה ובטחון ואהבת השי"ת וטוהר המדות. הרבה שתו ממימיו המתוקים ונהנו ונתעלו.

ועכשיו נתעורר להוציא לאור עולם חיבור על פרשיות התורה ולהעלות מטמוניות של יראת שמים ואהבת התורה ושאר מעלות העליונות הנמצאות טמונות בתוך הפסוקים והמדרשים של הפרשיות. "כמה גדולים מעשי חנוך", שזכה להתעוררות זו, שרבים צריכים לו, ועד כמה תועלת גדולה תצא לאור עולם ע"י ספר זה שוודאי יהא מקובל ומרוצה לכל אלו שיבוא לידם לקרוא וללמוד בו.

הנני מברכו מעומקא דליבא שיצליח בכל ענין לקרב הלבבות לכל אלו מעלות עליונות, ולהרים קרן התורה והיראה, שזהו באמת העיקר המבוקש של האדם באמונה. לראות בנין בני אבותינו אברהם יצחק ויעקב, עולים ממדרגה למדרגה על הסולם המוצב ארצה וראשו מגיע השמימה.

הכותב דורש׳ בכבוד וידידות

אליעזר גינזבורג

1478 East 9th Street • Brooklyn, N.Y. 11230 • (718) 645-4698

APPROBATION FROM
HAGAON HARAV Y. YAAKOV LICHTENSTEIN SHLITA

בי"ד דק"ק חברת בני ישראל, לונדון

Beth Din
OF THE FEDERATION OF SYNAGOGUES

ב"ה

65 Watford Way London NW4 3AQ Tel: 081-202 2263 Fax: 081-203 0610

RABBI Y. Y. LICHTENSTEIN
Rosh Beth Din

הרב ישראל יעקב ליכטנשטיין
ראב"ד

י' בתמוז תשנ"ו

לכב' ידידי הנעלה הנכבד והמפורסם הרב חנוך יונתן טלר שליט"א
מחבר הרבה ספרים שעוסקים בקירוב אחב"י לתורה ולי"ש

אחדשה"ט

שמחתי לראות שאתה עומד להוציא לאור ספר חדש באנגלית על פרשת השבוע מתובל בפנינים ממרביצי תורה ומוסר. כבר יצאו לך מוניטין בהרצאותיך ובספריך הקודמים שעסקו בעיקר בסיפורי מעשיות ומטרתם להשתיל בלבם של הקוראים התעוררות לי"ש ולתיקון המידות ונתקבלו ספריך באהדה בהציבור של בני תורה.

ראיתי שספרך החדש שונה מקודמיו בסגנונו אבל מהמעט שהצצתי בו התרשמתי שקלעת לאותה מטרה.

והנה כבר קבלת הסכמות על ספריך מגדולי התורה ולמותר מכתבי, וכן באתי לברך ולעודד אותך שתמשיך בעבודת הקודש לזכות הרבים ולקרב לבבם לתורה ולי"ש.

הכו"ח בברכת התורה

ידידך

ישראל יעקב ליכטנשטיין

Contents

Preface

As always it is my pleasure to acknowledge those who have helped the book and its author: Marsi Tabak was and remains the most dominant influence on my writing. This year we are celebrating the "bar mitzvah" of our association, of which each one of us claims to be the greater beneficiary.

Sections of this book were typed by Nechy Perry, Hannah Hartman and Barbara Wolfson. Lawrence Burian provided an invaluable service in expediting the preparation of the material. Sarah Scheller and the highly-talented and devoted Shlomo Krasnostein produced the book's attractive cover; Rabbi Aaron Lopiansky reviewed the manuscript.

It is an honor to have this, as my previous books, distributed by Feldheim Publishers, about whom it has been said, "When it comes to Torah literature, they wrote the book." Yaakov and Yitzchak Feldheim have always been especially gracious and cooperative in every aspect of my books' distribution.

If I were to thank 300 people for their kindness and assistance over the years, it would be neither an exaggeration nor inappropriate. I concede, however, that it might be a bit taxing for the reader. I shall therefore limit myself this time to the following individuals who have "been there" non-stop, always ready to extend a helping hand: my dear parents; the entire Paskesz family; Dr. and Mrs. Eli Eilenberg, Rabbi and Mrs. Shalom Seigfried. Special thanks to Rabbi and Mrs. Chaim Wakslak, Kalman and Ruki Renov and Mo and Linda Garson. My encounter with Craig Brod and Janet Weil was a Providential blessing.

Fortunate am I that Benjie Brecher and Rabbi Mutty Grunberg never know when to stop. The same can be said for Terry Augenbraun and Bennet Kaplan, whose humility almost succeeds in disguising the lengths they will travel to help out someone in need (like myself). Debbie Loebenberg and Nathali Ashkenazy are valorous women and none but

Shlomo *Hamelech* could do justice to enumerating their myriad saintly attributes.

I am gratified to have this opportunity to offer accolades to three of the most esteemed educators in America: Rabbi Yosef Willner, Mr. Isaac Fink and Rebbetzin Dubby Groner.

There are two components to Midrash: Halachah and *Aggadata*. The lion's share of this work deals with *midrash aggadata,* a subject with which I am more than familiar as the husband of Aidel Teller. Even those who have actually met her believe that she must be allegorical. I happily affirm that all of the incredible stories describing her boundless virtues are true.

Hanoch Teller

Erev Tisha b'Av, 5756
Jerusalem, May It Be Speedily Rebuilt

Introduction

As a rule, I have devoted my Introductions to a statement of mission and justification for the project. In the beginning of this humble career, I engaged in detailed excursus regarding the value of storytelling as a powerful medium for conveying an everlasting message. As time and titles progressed, my books became thematic, at which point the Introduction was devoted to justifying the choice of topic (or at least the need for a collection of stories on the subject).

But what need, pray tell, is there to justify writing about *parashas hashavua* and insights of *gedolei Yisrael* on the Midrash? Is there anyone who requires convincing regarding the importance of such an undertaking?

A profound insight of our venerated Sages, followed by a contemporary story that illustrates and emphasizes the point, is a formula that has withstood the test of time. Whether in the shtetls of Eastern Europe, or the *kuttab*s and *mellah*s of Northern Africa; the soaring, cathedral-like synagogues of Antwerp, or the tiny *shtiblach* of Williamsburg; the forests of Meziboz, or by the waters of Babylon. It is to that sublime genre that the title of this work refers.

As it is said, *"Lo hamidrash ha'ikar, elah hama'aseh"* (*Avos* 1:17) — brilliantly accomplished deeds are even more essential than brilliantly derived insights. Experience has corroborated an additional interpretation of this: Learning is the very essence, but it will be best remembered through a story. The following, I believe, will prove my point.

A warm kernel of happiness nestled in the center of Josh Silverman's being. Newly observant, he was deeply immersed in his studies at a Jerusalem yeshivah, experiencing a sense of fulfillment and meaning he had never felt before. And yet, his mind was not at ease. The thought that his older sister Robin was very far from where he was, in more ways than one, tormented him and aroused painful guilt feelings over his own inability to influence her lifestyle.

Robin was neither a drug addict, a drifter, nor a punk rocker; nor did she frequent bars or other unsavory places. Indeed, she was deeply religious — but her faith was pathetically misplaced: Robin's heart belonged to Vishnu. Not content with the "sacred cord" or the other vestiges of Hinduism, she sought an environment steeped in religious observance. Hence she had abandoned her home and the comfortable lifestyle of Lincolnwood, Illinois in favor of a drab, meager existence in the slums of Hyderabad, India, where she dwelled in squalor.

The effect on Josh was devastating. Here he was, studying and practicing the mitzvos of the Lord, and Robin was chanting mantras as she sipped the "sacred Soma."

Something had to be done, Josh knew, but lack of experience in this area limited his options. His solution would have earned him and "A" for effort, but a "C" — at best — for creativity.

He made Robin what he hoped would be an offer she could not refuse: an all-expenses-paid trip to Israel. Josh told her that he would cover the airfare, hotel accommodations, and everything else, *provided* she attend at least one class in a Jerusalem seminary for not-yet-religious women interested in Judaism.

The offer indeed proved irresistible, and since Robin missed her brother terribly and was intrigued by the Middle East, she accepted on the spot. His telegram could not have come at a better time — the rainy season was just starting in India and her shack was sure to be swept away by the anticipated torrents. Religion-wise she had nothing to fear from Josh's stipulation as she was totally in control of her Karma.

Josh was a gracious host and a perfect gentleman, biding his time for the right moment to raise the subject of the provision upon which he had made his largesse contingent. But as he hesitated and groped for words, Robin resolved the matter by informing her younger brother that on the Tuesday before she her scheduled departure she would have some time in the afternoon to attend a class.

Josh had embarked on the venture as a means of assuaging his guilty conscience and to prepare an answer for the Divine tribunal which would surely demand to know what he had done to save his sister from herself. Accordingly, he did not hold high expectations of effecting a turnabout, and after one week of shared company, any hopes that he might have harbored were dashed and relegated to the trash bin of wishful thinking. She was considerably more religious than *he* was, and had the conviction and degree of sober certainty possibly enjoyed only by those awaiting imminent execution by firing squad.

Josh took comfort from the fact that he had, at the very least, done his part, and as far as Robin was concerned, she was about to do hers.

She stepped into the seminary on a fateful Tuesday afternoon and inquired if there was a class that she might attend. Quick to size her up, the educator on duty urged her to come back the next morning when the senior lecturers would be giving their classes. The afternoon classes were generally less philosophy-intensive and beginner-oriented, and were more devoted to skills and the technicalities of "learning how to learn."

But, alas, Robin did not have a "tomorrow" option. After some consideration, she was directed to a class in Halachah.

Rabbi Rubinstein's Halachah classes were always well-prepared, informative, practical, and... capable of inducing somnolescent stupor in the most dedicated insomniac. That

Tuesday was no exception.

Had someone been inordinately curious about the various technical minutiae of the laws germane to returning a lost object, there is no doubt that Rabbi Rubinstein's Tuesday afternoon class was the place to be. But for someone only marginally interested, a logarithm chart would have held greater appeal.

The class was not a total waste, for as the lecturer droned on, reciting the list of identifying marks which the finder must proclaim, Robin did manage to write two letters and tally her expenses of the past week.

After one full hour the class was mercifully over, as was Robin's obligation to her brother. With a clear conscience she could head back to the high life of Hyderabad.

Robin hadn't been back in India a full two weeks when, while walking in the marketplace with her guru, he discovered a wallet lying on the ground, its contents strewn beneath the wheels of an abandoned pushcart. The guru examined the wallet and discovered that it contained no ID, but what it lacked in driver's licenses, credit cards, and health insurance data, it more than made up for in money. Without even a furtive glance left or right, he pocketed the wad of cash and prepared to dispose of the evidence before the incredulous eyes of his protégé.

All piety and self-righteousness, his holiness was quick to explain himself: The money was not for him but would be donated — in its entirety — to the Ashram.

"But what about the person who lost the wallet?" Robin demanded. "Isn't he entitled to get his money back?"

"Who knows who or where he is," the maharishi replied. "In the meantime, the money can be sanctified by being contributed to our house of worship."

"But the owner may prefer that his hard-earned money be spent otherwise," Robin protested. "I'm sure that there are some identifying marks in the wallet that would enable us to locate its owner. Who knows if he's given up hope of ever recovering it." Sentence after sentence of subconscious Rabbi Rubinsteinology came spooling out of the novice Halachah student, but the guru was not impressed.

Nor was Robin Silverman.

Unwittingly, most definitely unconsciously, she had absorbed a lesson, and it could not be ignored. A few days later she was back at the Jerusalem seminary — this time at her own expense — attending both morning *and* afternoon classes.

The lessons of the Midrash, like any component of the Torah, are often dry and unimpressive until they impact upon real life. As long as the details of returning a lost item were irrelevant to Robin Silverman, they contained all the excitement of a mausoleum. But once they came to life, they became life-*changing*. This is the point, and certainly the goal of these two volumes.

If this humble effort will make the Midrash more accessible to a wider public, and the lessons of the weekly portion better understood, then this effort will have been gloriously vindicated.

The effort, I hasten to confess, was a joint one. The Midrash would have remained a sealed book for me had it not been for my learned teachers and the plethora of *sefarim* that address the weekly Torah portions. I am indebted to all, especially the Almighty Who allows me to learn and teach His Torah.

In this work, wherever "Midrash" is the source indicated,

the reference is to *Midrash Rabbah*, the oldest Amoraic classical midrash on the Torah and the five meggilos. The two other Midrashim that are cited here are *Yalkut Shimoni* and *Midrash Tanchuma*.

Yalkut Shimoni is the most comprehensive midrashic anthology covering the entire *Tanach*. It is attributed to Rabbi Shimon haDarshan of Frankfort, who lived in the thirteenth century. *Midrash Tanchuma* is exclusively on the Torah and is ascribed to Rabbi Tanchuma.

Even my most devoted followers (individuals who have read over 6,000 pages of Teller tales) will find in this anthology numerous never-before-published stories written specifically for this project. You may also find stories that are recognizable from earlier works. Please bear in mind that the "classic" stories herein were culled from sixteen different volumes and numerous articles, spanning over 13 years.

Inevitably, certain turns of phrase and fictitious names which I have unwittingly become attached to may appear more than once. "As remunerative as playing with a yo yo," was an apt description in *Soul Survivors*, and it also worked ten years later in *Give Peace a Stance*. I confess that I am occasionally guilty of self-plagiarism. I beg your gracious indulgence and hope that this will not detract from your reading enjoyment nor impede the inculcation of the vital lessons contained in *A Midrash and a Maaseh*.

Bereishis

בְּרֵאשִׁית

Divine Prejudice

וַיַּרְא אֱלֹקִים אֶת הָאוֹר כִּי טוֹב וַיַּבְדֵּל אֱלֹקִים בֵּין הָאוֹר וּבֵין הַחֹשֶׁךְ.

And God saw the light that it was good; and God divided between the light and the darkness.

(Bereishis 1:4)

The Midrash explains:

> *At the beginning of Creation God foresaw the deeds of both the wicked and the righteous. "And the earth was null and void..."* (Bereishis *1:2) refers to the deeds of the wicked, '"And God said: Let there be light..." (1:3) refers to the deeds of the righteous.*

If not for the verse "And God saw the light that it was good...," one wouldn't know which [the deeds of the wicked or of the righteous] God prefers.

To explain this perplexing Midrash, Rabbi **Leib Gurwicz** taught that we can achieve our ultimate purpose of sanctifying God's Name in the world either through the deeds of the righteous or the punishment of the wicked.

As both means lead to the same result, one might have thought that God has no preference between them. Thus, the verse teaches that the Almighty favors the deeds of the righteous, who "tread in the light," over the deeds of the wicked who "grope in the dark." The light of the righteous is free of deceit and untainted by all of the schemes the wicked routinely employ before God foils their plans and sanctifies His Name.

Steeped in Torah learning and zealous in his observance of *mitzvos*, Reb Velvel (the Brisker Rav) was a beacon of confidence. He didn't flinch at any intimidation from the outside world nor succumb to pressures from within.

Once, many of his students, along with several notables, appealed to the Brisker Rav to permit electioneering prior to the *Motzai Shabbos Kehillah* (an organization responsible to the government) ballot. "If the Rav won't allow us to broadcast our platform, the irreligious camp will win by a landslide," they argued, and the Brisker Rav grudgingly agreed.

Ironically, the irreligious and the religious hired the same printer to run off their placards and literature. Apparently, for an additional fee, the printer showed the irreligious campaign organizers the text of the adherents of the Brisker Rav. The irreligious then printed an even more profanatory placard, strongly condemning and debasing the Brisker Rav. All of this resulted in a delay in producing the placards for the religious camp and they weren't ready until erev *Shabbos*. Because of the late hour, the students grabbed the posters directly off the printing press and ran to show them to the Brisker Rav for his approval before posting them throughout the city. Reb Velvel, however, took the placards and locked them in his room. "It is erev Shabbos and winning every seat in the election isn't worth a risk of desecrating the Sabbath..."

"But Rebbe, if we don't paste up our placards, the residents of Brisk will only see the posters of the irreligious and will be lured by their propaganda. We'll be careful to stop affixing the posters well before Shabbos. Please. PLEASE!!"

"Just as there is a mitzvah to fight the 'Enlightenists,' likewise is there a mitzvah to observe the Shabbos, and I cannot permit any risks in that regard!"

That Shabbos, Brisk was saturated with placards denouncing the religious platform and attacking the Brisker Rav — and no pro-religious posters appeared at all.

Nevertheless, it was beyond the imagination of the residents of Brisk, who had all of Shabbos to study the propaganda, what the Brisker Rav could have done to deserve such insults and ridicule. He had not posted any derisive remarks about the town's irreligious residents or their leaders. In fact, the "Enlightenist" posters appeared so unprovoked and in such poor taste that the religious camp emerged the overwhelming victors in the election — out of all proportion to their numbers.

Imperative Introspection

וַתּוֹצֵא הָאָרֶץ דֶּשֶׁא עֵשֶׂב מַזְרִיעַ זֶרַע לְמִינֵהוּ וְעֵץ עֹשֶׂה פְּרִי אֲשֶׁר זַרְעוֹ בוֹ לְמִינֵהוּ....

The earth brought forth grass, herb yielding seed after its kind, and tree yielding fruit, whose seed was in itself after its kind...

(Bereishis 1:12)

When iron was created, the Midrash relates, the trees became frightened, for the blade of the ax could fell them. God reassured the trees that their fear was baseless, for as long as the trees did not provide the wood for the ax handle, the iron would be harmless.

Rabbi **Avraham Twerski** highlights the poignancy of this lesson. Man is his own worst enemy — he provides the very instruments of his own destruction. No one can harm us as much as we can ourselves, but we always tend to shift the blame away from ourselves. We complain that our troubles come from without, but we would do well to first look within before casting suspicion elsewhere.

It's hard to say if Dr. Rappaport is a naturally exuberant individual. His perpetual, toothy smile and jovial demeanor are part and parcel of his work. His reputation as one of Jerusalem's finest and most respected pediatricians derives from his medical prowess, while his popularity derives from his concern and friendliness. When asked how he is able to maintain so cheerful an outlook with a hectic practice such as his, he shrugs and explains that *someone* has to look cheerful in an office always crowded with chicken-pocked children and bawling babies. But for all of Dr. Rappaport's congeniality, he was not about to brighten Rivkie Shreiber's Wednesday morning.

Rivkie was the consummate, Brooklyn-born-and-bred wife of a *kollel* fellow: gregarious, endearing, wide-eyed, a touch flamboyant — in short, very American-*frum*. But beneath the façade of stylish wig and fashionable attire beat the faint heart of a timid Bais Yaakov graduate terrified to be on unfamiliar turf. A newcomer to Israel, Rivkie did not have local family or close friends, and barely spoke the language. The little Biblical and Mishnaic Hebrew she could muster evoked gales of laughter from the natives. To have found a pediatrician who was not only well-qualified but able and willing to speak to her in her own tongue was a relief.

As Dr. Rappaport's deft fingers examined Rivkie's seven-month-old baby Deena, however, his smile faded. This was not the common ear infection or simple case of bronchitis for which a standard prescription and best wishes for a *refuah sheleimah* would suffice. The baby's chronic listlessness and soaring temperature were the symptoms that alerted him; stool specimen tests corroborated his tentative diagnosis. There was little doubt now as to the nature of Deena's ailment.

As gently as he could, Dr. Rappaport broke the news. His diagnosis etched painfully sharp lines in Rivkie's brow, reducing her vivaciousness to stony silence. She had never heard of shigellosis before, but she had realized that her Deena wasn't suffering from an ordinary case of diarrhea.

To make sure that the baby received the proper care, Dr. Rappaport told Rivkie the truth: "This disease can be fatal in infants. It is also highly contagious. The baby must be admitted to a hospital immediately."

"Fatal?!" Rivkie thought to herself, her heart pounding loudly in her ears. "Oh, my God!" Her hands trembled as she attempted to button up Deena's creeper. If this simple chore of closing a button seemed a near impossibility to her now, how in the world was she going to manage to bring Deena to the hospital? Besides being nearly hysterical with fright over her baby's condition, Rivkie could barely breathe at the prospect of all the red tape that would surely confront her there. She often became flustered and embarrassed when attempting minor transactions at the bank or supermarket; how, then, could she overcome the infamous *bureaucratzia* to admit her baby into an Israeli hospital?!

Rivkie's thoughts drifted back to the more carefree times of her childhood, when her warm, large family was always there to help her over even the most inconsequential hurdles. Tears welled up in her eyes as she recalled her mother's kind, loving face. But Rivkie's daydream lasted only a split second; her maternal instincts galvanized her into action, penetrating the inertia of despair. This was no time to sob on the phone to Mommy in Brooklyn. She had to take care of Deena herself, and she had to act *now*.

Reaching down into herself for the fortitude she had to have, she turned to the doctor and said: "Just tell me exactly what I must do."

"I am preparing all of the papers," he told her while he quickly tended to a veritable ream of printed forms. Dr. Rappaport punctiliously explained each item, repeating himself where he thought it was necessary. He then escorted mother and child out of his office, ensuring that the infectious baby did not come into contact with the dozen patients in his waiting room.

Once outside, however, Rivkie's courage waned. Of all the times to be left on her own! Her husband had flown to the States the night before for his brother's wedding. Even before the present crisis, she had felt incompetent dealing with the normal rigors of daily existence without her husband's patience, calmness and fluency in Hebrew. She had never been so completely alone before.

Rivkie had come to Israel for the same reason many of her peers had: she wanted her husband to ascend in learning, and *"ain Torah k'Toras Eretz Yisrael."* Attaining that goal entailed a sacrifice on her part in terms of separation from family and friends, but she was sure it was worth it. Besides, it was sort of a tradition. Hadn't Rabbi Akiva's wife, and all of the wives of *talmidei chachamim* before and after her, made sacrifices for Torah's sake?

Because of budgetary considerations, Rivkie had not traveled with her husband, but she no longer regretted having remained behind. The thought of toxins attacking her baby in mid-flight with no proper medical attention available was even worse than the current state of affairs, as bad as it was.

Rivkie raced through her apartment, stuffing into a bag whatever she thought Deena would need in the hospital. Just when time was so critical she found everything disorganized and nothing in its place! Frantically scurrying from the baby's room to hers, she improvised, settling for anything that was clean and serviceable. She snatched the *sheitel* off her head and put a *tichel* on in its place, knowing intuitively that she would be in for a long, draining ordeal where looking her best was the lowest priority. She grabbed pajamas for Deena and a denim skirt for herself, as her fingers fumbled for the *Tehillim* on the shelf below her husband's *Shas*. Grasping the little book tightly, she reassured herself, "I'm not really alone," in an effort to fight off the terrible thought that Deena might never return to their apartment.

To complicate matters, one of the pediatrician's forms had to be stamped by the *Kupat Cholim* ["Health Fund"] office in downtown Jerusalem before Deena could be admitted by the hospital. Rivkie's few encounters with *Kupat Cholim* led her to fear a protracted process involving several offices and interminable lines. But even if it were to go quickly this time, how could she take Deena with her? On the other hand, how could she leave her very sick and contagious baby with a sitter or a neighbor? The walls of her apartment seemed to be closing in on her. There were no doors in sight.

Rivkie's instincts impelled her to get the baby to a hospital without delay. If necessary, she would turn on the charm and hope for the best. If a womanly approach failed to get her any medical attention, she would... she would... she'd just scream!

Rivkie dialed for a taxi and explained that it was urgent. But the problem with taxis is that *every* caller feigns urgency, desperation, or the like in order to receive a cab quickly. Waiting for a taxi at any time is a trial of patience; waiting for one in an emergency is a test of nerves. Rivkie failed both.

But the mother was not the worse off. While Rivkie and her daughter were waiting for the cab to arrive, Deena began to convulse. Her fingers kept clenching and unclenching. Her eyes rolled wildly and she hissed through her closed mouth. Rivkie clutched her baby tightly in her arms, her eyes darting up and down the street frantically. Just then the taxi pulled up at the curb.

As they sped away, Rivkie implored the cabbie to drive as fast as possible. She nearly screamed each time he slowed down for another red light. Her body tightened like a spring around her baby's contorted form, and she prayed that the hospital would soon be in sight...

Deena's grave condition circumvented the admission procedure. When the taxi finally arrived, it went straight to the emergency room entrance. Layers of red tape fell away when the medical personnel saw the agonized baby and her panic-stricken mother.

The convulsion passed but its effects lingered. The insidious toxins attacking Deena's brain had turned her into a baby her mother couldn't recognize. An alert attendant in the ward sized up the situation at once and rushed to notify a doctor. Within seconds Deena was injected with a tranquilizer.

The baby was placed in a crib, and a medical team huddled around. One nurse inserted an IV tube into Deena's tiny wrist, while another left to arrange a spinal tap and a third took her blood pressure. The doctors prepared a stool sample and ordered a battery of other tests.

Rivkie was unable to comprehend the Hebrew words flying back and forth, but the word "*shigella*" cut into practically every sentence. "What's happening with my baby?" she pleaded several times, but the doctors were too intent on their work to respond. They motioned for a nurse to remove her so that they could continue unhampered.

"Not to vorry," a nurse tried to assure Rivkie in broken English, "you baby go upstair to qvarantine and get good care." Not worry?! Rivkie was terrified! The doctors' looks of concern and the pediatrician's earlier warning about fatality converged like cymbals crashing in her ears. She trembled and began to cry hysterically.

Rivkie loved her baby more than anything in the world, and the thought of her demise was... God forbid! She refused to allow that unimaginable thought in her head; it was too horrible even to contemplate. The death of a child was the kind of tragedy no one ever thought could befall his or her own family; it only struck hapless strangers and was only discussed in dark whispers that hovered somewhere between sympathy, shock and *lashon hara.*

It was astounding that in just a few short months one could grow from a teenaged *kallah* into a mother willing to endure the worst tortures ever conceived in order to save her child. Rivkie would have gladly changed places with little Deena if only to spare the baby even a second of pain. She chastised herself for having earlier indulged in homesick thoughts of Brooklyn, and wasting precious seconds — seconds that might have meant the difference between life and death.

As helpless as she felt, Rivkie was determined to do anything to save her Deena. But for the time being, her lonely crib-side vigil, her constant *tefillos,* and her continuous loving caresses were all she had to offer.

At six forty-five in the evening Deena was moved from the emergency room to the Quarantine Section of the Pediatrics Pavilion. It had been eleven hours since Rivkie had last eaten, but she was still too inexperienced to know that in order to tend to her baby properly she had to take care of herself as well. It was so hard to be separated from Deena, even for the few minutes she would have needed to find some food. Feeling as alien and vulnerable as she did, Rivkie instinctively sensed a hostile environment. Even though she knew that the hospital housed a professional, caring staff, Rivkie felt an evil presence lurking in the corridors. Dizzy from hunger and fatigue, and consumed with anxiety over her daughter, she was unable to think rationally.

As the attendant wheeled Deena's crib out of the elevator, Rivkie's worst fears were realized: from the corner of her eye she suddenly caught sight of a hideous black monster. A gasping shriek escaped her lips and she fell upon her baby to protect her from the creature's sinister gaze.

"What is that?" she whispered urgently, but the attendant, a cold, seasoned hospital worker, neither replied nor flinched. He continued to push the crib, dragging the stumbling, hysterical mother along.

"Wait, wait, please!" Rivkie begged as little Deena was wheeled straight toward the monster. Frantically tugging at the crib to prevent the attendant from advancing, Rivkie alarmed the whole floor. "Can't you hear me?" she yelled. "Please, let's go the other way. Can't we go the other way?" Nurses and patients rushed to the scene of the commotion and began to jabber in Hebrew about the crazy American. A nurse tried to get her to let go of the crib and calm down, but it was no use. A security guard was called.

Rivkie thought she was living a nightmare. The spasmodically twitching monster, emitting a fetor as foul as the stench of a charnel house, was advancing closer and closer, and everyone was conspiring to bring Deena into his vile clutches. "Help! HELP ME!" Rivkie screamed. But her pleas fell on deaf ears.

The security guard arrived and first set about dispersing those who had gathered to watch the spectacle. He and the attendant exchanged a knowing look. Then, approaching Rivkie from behind, he grasped her arms and removed her bodily from the path of the crib. Rivkie struggled to wriggle free, but she was no match for this burly, experienced guard.

Devastated, Rivkie watched helplessly as Deena's crib was wheeled inexorably closer to the monster. How could they do this to her baby? Clearly the beast sensed another victim approaching. It raised its massive head, displaying gruesome, bloated lips that opened and closed like the mouth of a giant fish. Rivkie moaned, and the guard tightened his grip. She felt faint, but she forced herself to maintain consciousness. She had stumbled into a nightmare world: this was some voodoo temple behind the façade of a hospital. Before her very eyes, her baby was about to become a heinous sacrifice on the altar of a hideous god. The crib was nearing the monster, which raised itself on its elbows in anticipation, a white froth forming around its distorted lips. Rivkie's breath caught in her throat as her eyes bulged out of their sockets. She had no voice left to scream.

When the attendant came within the creature's reach, it thrust out a blackened limb to arrest the advance of the crib. But miracle of miracles, the attendant waved it off and continued into the pavilion. Rivkie started to breathe again. Deena was safe from this *bête noire* for the moment... but who knew what perils awaited her inside? The guard released her at last, and Rivkie ran after her baby.

But as she approached the frightful miscreation, it once again extended a ghoulish black limb. She leaped out of its reach, racing to catch sight of the attendant pushing Deena's crib into a private room. A nurse was busy taping a sign to the door — *Highly Contagious.*

Rivkie had almost forgotten her earlier hellish encounter, attributing it to nerves and exhaustion. But as she dropped off to sleep, she again found herself face to face with the frightening monstrosity she had seen in the corridor a few hours before. In her dream he was standing over her, trying to pull Deena from her arms. His black talons ripped her daughter away and carried her toward a raging fire. With arms raised, he held the little body above the flames, ready to hurl her into a fiery furnace. Rivkie shrieked uncontrollably, waking herself and baby Deena. It took some time before she was able to restore both the child and herself to normal. And even then, alone in the dark, all her fears resurfaced. Was she safe from his vile clutches here in this ward? She could not shake the haunting feelings that he had aroused in her.

Shigellosis, Rivkie soon learned, is a disease not quickly cured. The nerve-racking experience of a prolonged stay in the hospital was somewhat ameliorated by the slow but steady improvement in Deena's condition. After two days the baby's temperature dropped and she appeared less sickly. The diarrhea, however, did not relent.

Toward the second evening, Rivkie detected some difficulty in Deena's breathing. Her observation was confirmed by a doctor, who quickly ordered a chest x-ray.

Alarmed by the new development, Rivkie accompanied Deena to the radiology department. When they emerged from the elevator the terror of that first night was abruptly rekindled. Propped up in a bed, only meters away, was the same jet-black beast, his face indiscernible but for the opening and closing of gruesomely swollen, protruding lips.

Rivkie flinched involuntarily and tried to prevent herself from again emitting a terrified shriek. She instinctively threw her hands around Deena to shield her from the gaze of the creature and kept her own eyes riveted to her daughter.

After a few brisk strides Rivkie realized, to her profound horror, that they were headed directly into the path of the dreadful beast. She had begun to hyperventilate with fear. What could she do? She turned sharply and walked backwards, pretending the attendant needed her to help pull the crib.

Suddenly she felt a hand brush against her back and Rivkie jumped as if stung by a live wire. She was too petrified even to scream. She ran, pulling the crib all the way back down the corridor to their room.

He had touched her, there was no doubt about it. She felt that she immediately had to have her blouse incinerated. What *mikveh* was wide and deep enough to cleanse her of the contamination of that demonic contact? Was it the Satan that had grazed her, or the Angel of Death? Rivkie was shaking and sobbing, gagging from terror.

The attendant caught up with Rivkie and threw her an angry look. He grabbed the crib and deliberately began pushing it back toward Radiology. Rivkie simply could not believe how nonchalant the hospital staff was about that most craven of creatures! Surely that thing should be kept away from good, healthy people. Didn't they realize that God would not punish one so unless he truly deserved it? She couldn't imagine what iniquity could be so grievous that the Almighty would mete out such a punishment.

The x-ray technician asked for her help in placing the baby on the x-ray table. Rivkie froze, afraid to touch her precious Deena. Who knew what pernicious disease could possibly be transmitted by contact with that Frankenstein? The technician let out an exasperated sigh and repeated his request through clenched teeth. With a sudden shock, Rivkie realized that *her* child was the contagious one on this floor, and she had no time to worry about whether she had contracted some horrible disease from the monster. She'd have to save her own personal worries for that silent hour of the night when banished, subconscious thoughts invade the conscious mind, robbing the soul of sleep.

The head radiologist examined the x-ray of Deena's chest and scribbled some notes. Everything was in order and they prepared to return to the ward. Rivkie begged the attendant to tell her if "it" was still in the corridor. He informed her with a smirk that he had been moved, and she prayed that the man was telling the truth. Rivkie had heard that hospital employees become inured to everything, but that accursed creature's condition was far worse than any debilitating disease or chronic ailment she could ever imagine. She was still frightened, and couldn't expel the horrible visage from her memory.

Rivkie was quivering from head to toe from the experience, which no one had bothered to explain to her. After seeing it at close range, she now understood that the "monster" of her hysterical imagination was actually a pathetic human being with some unspeakable disease or congenital defect. Surely the mark of Cain had not been as pronounced, she thought, and wondered again what abominable sin this person must have committed to have deserved such a frightful disfigurement. She hoped she would never know. Rivkie prayed that she would never see it again and that she would be able to erase the memories of this harrowing day. She needed to concentrate on her baby now, she tried to tell herself, not on the few moments of horror with that malevolent creature. But the image of the monster made her shiver suddenly and violently. It somehow embodied all of her fears, everything she couldn't face.

Later that night, a nurse brought Rivkie a cot so that she could sleep alongside her daughter. Her presence was needed to change the diapers that Deena was soiling with such frightening frequency. She also had to notify the nurses when the intravenous solution ran out, since they paid less attention than normal to the quarantined patients.

Rivkie collapsed on the cot, a little more in control of herself after the quick meal she had virtually inhaled while standing over Deena's crib. Her thoughts drifted to her husband, Yossie. His brother's wedding was to take place tonight, she recalled. Tears swam in her eyes as she visualized all the happy, smiling faces of friends and relatives who would be dancing with the bride and groom... while her baby was here in this sterile, unfriendly hospital, hovering between life and death.

How Rivkie had wanted to join Yossie on his trip to America! But in the end, she herself had decided to remain in Jerusalem, knowing full well that they could scarcely afford a second plane fare. Her parents had been generous enough when Deena was born, and Yossie's parents were already strapped with all the "extras" a wedding calls for.

The thought of being alone in a foreign country had been daunting, but she had not dared to tell him for fear of spoiling his trip. Now she wondered what she could possibly have done to have brought this torment on herself and little Deena.

Rivkie glanced down at her baby. Deena was looking so much better, thank God. But what use was her recovery if this monster would cast some satanic spell upon her? If ever there was an "evil eye," it was his to give.

Because Deena was kept in isolation, Rivkie didn't have the opportunity to discuss the matter with other patients or visitors to the hospital. The next morning, she told herself she would bring up the problem with Deena's doctors. Rivkie had no intention of asking for a history or medical analysis of that poor soul's condition: she simpy wanted to know how they could allow such a thing to remain in plain sight — roaming all over the hospital and terrorizing patients and any sane visitor.

But the opportunity never arose. The next morning a physician came to visit Deena, flanked by interns and residents. He turned to Rivkie and said in near-perfect English: "I have good news for you. Your daughter is showing real improvement. She's making a far more rapid recovery than we had anticipated considering her condition when she was first admitted to the hospital. I imagine she will have to remain here for another day or two — pending examination by the head of Pediatrics. He will probably put your daughter on phenobarbital tranquilizers for several months, and, as a matter of course, order an EEG six weeks after discharge to see if the convulsion has left any lasting effects."

The doctor's "good news" didn't sound all that cheery to Rivkie. Aside from the part about leaving the hospital soon, the prospect of an EEG made her fearful once again. Then the nagging, subliminal question that had been haunting her every night came to the surface:

"Will my daughter have any brain damage because of the convulsion?"

The doctor tried to allay her fears: "Electroencephalograms are performed routinely on anyone who has experienced a convulsion. Undoubtedly in your baby's case it was a *shigella* toxin that caused the seizure, but we just want to make sure she doesn't have a tendency to convulse — data which would be very valuable for you to know."

The prospect of being released from the hospital was blissful — but it was marred by the nightmares and the overwhelming stress Rivkie had suffered from her grisly encounters with the ubiquitous monster. Who knew what ghastly scars this experience would leave on her and the baby?

The next morning the head of the department examined Deena as promised, and announced that she could be released that day if lab results confirmed his prognosis. Needless to say, Rivkie was elated when the lab gave Deena the green light; the dreadful week in the hospital would soon be over. Rivkie had to go downstairs to handle the paperwork before the release could be authorized — a procedure that took close to an hour.

When she returned to Deena's room she found a nurse getting the baby dressed to leave. "Well, you're all set to go," she cheerfully greeted Rivkie. The nurse was British, the first native English-speaker Rivkie had met all week. "Submit a copy of the papers you received downstairs to the nurses' station near the entrance to this ward, dear, and you'll be on your way. Oh, yes — I also have a message for you: Yigal wants to say goodbye."

"Yigal?"

"Yes, you'll find him at the desk."

Rivkie wondered who "Yigal" was. Maybe he was the intern who had received them in the emergency room and had come up several times to check on Deena's progress. Or perhaps he was the taxi driver who had driven them to the hospital and who had refused payment — that first day and again when Rivkie subsequently met him near the outpatient clinic.

Rivkie packed their few belongings, picked Deena up and turned to the nurses to thank them for their care. Each glorious step was bringing them closer to freedom. She was finally leaving, just in time to get ready for Yossie's return in only two more days. She would need that time to get the house back in order and put this whole ordeal in proper perspective. What was she meant to have learned from it?

Rivkie approached the nurses' station and began kissing Deena's forehead excitedly while she waited for someone's attention. Deena's lively personality had been almost fully restored and she babbled merry gibberish while her mother *kvelled.*

A nurse finally turned to them, and Rivkie handed over the mass of papers. After a brief perusal, the nurse said she required the passport numbers of both Deena's parents. Rivkie smiled and reached for the purse she had placed on the counter — and nearly jumped out of her skin.

There he was, looking directly at her from down the corridor! "Oh dear God," Rivkie whimpered. "Not now, when we are almost out! Please, just let us leave this place!" She clutched Deena tightly, pressing the baby's head into her side. Deena struggled to wriggle away but her mother refused to relax her grip.

"*Nu?*" the nurse demanded, rolling her eyes.

"I... I don't... know," Rivkie spluttered back. "I... I must go now, and I will call in the information."

"Wait just a minute," the nurse replied sharply, "I must ask the head nurse." The nurse stood up and went into the head nurse's office. Rivkie remained frozen in place, her eyes tightly closed. She didn't know what to do. She wanted to run away, but was afraid they might call downstairs and not let her out of the building. Without an official release from the ward she would be ineligible for reimbursement of both the hospital fees and the cost of the EEG, which the head of the department had said was so crucial. She was trapped, a captive victim of his vile gaze. She began to tremble once more, her earlier elation forgotten.

"Mrs. Shreiber... Mrs. Shreiber?"

She was being spoken to. "Yes," she answered, startled, and opened her eyes.

"Do you have at least *one* of your passport numbers with you?" the head nurse asked. She was a middle-aged woman with an air of efficiency about her, and she appeared more cooperative than the nurse who had gone to get her.

"Uh, uh... yes, sure."

"Then that will be adequate. Now, if you don't mind my saying so, your baby appears to be very uncomfortable. It seems you're crushing her! Are you trying to conceal something?"

Rivkie realized how foolish she must have looked, but she was scared, scared for herself and for poor Deena. She and her baby had gone through enough. She did not need to look at the monstrous face of sin in the form of a man.

But why was everyone else so calm about his presence? Irony of ironies, *she* looked like the queer one, and "it" was treated like a cherished patient to be wheeled everywhere, deposited wherever he wished, and tolerated throughout the hospital by one and all.

Grabbing hold of herself, Rivkie reached out again for her purse. This time she saw that he was inching closer to her and, to her consternation and utter chagrin, she let out a high-pitched, long-suppressed screech.

"What's the matter?" the head nurse asked in alarm.

"N... nothing," Rivkie responded, controlling herself. She fumbled for her passport and hastily read off the number. The nurse jotted down the information and nodded her approval.

The last hurdle was behind her now, and Rivkie could finally leave. As the nurse stamped the document and handed it back, she told Rivkie that Yigal was waiting for her, and would she just take a few more minutes of her time to speak with him?

With all of the tension, Rivkie had completely forgotten about the mysterious Yigal. With the monster so close she did not wish to remain an extra second. But who was this Yigal?

"Please tell him that I'll call him," Rivkie said hurriedly, "but I don't remember exactly who he is."

"You don't know who Yigal is?" the nurse asked with surprise, as though Rivkie had not recognized the name of the Prime Minister. "Why, he is lying right at your side!"

Rivkie cowered. "What *is* he?" she asked, ashamed that her tone evinced such disgust.

"What *is* he?" the head nurse repeated in bewilderment. "Yigal is our favorite patient, that's who he is."

At this point Rivkie's anger overcame her fear. "Favorite patient? How dare you all treat him like some privileged character when obviously he's a living example of the wrath of God!"

The nurse's expression reflected her astonishment. "Why don't you ask him yourself how he got to be this way? Go ahead," she cajoled, "he's waiting for you. He has wanted to talk to you for some time now."

Rivkie, her anger spent, became flustered and stared pointedly at the counter. She felt faint again, and wished she were somewhere, *any*where but in the company of that malfeasant.

In the meantime the head nurse wheeled Yigal right over to her. Remembering the interdiction of the Rabbis forbidding one to look an evil person in the face, Rivkie felt no urge to violate the rule at this time. Close up, she was certain, his features would be even more gruesome than they had appeared from a distance.

The grossly ballooned lips parted and the creature uttered a muffled "Shalom."

"This young lady," the head nurse told Yigal, "would like to know how you came to look like this."

"*Motek*," Yigal mouthed laboriously, "for my buddies I would be willing to burn a hundred times, just so that Jewish boys might be saved."

All this time, Rivkie had not shifted her gaze from the counter. But when she heard these last words about saving Jewish boys, she lowered her eyes to the foot of Yigal's bed. Deena had fallen asleep and Rivkie supported her on her shoulder.

"Go on, Yigal," coaxed the head nurse, "tell Rivkie your story." A few people in the hallway gathered around him.

"It was the first day of the war," he began in such surprisingly perfect English that he might have been a foreign correspondent, "Operation Peace for Galilee, that is, when we set out. We were part of the armored brigade which was to lead the attack on the western axis up the coastal road. Almost all the boys in my unit were *Hesder* yeshivah students, just eighteen- to twenty-year-old conscripts who were seeing action for the first time.

"We had regrouped within Major Haddad's enclave in Lebanese territory, and at 11:00 A.M. we headed out for the U.N. zone.

"Half an hour after starting out, shells began erupting. From a fortified position on the road to Tyre, Palestinian terrorists showered the lead tanks with a barrage of rocket-propelled grenades, but it didn't take us long to destroy their position.

"Just a little while later those same tanks were blown off the road when our own planes mistakenly bombed the crossroads just as we were approaching. Fortunately our tanks sustained only minor damage.

"Since the directive was to reach the Kasmiye bridge over the Litani River as fast as possible, the lead tank unit did not engage in any mopping-up operations after we destroyed the Palestinian stronghold. This enabled them to regroup before the advance of the second unit.

"The problem was that the commander of the paratroop battalion farther back in the column was unfamiliar with the area, not having been briefed as fully as we had been. To compound the problem, his communication system became inoperative just as his armored personnel carrier crossed the border.

"The battalion mistakenly traveled through some citrus groves. This made visual contact very difficult for us, while it allowed the terrorists easy access to the battalion. From out of nowhere, RPGs were fired and several tanks and APCs suffered direct hits. My unit was trapped.

"We were being hit from all sides and lost contact with our commander. Soldiers started leaping out of their disabled vehicles before they exploded, frantically running for cover in all different directions. Several, including our commander, were captured by the enemy.

"I also had to bail out of my APC; the steering mechanism had been jammed by a rocket. I was painfully aware of the fact that many of my buddies could not escape from their vehicles. A little ahead of me I saw a Merkava tank get hit and burst into flames.

"The rear escape hatch was engulfed in fire and I knew that the tank's crew was roasting inside. I pried the hatch open and crawled in to save my comrades. My clothes were on fire."

By this time even more people had congregated around Rivkie and Yigal. They urged him to continue as he paused to catch his breath.

"I found the entire crew alive," Yigal rasped, "but they were unable to extricate themselves from their positions. I pulled and shoved with all my might to maneuver them toward the escape hatch. The door at the end was still burning, but once you were out you could roll on the ground to extinguish the flames. The tank's gunner was in shock and bleeding badly but we somehow managed to push him out. Thank God, those boys are all fine today."

"And you, Yigal? What happened to you?" asked an orderly who had heard the story many times but never ceased to be amazed by it.

"By the time I was able to escape, the chute was red-hot. My skin melted right off of me. Most of it remained on the walls of the slide." He paused, dropped his head, then added with renewed animation, "But I'm telling you, *chabibi*, if I could have, I would have climbed into a dozen such tanks — anything to save our boys!"

Yigal fell silent. There were tears coursing down his own charred cheeks, and his damaged hands were shaking.

Rivkie had been crying for some time now. So these stories *did* happen to real people, not just to nameless faces you read about in the *Jerusalem Post*. *These* were the valiant individuals who risked their lives to save fellow Jews, men who fought and suffered the most horrible disfigurements so that women like her — and infants like Deena — could live safely in the Land. Heroes, she realized with a sense of profound shame, weren't the child-women who braved a stay in a hospital for a few days.

How she had incriminated this courageous man, accusing him in her mind of terrible deeds! Rivkie had been so involved in her own troubles she had failed to consider his possible sorrows. She had shunned and castigated a fellow Jew based on nothing but her own fears and weaknesses. How could she ever make up for the pain she had inflicted, the untold suffering she had heaped on him?

"Please," Yigal said, speaking directly to her now, "forgive me for frightening you. You see, I sometimes forget how I must look to others. When I saw you with your sick little baby, all alone and so worried, I wanted to comfort you. I, too, would love to have a family, a home, someone to care — *really* care — about me. But the truth is, I have no one. I've been here so long that even my old comrades have tired of visiting me. So I live through others, experiencing the pain and the joy of people here in the hospital. It's become a sort of hobby. Believe me, I only wanted to help you. Instead, I scared you. I forget how ugly I must look. Please, please," he said softly, "I've been wanting to ask your forgiveness."

Rivkie looked deeply into the *tzaddik*'s moist brown eyes. "*Ashrecha*, Yigal," she began through her tears, "*halevai* there should be more like you among our People."

After a few parting words, Rivkie Shreiber finally left the hospital, but she knew the ugly scars would remain on her *neshamah* for some time, a small reminder and a cheap price to pay for her unpardonable act of misjudgement. She stood on the sidewalk a moment and inhaled the crisp, fresh air of Jerusalem. The streets were awash with sunlight.

Rivkie stared out the bus window all the way home, her

thoughts in turmoil. "As soon as we get home," she told her precious sleeping baby, "I'll bake him a cake. And tomorrow I'll bring it to him — can you imagine, no one visits him?" She smiled to herself, thinking how happy it would make Yigal to have company.

All at once, Rivkie felt buoyant, lighthearted. One small scar had suddenly disappeared.

Eternal Reward

אֵלֶּה תּוֹלְדֹת נֹחַ נֹחַ אִישׁ צַדִּיק תָּמִים הָיָה בְּדֹרֹתָיו אֶת הָאֱלֹקִים הִתְהַלֶּךְ נֹחַ.

These are the offspring of Noach: Noach was a just man, perfect in his generations; Noach walked with God.

(Bereishis 6:9)

Why does the Torah promise a list of Noach's progeny, then discuss only his piety? In answering this question, the Midrash Tanchuma teaches a fundamental principle: "When a righteous person dies childless and weeps over his barren state, God assures him that he leaves behind something even more precious than children — the Torah study and good deeds accomplished during his lifetime. As it says, "The fruits of the righteous are a tree of life" *(Mishlei 11:30)*, and "a tree of life" always implies the Torah, as in, "[Torah] is a tree of life to those who support it..." *(3:18)*.

Rabbi **Yissacher Frand** points out that this Midrash flies in the face of conventional thinking that progeny are a parent's highest priority. There is apparently something more important than one's own children: one's Torah study and mitzvah observance. Hence, we mustn't bank on enjoying the merits of our children's Torah pursuits and neglect our own.

Children are a wonderful blessing, but they should never substitute for one's own spiritual development. The ultimate blessing, the Midrash maintains, is that of Torah learning and other good deeds.

The Bostoner Rebbe's appearance at the funeral of Yosef Gadish turned many a bare head. What possible connection could there have been between the distinguished leader of the Bostoner *chasidim*, and a stalwart of Mapai — a political party noted for its socialist/Marxist values and policies antithetical to Torah?

The Rebbe explained that Yosef Gadish, in his capacity as Deputy Mayor of Jerusalem, had been instrumental in giving the Boston community its foothold in the Har Nof neighborhood of Jerusalem.

It all began in the summer of 1983, at the *sheva berachos* of a Jerusalem family who had had some contact with the Chasidic Center in Boston. The Rebbe was introduced to Mr. Gadish there and the two hit it off very well.

A few weeks later, as the Rebbe was preparing to return to America after a somewhat fruitless pilot trip for the Har Nof Boston community, he decided to call Mr. Gadish as a gesture of courtesy, to say good-bye. To the Rebbe's surprise Gadish told him that he must see him right away.

"I wish I could accommodate you..." the Rebbe said, "but I'm leaving for the States tomorrow evening."

"Well, then, there's still plenty of time," Gadish responded. "I would come to see you, but I have meetings in my office all day. Please try and be here by seven tonight."

Something in the tone of Gadish's voice urged the Rebbe to comply. When he walked into his seven o'clock meeting he found the Deputy Mayor animated and extremely friendly. Gadish told him that he had just read a most impressive newspaper article about the work the Rebbe does to help the infirm. He had also heard from a friend who had undergone extensive medical treatment in Boston and who was full of praise for the Rebbe's and R.O.F.E.H.'s* assistance.

"Now," Gadish declared, "I would like to see how I can help you. Tell me, how are the plans for your community developing?"

In truth they were undeveloped, or perhaps better expressed, needed quite a lot of development. A chasidic community without a shul was patently absurd, but despite all of the Rebbe's meetings and explorations during his visit to Israel, no progress had been made in this area. The Rebbe, chagrined over having nothing to report, responded instead with a more face-saving, "We are negotiating."

"And how about the shul?"

The question took the Rebbe by surprise. The shul was the crux of the entire project! The thought that someone in a position of influence might now be taking an interest ignited the Rebbe's imagination and rekindled his hopes. As nonchalantly as he could, he replied, "Why, that is *your* domain."

The Deputy Mayor nodded and said, "I'll give you a shul. The cost of building one, and I'm referring to the real cost — no frills — is $150,000, with all the infrastructure and land rights thrown in by us. Give us a third and it's yours."

The Rebbe was absolutely flabbergasted. Yes, yes, of course the answer was yes, he wanted the shul with all his heart. This was the windfall he had prayed for. The glorious dream of settling Boston in Israel was about to come true — but there was one hitch: the family tradition. The Rebbe's father, in his day, would not relocate to a neighborhood unless there was a *mikveh* there, even if that entailed constructing one on his own. Could the Rebbe have the audacity to ask his new-found friend, who was already offering him so much, for *mikveh* facilities as well? But then again, could he not?

As diplomatically as possible, the Rebbe explained that although he was most grateful for the exceedingly generous offer, a shul without a *mikveh* was out of the question.

Gadish seemed sympathetic but his response was negative: there was no room on the site for a *mikveh* as well as a shul. "It needn't be a big *mikveh*," the Rebbe urged, "just a *mikveh*."

Gadish grabbed the phone and got his engineer on the line. A fast-paced discussion took place, and arrangements were made for the engineer to go to the site the following morning, meet with the Rebbe, and look into the possibility of constructing a *mikveh* on the same plot as the shul.

Two hours before check-in time for the Rebbe's return flight to the States, a suitable location for the *mikveh* was indeed discovered and the engineering feasibility resolved, but unless a contract was signed within the next 45 minutes all the efforts would have been in vain. When the Rebbe would next visit Israel, this prime property would surely have been allocated to someone else. The Rebbe and Dr. Moshe Singer, general manager of Boston-Jerusalem, sped to Gadish's office with their pens poised — they had to seal this deal NOW!

The Rebbe made a somewhat uncharacteristic entrance into Gadish's office, an exuberant expression on his face. "*Mazel und bracha*!" he exclaimed. "The deal is on!"

The Rebbe withdrew a spare *kipah* from his pocket for the Deputy Mayor, to insure that this moment would be consummated in the appropriate atmosphere, but Gadish declined the Rebbe's offer. Reaching into his top drawer, Gadish produced a *kipah* of his *own*. Then, insisting that the Rebbe be seated in his executive chair, he arranged the papers on the desk for all to sign.

With the signing completed and a round of *L'chaims* toasted for the auspicious occasion, the Deputy Mayor rose from his seat, embraced the Rebbe and planted a kiss on his cheek. "I love you!" he said, and the Rebbe warmly returned his embrace.

A year later, when Yosef Gadish passed away, not only did the Rebbe attend the funeral, but he instructed his *kollel* to recite *Kaddish* and learn *mishnayos* for one year in Gadish's memory. "Because of this man," the Rebbe declared, "thousands of Jews have a beautiful shul and *beis midrash* to learn and *daven* in all day and all night."

* R.O.F.E.H. is the acronym for Reaching Out — Furnishing Emergency Healthcare, a branch of the Boston Chasidic Center which assists people from all over the world who are compelled to seek specialized medical treatment far from home.

Parashas Noach

No Questions Asked

וַיְדַבֵּר אֱלֹקִים אֶל נֹחַ לֵאמֹר: צֵא מִן הַתֵּבָה אַתָּה וְאִשְׁתְּךָ וּבָנֶיךָ וּנְשֵׁי בָנֶיךָ אִתָּךְ.

And the Lord spoke to Noach, saying: "Leave the ark, you and your wife, your sons, and your sons' wives with you."

(Bereishis 8:15,16)

The Midrash comments that the verse "If the spirit of the ruler rises above you, do not leave your place..." *(Koheles 10:4)* refers to Noach. For Noach said, "Just as I entered the ark with permission, I shall not leave without permission. Furthermore, "'For everything there is a season, and a time for every purpose under Heaven' *(Koheles 3:1)* — there was a time for Noach to enter the ark and a time for him to leave."

Had God commanded Noach to construct the ark simply to save his life, it would have been obvious that this was its purpose and Noach would have entered of his own volition. God wouldn't have had to order him to enter it. Nor would there have been any need for a Divine directive to leave the ark afterward: having survived the flood, Noach would have known that the ark had served its purpose and that it was time to disembark. Our Sages therefore contend that it was not the ark that rescued Noach but that he was saved by a miracle; the purpose of his building an ark is beyond our ken.

Thus, "If the spirit of the Ruler rises above you...," meaning, if God commanded Noach to enter the ark for some reason that was "above him," "do not leave your place" — he was not to leave the ark until God instructed him to do so. By remaining in the ark until he received the Divine directive, Noach essentially declared, "Just as I entered the ark with permission, I shall not leave without permission." Noach acted with pure faith even when the events were beyond his comprehension.

Seventy-two hours can seem like an eternity when one is awaiting glad tidings. Seventy-two hours is more than enough time to prepare oneself for joy. But for sad news, seventy-two hours is not nearly sufficient; it passes like a tiny fragment of a fraction of a second. The thought that someone so dear could suddenly be gone — that thought can barely reach the information processing center of the brain in seventy-two hours, let alone penetrate the heart. The emotional barriers which block the passage of such terrible messages are too formidable to be breached in so short a span of time.

Seventy-two hours — but three short days — was all Reb Shlomo Zalman had to absorb that terrible message about his beloved Rebbetzin, his *eishes ne'urim* who had served as partner and helpmate for over fifty years. Thursday night she felt unwell; Shabbos she was gone. At the *seudah shelishis* the Auerbachs' eldest son, Reb Shmuel — the Rosh Yeshivah of Ma'alos Ha-Torah — began to weep, and his father admonished him for allowing his sorrow to desecrate the holy Sabbath.

When the Sabbath Queen had departed, Reb Shlomo Zalman's own sorrow burst its bounds. He traveled to the hospital to sign the documents and whatever other papers the administrative staff thrust before him, and then made his way to the ward where his Rebbetzin's body still lay. He handed his overcoat to the student who had accompanied him, and then entered the room alone.

His grief was overwhelming, but it was *his* grief, not to be imposed on others. When he emerged from the hospital room, his anguish apparent, the student meekly offered Reb Shlomo Zalman his overcoat, and the Rav accepted it with a gracious smile. As he neared the hospital exit, a former student from the Kol Torah Yeshivah, unaware of the tragic circumstances which had brought the Rav to the hospital, greeted Reb Shlomo Zalman with the good news that his wife had just given birth to a baby boy. Again Reb Shlomo Zalman detached himself from his personal agony and showered the young father with blessings.

If behaving with *derech eretz* even in a moment of profound *tza'ar* presented a challenge to Reb Shlomo Zalman, there was no evidence of it. On the contrary, expressing gratitude for even the smallest of favors and joy for someone's happy event was as natural for the Rav as breathing. The real challenge of this sorrowful time yet lay ahead.

In the modest home of Reb Shlomo Zalman and his Rebbetzin lived the Rebbetzin's frail and elderly mother. At the advanced age of ninety-six and in so fragile a state of health that whenever she would place her head down to rest the family feared that she would not lift it again, she could hardly be expected to receive the news of her only daughter's demise with equanimity. The consensus among the family members was to conceal the tidings from their grandmother, at least until after the funeral, lest the news alone prove fatal to someone in such a delicate condition.

Reb Shlomo Zalman emphatically disagreed. It was the

woman's right, he declared, to be informed *before* the funeral and even to attend, if she so chose. Furthermore, he would allow no one but himself to accept the awesome responsibility of delivering the news to the Rebbetzin's mother. To do otherwise would be blatantly disrespectful. And with that, he turned toward her room to meet the challenge as only Reb Shlomo Zalman could.

Quietly the Rav entered his mother-in-law's room and gently closed the door. She lifted her eyes to him expectantly and saw the pain engraved on his face. With the utmost respect he said, "You know that the Holy One is good and all that He does is good. Sometimes we understand His ways, and sometimes we do not. You should know that the Almighty in His wisdom has taken your daughter to a place that is entirely good, and now you and I will together recite the blessing of *Dayan Ha-Emmes*, word by word, without crying."

Silence filled the tiny room. Then the elderly woman, whose own life seemed to hang by a tenuous thread, asked in a quavering voice, "How can I say it without crying?"

"All your life you have been a *tzaddekes*," her son-in-law replied. "You are able to accept this trial as well."

Together the grieving mother and husband recited the blessing, word after word, without a tear, affirming their conviction that the Almighty God is the True Judge.

Ladies First

וַיַּעְתֵּק מִשָּׁם הָהָרָה מִקֶּדֶם לְבֵית אֵל וַיֵּט אָהֳלֹה בֵּית אֵל מִיָּם וְהָעַי מִקֶּדֶם וַיִּבֶן שָׁם מִזְבֵּחַ לַה׳ וַיִּקְרָא בְּשֵׁם ה׳.

And [Avram] moved from there to the mountain east of Beis El and pitched his tent, with Beis El on the west and Ai on the east; and he built an altar to the Lord there and invoked God by name.
(Bereishis 12:8)

A feminine suffix is used to describe Avram's pitching his tent [*ohaloh*]. From this anomaly the Midrash deduces that he attended to Sarai's tent before his own. The lesson we glean here, Rabbi **Zelig Pliskin** explains, is that when a husband must do something for himself and also something for his wife, he should see to his wife's needs first.

There have been many famous couples throughout Jewish history. Dozens of names come to mind; but foremost among them are surely Zish Gutnick and his second wife, Briendel.

WHAT? You mean to say you've never heard of Zish Gutnick and his second wife Briendel? Let me introduce you.

Reb Zish Gutnick was a survivor of the Great War. As a young war orphan, he was shoved, along with scores of other

Jews from war-ravaged Rumania, down the hold of a smelly, leaking tanker, and together they bobbed and rolled their way over the ocean to Palestine. The trip from Rumania to the Holy Land was the worst and best trip of Zish's life. He was seasick and cold and thirsty, excited and happy and joyous, scared and full of hope and confidence, all at the same time. When the long voyage was finally over on a moonless night in the summer of 1921, Zish and 83 of his compatriots waded ashore to live as Jews in the Land of their forefathers.

Zish was welcomed by a family and raised on what was the first attempt at a religious *moshav*. School was out of the question (the *moshav* had none), so Zish spent his youth bouncing around from one job to another. After some years, it became apparent that *moshav* life wasn't for him. What *was* for him, no one knew. Unfortunately, the notion of vocational counseling hadn't been thought of yet. So Zish left the *moshav* and went to Jerusalem to live with a distant relative.

In Jerusalem, Zish got a job as a handyman, a misnomer if ever there was one. And if ever there was a man who shouldn't have been trusted with tools, it was Zish. It wasn't that he was incompetent. No; if he fixed a roof, it usually stayed fixed — at least until he got paid. It was just that tools and Zish appeared to be mortal enemies. If he had a hammer, he would smash any nail in sight, especially his fingernails. A saw was an invitation to perform the ancient medical practice of blood-letting. His face, hands, arms, legs and back were always finding new ways to get battered and bruised.

And behind every bruise, there was a story; if Zish was working on top of a building, there were usually two or three stories. How many times he actually fell off one was anybody's guess. Even Zish had lost count. Several times he'd also lost consciousness. But a little shpritz of water or a shot of whiskey ("Dat's de only kinda shots I take") was usually all he needed to find it again.

When Zish was an *alte bochur* of 45, he married Zelda. She was 46, the first of five sisters to get born and the last to get married. It wasn't that she hadn't tried; it was just that she had never found the right person. Zish came closer than anyone else, and by the time he came around, that was close enough.

For twenty-three years, Zish and Zelda had an ideal partnership. Whatever part of his body he would fracture, break, puncture, cut, bruise, crack, abrade, tear, chip, sever, smash or split, his devoted wife would bandage, salve, disinfect and heal.

It's one of life's ironies that, although Zish spent so much time with one foot in the grave, Zelda was the one who put both feet in first. Maybe all those broken bones broke her spirit. Perhaps she just got sick of playing Florence Nightingale. Whatever the reason, she left life to the living, and at the age of 68 Zish found himself living alone.

"*Oy*!" he said to the mirror. "Do I feel bad! Mein bones ache!"

The mirror did not respond. It just stared back at him. Still, Zish got the message. "*Oy*!" he groaned again as he noticed his reflection. "I look even vorse den I feel!"

Zish made himself a glass of tea to relax before going to bed. As he sat down at the kitchen table to drink it, he automatically looked for his wife. All he saw was an empty seat. "Zelda, Zelda," he called out, "I'm a sick man! How'm I gonna take care of myself? I don't eat. I don't sleep. Vhat's gonna become of me? If you don't vatch over me, pretty soon, you'll haf company!"

The next morning, Zish miraculously knew what to do. "Vhy didn't I tink of it before? I'll find for me a younk vife. Somevone who can cook and clean. Somevone who can sew and mend. Somevone who can vash mein clodes."

Zish went off to shul a changed man. As he laid his *tallis* bag on the table, he turned to a geriatric friend of long standing, "Zelig, I gotta get married. Find for me a younk vife."

Reb Zelig was used to Zish's complaints. But this time, it sounded like he was truly serious. "Zish, did you fall off a building again and hurt your head?"

"No. It's like dis: I can barely get up in de mornink. Mein arms is bodderink me. Mein back is killink me. Mein head is achink me. Dat's vhy I need a vife."

"Zish, you don't need a wife. You need a chiropractor."

"I got vone. He don't help. I'm tellink you, I need a vife, like my Zelda. Only younk. Maybe tirty-sometink."

"Thirty-something? You mean *19*30-something! Listen, Zish, do yourself a favor. Forget about getting married to anyone. Believe me, you'll be happier."

Zish was insistent. "If you can't help me, I'm gonna find somevone who vill!"

That evening, on his way home from work, Zish made an unscheduled stop. He dragged his broken body and his heavy tool box up four flights of steps and knocked on the door. The sign on the mailbox downstairs read:

Miriam Goldwasser, SHADCHAN

"I sure hope so!" Zish muttered to himself. "Four flights of stairs shouldn't be for notink!"

Before he had a chance to even catch his breath or in any other way prepare himself, a silver-haired lady came to the door. By her elegant appearance, refined manner and fancy jewelry, Zish figured he had the right person. "Goot evenink."

"I'm sorry," the lady said, "but I didn't call a carpenter."

"No, you didn't call me. I'm callink you. I'm lookink for mein vife."

"Why, I haven't seen her."

"Either did I since she dite. Dat's vhy I'm here. I need a new vone!"

Miriam Goldwasser smiled in spite of herself. "Come in. What did you say your name was?"

"I didn't. Gutnick. Zish Gutnick. Tenk you."

For the next forty minutes, Zish gave the *shadchante* a rundown on every time he had been run over. When he was finally finished, so was she. "Mr. Gutnick, I really do feel for you."

"So you'll marry me?"

Miriam was accustomed to many things, but Zish's head-on approach wasn't one of them. Her poise exploded in a paroxysm of coughing at the very thought.

"No! No! I-I mean you're very nice..."

Seeing how choked-up she'd gotten, Zish was encouraged.

"Is dat a yes?" he asked.

"Please, Mr. Gutnick."

"Call me Zish!"

"Zish, I'm flattered. I really am. But I don't think we were made for each other."

"Vhy not?"

"Well, I don't know the first thing about first aid!"

"You could learn. Zelda did."

"Mr. Gutnick..."

"Call me Zish!"

"Mr. Gutnick!"

"Vhat?"

"Listen to me. I am not interested in marrying you. And I don't know of anyone who would be interested in marrying you! Is that clear?"

"Vhen do you tink you'll find somevone? By next veek maybe? I'm not gettink any younker, you know."

"Believe me, I can tell," Miriam said curtly. Then she softened. "My advice to you, Mr. Gutnick, is to check the newspapers."

"I'm not lookink to buy a car."

"No, I mean the personal columns section. Perhaps you could find someone who would be compatible. In the meantime, if I hear of anyone, I'll let you know."

Zish wanted to pursue the matter further, but Miriam politely though firmly showed him the door. Slowly, he descended the four flights of stairs and walked out into the cool Jerusalem breeze.

Down but not out, Zish found himself near a newsstand. "Buy a paper!" he harumphed to himself. "Vhat kind of advice is dat?"

Still, it was the only advice he had. So Zish plunked down a couple of coins for a copy of the evening paper. Impatiently, he scanned the headlines. "Inflation. Crime. Politics. Bah! Dere's notink here for me!"

Still, he kept on reading. Finally, he found the personal column. His eyes grew wide as he studied the ads.

"Seeking a fun-loving, sports-minded, athletic type to work out together."

"I doubt she vould go for roof climbink."

"Elementary school graduate wishing to wed simple woman without intellectual pursuits or aspirations."

"Wrong gender — I tink!"

"Champion swimmer seeks lifesaver."

"Dey can bot jump in de lake togedder."

"Female, Orth. 22, looking for Yeshivish type. No smokers."

"Too younk," he said to himself.

The next entry caught his attention. *"Modern Orthodox woman, mature but young at heart, seeks similar. Obj: matrimony! Write Box 543."*

"Binko! Dat's more like it!" Zish said enthusiastically. He ripped the ad out and stuffed it in his pocket. At home, he searched frantically for a sheet of paper, but all he could find were estimate forms he'd once had made up. On the back of one of them, in his best penmanship, he scrawled this note:

בס״ד

Dear Box 543,
I am self employed Vidver looking to remarry.
If interested call dis number.
Zish Gutnick

For the next week, Zish jumped every time the phone rang. This was not easy, since he had broken both his legs on several occasions and they screamed in outrage and pain whenever he asked them to function. Furthermore, his body was one big arthritic creak of joints in need of oil.

After ten days of calisthenics, however, his note — and his prayers — were answered.

"Hello?" a warm feminine voice asked quietly. "Is this Mr. Zish Gutnick?"

"Yeah," Zish replied, hoping his pounding heart wasn't audible on the other end of the line.

"My name is Briendel Kranovsky. I placed the ad in the newspaper."

"I know," Zish said.

"You know?" Briendel asked, taken aback.

"I mean, I don't know you. I know about de ad."

"Oh, I, uh, understand. Well, I'm not quite sure where to begin. You see, I've never done anything like this before. But my first husband passed away and I..."

"My first vife pessed avay, too! Vhat a coincidence!" an exuberant Zish interjected.

"I'm really not sure," Briendel said hesitantly. "Maybe we could meet someplace and talk?"

"Sure," Zish agreed in a confident tone. "How about de Central Bus Station? It's easy to get to. Vhat if I'm meetink you dere tomorrow afternoon, say two o'clock?"

"That sounds fine."

Zish hung up the phone a new person. He quickly pulled out his *yuntifdikka* suit and tried it on — just to see how he looked. "Not bad," he told himself.

It was only later that night that a frightening thought struck him. He didn't have the slightest idea what she looked like! Zish attempted to form a mental picture of the person behind the voice. "I vould say younk. Must be maybe forty-fifty. Nice lookink. I'll know her vhen I see her," he decided finally, and blissfully drifted off to sleep.

By 10 AM, Zish had showered three times. He had also

dressed and re-dressed himself, trying every shirt he had with his suit. He made himself a glass of tea to calm down, but was too nervous to drink it. His heart was pounding and that made his legs ache. His bursitis was acting up in his shoulder, so he couldn't lift his arm above his head. His left hand was still bandaged after losing a battle with a hacksaw. Still, Zish felt terrific. By one o'clock, he couldn't stand the tension anymore, and departed for the Central Bus Station.

If you've ever been to Jerusalem's Central Bus Station, you know that it's the *last* place in the world you would want to find or meet anyone! Crowded, noisy, chaotic, it's the city's hub of activity and at any given moment you can see hundreds, if not thousands, of citizens, soldiers, students, street vendors, tourists, taxi drivers, beggars, bus drivers, policemen and others milling around. As soon as Zish entered the center of the confusion which also serves as a lobby, he knew he had made a mistake.

"How am I ever goink to find Briendel in dis place?" he asked himself. There was only one thing to do: Start asking.

"Excuse me," Zish innocently inquired of a tall girl who must have been all of twenty-two years old, "did I talk to you on de phone de odder night maybe?"

"You get out of here!" she quickly replied. "Or I'll notify the authorities!"

Zish tried again. This time, he picked on a raven-haired lady. "Excuse me, by any chance are you lookink for a husband?"

"No!" she said definitively. "And especially not you!"

Zish was used to a lot in his life, but he wasn't used to this. In seconds, his self-confidence was shattered. He beat a hasty retreat to a remote corner of the bus station. "Dis is much harder den I tought," he muttered.

After considering the matter for a few minutes, Zish came up with another plan of attack. "She's obviously lookink for me, so all I gotta do is let her find *me*!" At this, he began to stare meaningfully at every eligible-looking female in the bus station.

Unfortunately, this approach did not have the desired effect. If anything, it was even worse! One young woman was so offended at a steady gaze from a 70-year-old (even if he was a kindly-looking 70-year-old) that she brought a cop over and pointed at Zish accusingly. "That's the one, officer!" she said in a shrill voice.

The policeman told Zish to behave himself.

"Dis is too much!" Zish said, throwing his hands up in despair. "How can I marry Briendel if I can't even meet her?" Still, his determination was so great that Zish tried again. Only this time, he began to make his way slowly through the moving throngs asking young and old alike, "Briendel? Are you Briendel? Briendel?"

Meanwhile, Briendel was having troubles of her own. When she had spoken to Zish on the phone, she had thought that it might be hard to find him in a crowd. But he had sounded so self-assured that she didn't have the courage to ask him what he looked like. Now she realized what a mistake it had been to agree to meet at the bus station, and she too was moving slowly through the crowd asking all the men, "Zish? Are you Zish? Zish?" Their responses ranged from a polite "*Gesundheit!*" to something less polite.

Finally, Briendel asked, "Zish?" as Zish posed, "Briendel?"

Zish was the first to react. "Briendel? Is it really you? "

"I-I-I think so. Are you Zish?"

"Yeah. Now let's get outta here. I don't wanna attract any more attention."

Briendel and Zish shuffled over to a restaurant. Zish desperately wanted a shot of whiskey to calm his nerves, but he settled for a seltzer. Briendel countered with a glass of tomato juice.

In the quaint atmosphere of Sami's Snackiya, Zish studied his mail-order bride. He had memorized the personal column ad by reading it some 2,486 times. Now he compared it with the real thing. She was a good deal older than he had imagined. Instead of a woman in her early forties, she was a grandmotherly matron in her late sixties. In fact, she looked like everybody's *Bubbe*, from her bifocals down to her orthopedic shoes.

Slowly, formally at first, they began to talk and to compare notes. The two hours that they sat in the restaurant seemed to both of them like two minutes. At the end, Zish offered to take her home by cab. As they walked to the street, he noticed for the first time that she was limping. "Is your leg okay?" he asked.

"I think so. My knees aren't what they once were."

"So whose are? I got de same problem."

They waited in the shade of a tree for a taxi to pass by. Briendel took a little bottle of pills out of her purse.

"Vhat are dose?"

"The dose the doctor said, a couple of liver pills a day. Nothing serious. In fact, except for a few minor aches and pains, I'm as fit as a fiddle." Zish beamed at his good fortune. Briendel just smiled shyly.

That's how it all started. Zish courted Briendel for three weeks and then they became man and wife according to the Law of Moses and the State of Israel. For five years, Zish and Briendel lived in perfect harmony. They walked, talked, ate and popped pills together. They became so close that it was soon hard to tell them apart.

"Briendel, mein back," he would *krechtz*.

"Zish, your back, my feet!" she would reply.

"Briendel, mein *kop*!" he would groan.

"Zish, your *kop*, my gall bladder!" she would moan.

And so it went on, one "*krenk* call" after another. For every "*Oy!*" of Zish's, Briendel had an "*Ay!*"

Eventually, Zish had had enough."Briendel," he said one night as they met in the kitchen to toast each other with tall, cool glasses of Milk of Magnesia, "we made a mistake. I shoulda found a younker voman and you shoulda found a younker man."

"Now you tell me?"

"*Oy*, Briendel, mein *kishkes*. Listen, maybe it's not too late. You're in better shape den I am. It vould be easy for you to find a *shidduch*, somevone who could take care of you."

"*Ay*, Zish, my arthritis. You may be right. But what about you?"

"I'll see vhat I can find. Maybe I could get a younker voman to take care of me too." Zish looked at his beloved Briendel. This was not the way he had planned things, but what could he do? It was obviously God's Will that they find new partners.

After a minute's silence, he asked, "Vhat do you tink, Briendel? Tell me de trut."

"The truth? Zish, the truth is I'll do whatever makes you happy. But are you sure?"

"I vas right vhen I decided ve should get married, no?"

"Well, yes."

"So I'm right vhen I decide ve should get a divorce!"

The next day, Zish called a *Beis Din*. He explained the situation over the telephone — how he and his wife needed a divorce. Between her low blood sugar and his high blood pressure, they were obviously incompatible. He was told to gather as much documentation as he could and appear with Briendel the following Wednesday.

The week went by much too quickly for both of them. Zish was still working and self-destructing bit by bit. Cut hands, banged-up shins, a strained back. After fifty years of accidents and pain, you'd think his body parts would have learned to get out of the way, but they never cooperated. And whenever something happened, Briendel was there to patch him up.

Unfortunately, the strain of their impending divorce was beginning to tell. They found themselves snapping at each other, they even bickered, and once they actually went to sleep without their companionable Milk of Magnesia cocktails.

By the time "D-Day" arrived, they both felt as though they were airsick without ever having left the ground. While Zish went to see the Rabbis, Briendel went to see her doctor. It was just as well; Zish didn't really want her around when he made his big speech.

The Rabbinical court convened promptly at ten. At ten-oh-five, Zish began. "Honored Rabbis," he declared, borrowing a term he had heard used during the *divrei Torah* at *chassunahs*, "I'm a poor but honest man. All my life I haf vorked very hard. And I can tell you I haf a lot to show for it — see dis scar? Dat's vhere I fell off a ladder. And dis arm? It vas broken tree times and fixed tvice. And I got more bruises den de tomatoes on my old *moshav*. And my back, I can't even remember how many times I trew it out. Even my knuckles, dey don't crack no more. Dey just groan."

For the next thirty-five minutes, Zish filled them in on every ache and pain of his existence. After describing a particularly gory encounter with a circular saw, Zish watched the Rabbis nodding their heads compassionately. It was obvious to him, and to them, that he needed someone who could take better care of him than he could himself. To add weight to his case, Zish brought in notes from doctors and friends testifying to both his honesty and his klutziness. He related his entire medical and personal history in minute detail while the Rabbis took turns dozing. He was just getting to the part where he met Briendel, when she walked in.

"Briendel! Are you okay?" he asked, interrupting himself. "Vhat did de doctor say?"

Briendel looked at the *Beis Din* and tried to force a thin smile of a greeting, but she felt too weak. *"Ay!"* she groaned.

Zish responded with an *"Oy"* of his own and sped to her side, "Briendel, look at you," he cried. "I bet you forgot to take your liver pills again! Here, I'll get you a *glezl vasser.*"

Zish excused himself and left the room. He returned with a paper cup filled with warm, cloudy water. "Drink dis," he ordered his soon-to-be ex-wife. "Now, vhere vere ve? Oh, yeah, I first met my vife at the Central Bus—"

"Zish, did you wear your back brace? You know you're not supposed to leave home without it," Briendel interjected.

"Yeah, yeah. I knew you vere goink to ask, so I put it on. And I took mein blood pressure medicine too. Back to the bus station... Oh, I just remembered sometink — Briendel, vhen ve get de divorce, de first tink you haf to do is to promise me

— and I mean *promise* me — you'll check your sugar tvice a day. You know I von't be around to remind you."

"I promise, but only if you'll check your pressure twice a day too. Salt herring isn't good for a man in your condition! And you have to find someone who can make *kishke* like I make."

"I'll try. But let's get back to—"

"Zish!"

"Yeah?"

"Your back! Who's gonna rub your back? You know you can't get out of bed in the morning unless someone rubs your back."

"*Oy*, mein aching back! I forgot all about it. I guess I'll haf to get used to de pain, but de tink dat really vorries me is your dizzy spells. Did you ask de doctor about dem?"

"Yes, he thinks they have something to do with either my heart or my eyeglasses, he's not sure which."

"Right after de divorce, you're gonna haf both checked. You see, Your Honors?" Zish said, turning to the Rabbis. "It's impossible. Ve both need somevone to take care of *us*. Ve're too sick to take care of each odder."

Before beginning their deliberations, the Rabbis asked Briendel for her opinion of the impending divorce. With a great *krechtz*, followed by two "*ays*" and accompanied by a giant "*oy*" from Zish as he finally sat down, she made her way to stand (or more accurately, lean) before the court.

"Whatever my husband says is fine with me," she said. "I want what's best for him." Slowly, she creaked back to where he was sitting.

That matter dispensed with, the Rabbis adjourned to their chambers. In the meantime, Zish and Briendel exchanged phone numbers, addresses and medical prescriptions.

Ten minutes later, the court reconvened. With a low but highly audible groan, Zish pulled himself out of his chair. Briendel felt too weak to move. "Mr. and Mrs. Gutnick, based on the medical and emotional evidence you have provided, it is obvious to us that you both need qualified people to care for you."

"Vhere do I sign?" asked Zish, congratulating himself for having presented the most compelling argument since Moshe took on Pharaoh in Egypt.

The *Av Beis Din* continued, "By the power vested in us as duly constituted members of this *Beis Din*, we hereby **deny** your request for divorce. You are to remain married to each other for the rest of your years."

Zish looked at Briendel with tears in his eyes. Briendel smiled back shyly. The same shy smile from Sami's Snackiya, Zish noted. They helped each other up and limped out of the courthouse together.

And they lived happily (*oy!*) ever (*ay!*) after.

Disdain Disgrace

וַתֹּאמֶר שָׂרַי אֶל אַבְרָם חֲמָסִי עָלֶיךָ אָנֹכִי נָתַתִּי שִׁפְחָתִי בְּחֵיקֶךָ וַתֵּרֶא כִּי הָרָתָה וָאֵקַל בְּעֵינֶיהָ יִשְׁפֹּט ה׳ בֵּינִי וּבֵינֶיךָ.

And Sarai said to Avram, "My outrage is due to you! I placed my maid in your bosom, and [when] she saw that she had conceived, I became lesser in her eyes; let God judge between me and you!"

(Bereishis 16:5)

As Sarai was barren, she urged her husband to wed her maidservant Hagar, so that he might have children through her. When this indeed occurred, Hagar disgraced Sarai. The Midrash notes that the idiom "outrage" which Sarai used — *chamasi alecha* — alludes to its literal meaning: "You have stolen [from] me." The implication is that Avram's silence amid Sarai's disgrace was equivalent to theft.

In what way was his silence tantamount to stealing? As Rabbi **Yosef Leipowitz** explains, if one witnesses his fellow man being humiliated and makes no attempt to defend his honor, this inaction is an act of thievery. One is withholding that which rightfully belongs to every individual: his honor and dignity.

One day, Reb Avigdor Halberstam was invited to be the *sandak* for the first son of Reb Michel the *baal agalah* (wagon driver). Reb Michel and his wife, Sheina Brienda, were blessed with six daughters before the Master of the Universe bestowed upon them a son. Perched atop his wagon Reb Michel had witnessed Reb Avigdor's holy ways from near and far and therefore asked the pious *parush* to do him the tremendous honor of being his son's *sandak*. Reb Avigdor agreed.

He cradled the newborn in his arms, and his thoughts concentrated on the mystical significance of *bris milah*. Reb Avigdor watched as Yosel the *mohel* bent over the baby, heard Reb Michel recite the blessing, and felt the little baby's body tense up. But his thoughts never wandered from their lofty plateau. In seconds, it was over and the townspeople cried: "MAZEL TOV! MAZEL TOV!"

The beautiful ceremony of *bris milah* was followed by an equally beautiful and bountiful *seudah*. Reb Michel and his wife were not wealthy in a monetary sense, but they had a wealth of friends who wished to share in the *simchah* and mitzvah.

"Eat... eat, Reb Avigdor. It's a mitzvah!" Reb Michel urged his honored guest.

"I'll wash and have a little bread. But please do not be offended if I refrain from partaking of the main course. You realize, of course, that consuming a full plate is not necessarily a sign of a full heart — merely a full stomach!" Thus Reb Avigdor managed once again to spare his host an expense, and at the same time retain his regimen of physical denial.

In the earlier stages of Reb Avigdor's journeys he had traveled alone and actually shunned company. But before long, a devoted group of disciples gravitated to the *parush* and followed him wherever he went.

As his fame spread, Reb Avigdor regularly received invitations to the homes of the more prominent members of the local communities. He frequently used these opportunities to build a bridge between those who were in a position to give and those who were in a position to receive.

One *erev Shabbos*, Reb Avigdor and several of his students were invited to spend the Holy Day of Rest at the home of Berke, the grain merchant. Berke was a man of means, observant, generous and, if the truth be known, accustomed to having his own way.

Early Friday afternoon the table was arrayed just the way Berke liked it. The company observed settings of gleaming silver, sparkling crystal, and an exquisite lace tablecloth that was said to have come all the way from Warsaw. With a look of contentment Berke surveyed the scene with his distinguished guests, and then commented in a satisfied tone, "I don't believe that there is anything more beautiful than a Shabbos table..." Suddenly, he stopped in mid-sentence.

"Wait a minute!" he shouted. "Where are the saltcellars? Masha, get in here right away!"

A slight girl of about fourteen came scurrying out of the kitchen, wiping her work-worn hands on her apron. "Wh... what is the matter?" she stammered timorously. "Did I do something wrong?"

"I told you to set the table!" Berke said sternly. "You have forgotten the salt!"

"I'm... I'm so... so sorry. I must have been in a hurry to finish making Shabbos."

"Well, see that it doesn't happen again! When my guests and I return from shul, we expect everything to be perfect."

"You must understand," Berke told his guests apologetically, as the exhausted and obviously despondent girl scuttled back to the kitchen, "she's an orphan. We took her in two years ago. Not terribly bright, but at least she's a hard worker. I suppose one of these days she'll get married, but in the meantime we keep her here."

Reb Avigdor tried to encourage Berke to be more understanding. "God chose the Jewish People," he explained, "because they were 'the smallest of the nations.' This refers to the ability of the Jew to make himself 'small,' to subjugate his own will to the will of his Maker.

"By taking the poor girl into your home you have done this, but in order to really fulfill the mitzvah properly, you have to treat her as one of your own, and that includes giving her the benefit of the doubt. In fact, it's a good idea to get into the habit of judging others favorably, particularly if you yourself wish to be judged this way. Sometimes even a great rabbi may do something that appears to be the opposite of good!"

"Thank you for your words of Torah," Berke countered. "Let me assure you that I treat her just as I treat everyone in my family. I give her clothes, food and a place to stay. And if I demand a lot from her, it's only because I also demand a lot from myself! But enough of this, we're going to be late for shul."

Berke and his honored guests joined the townsfolk in the humble shul. Berke was chosen to lead the congregation and his booming voice and joyous energy brought all those assembled into the Shabbos spirit. Before departing everyone paid tribute to Berke's masterful davening, and calls of "*Gutt Shabbos*! *Gutt Shabbos*!" echoed through the streets.

Reb Avigdor and his disciples slowly made their way to Berke's home. The darkness outside made the candles inside glow even brighter, and the light leaped and mirrored off the elegant candlesticks, crystal goblets and gleaming silverware. The missing saltcellars had been placed neatly at the head of the table.

After *Kiddush* and *Hamotzi*, Berke graciously invited his guests to partake of the *seudah*. "If anyone leaves this Shabbos table hungry," he exclaimed, "it's his own fault!"

As was his custom, Reb Avigdor ate sparingly.

"Is there anything wrong, Rabbi?" Berke inquired. "Why aren't you eating like your colleagues?"

Reb Avigdor smiled. "As you know, sublime thoughts accompanying the actual act of eating are capable of raising the holy sparks found only in food that is kosher. I can tell by the way everyone is enjoying himself that my help isn't required in this regard."

The guests continued their meal and the evening passed, bathed in the sweet warmth and glow unique to the Sabbath. It would have been superfluous, and indeed might have detracted from the joy of the Sabbath meal, had mention been made of the incident of Masha and the saltcellars, so the subject was discreetly avoided.

In fact, everything continued to go quite well until Shabbos lunch, when Reb Avigdor did something that evoked a sense of awe, curiosity, and utter amazement.

Berke, his wife, his four children, and his guests were all unusually hungry. It seemed that both the Rabbi's eloquent *derashah* and the *chazzan's* mellifluous *musaf* had been delivered in a way expressly designed to impress Reb Avigdor, and as a result the Shabbos davening had lasted much longer than usual. The scent of the simmering cholent that filled the house was more tempting than ever. The challah, as delicious as it was, did little to satisfy everyone's whetted appetite.

"We observe a little custom in our house," Berke announced, "of allowing a special guest to serve the cholent. Please, Reb Avigdor, do the honors, if you will."

Reb Avigdor was about to demur, but the savory cholent

was ceremoniously placed before him. He gripped the handles of the pot, intending to pass it back to his host, when he smelled the steaming mixture of meat and potatoes. Suddenly, Reb Avigdor stopped. He hauled the cholent back toward his plate, and began sampling it straight from the pot!

"It's really quite good," Reb Avigdor declared. "Very, very tasty!" At least that's what it sounded like, because frankly it was difficult to understand what he was saying. He kept eating and eating, stuffing overflowing ladlefuls of cholent into his mouth faster than he could swallow them! Chunks of meat and gelatinous globs of potatoes fell into his beard, looking like boulders in a hairy forest. Clusters of beans and other unidentifiable ingredients showered down and around his plate.

Berke coughed politely in order to get his guest's attention. Other members of the family merely stared thunderstruck, eyes bulging and jaws agape. Reb Avigdor's devoted disciples looked at one another uncomfortably; never before had they witnessed such outrageous behavior, and certainly not from their Rebbe!

Reb Avigdor was unfazed by the reactions. He continued to push, cram and stuff meat and potatoes, onions and carrots, and barley and lima beans into his gaping mouth as fast as he could scoop them up.

Berke's family and guests watched in dismay as their erstwhile meal disappeared before their eyes. Reb Avigdor was insatiable. What would make an ascetic who looked as if he could survive on air suddenly eat like a boorish peasant? they wondered. Did he not realize there were others at the table? Was he unaware of the scene he was causing?

When every globule of glutinous meat, every sliver of succulent potato, and every slice of sugar-sweet carrot were gobbled up, Reb Avigdor asked innocently, "Do you have any more?"

Dumbfounded, Berke brought out the remainder. This, too, was voraciously devoured by his guest, down to the last scrap and morsel. When he finished he scraped the pot with the spoon one more time, as though to make sure that no vestige of what once had been a colossal cholent remained around the rim.

"Is there any left?" Reb Avigdor asked when even the servants' portion was eaten up.

"Eh... no. I'm afraid not," a thoroughly shaken Berke lamented.

"Excellent. Truly excellent," Reb Avigdor exclaimed. "That was a Shabbos meal to remember!"

"It certainly was!" Berke replied, still in a state of shock.

After Shabbos, it came time for the guests to bid their host good-bye. Reb Avigdor shook Berke's hand warmly, and related, "Our Sages have declared that an act of hospitality is even greater than greeting the Divine Presence. We derive this lesson from the fact that God waited, as it were, while Avraham ran to invite the three angels disguised as men into his tent.

"My dear Berke, you too have fulfilled the mitzvah in a manner worthy of Avraham *Avinu*."

"Thank you, Rabbi," Berke replied, still remembering his cholent. "And if you are ever in this area again, please stop by," he added somewhat unenthusiastically.

"It would be my pleasure," Reb Avigdor responded. "And please thank Masha for that wonderful cholent."

Once on the road, Reb Avigdor's *talmidim* respectfully remained silent. They knew their Rebbe, and their Rebbe knew them.

After a while, he turned to them and defused the tension. "You know what my illustrious brother has said about living a life of holiness and avoiding luxury, how he has stressed that one's outer garb or appearance serves only as a reminder of the tenuousness of this world and the eternal promise of the World to Come." They all nodded pensively.

"So what then are your thoughts concerning my consuming the cholent?"

"You were trying to raise up certain holy sparks," replied one of his students.

"Not that I'm aware of," their master answered.

"You knew we were hungry, and wanted to prevent us from succumbing to our desires," said another.

"No, I didn't think of that either."

"You really wanted the mitzvah of '*oneg*' on Shabbos?" proposed a third.

"Yes, but certainly not at everyone else's expense," Reb Avigdor responded.

"Maybe you were extremely hungry yourself?" suggested a fourth *talmid*, offering an ignoble explanation in his zeal to solve the mystery.

"You're right — I guess I *was* hungry... hungry to do a mitzvah! As soon as I smelled the cholent, I knew something was wrong and my first taste confirmed my suspicion. Somehow Masha had flavored it with kerosene. If Berke had found out, I feared the poor girl would have been sent away on the spot. Something had to be done to save her position."

"But what about Berke?"

"I traded his ephemeral Shabbos meal in *Olam Hazeh* for something eternal."

"And what is that?" they all chimed in.

"The paramount mitzvah of supporting an orphan —

and meriting *Olam Haba*!"

The disciples, witnesses to Reb Yisrael of Ruzhin, admirers of Reb Chaim of Zanz, and adherents of Reb Avigdor Halberstam, exchanged a look of consummate understanding.

Remiss in His Mission

וַיִּשָּׂא עֵינָיו וַיַּרְא וְהִנֵּה שְׁלֹשָׁה אֲנָשִׁים נִצָּבִים עָלָיו וַיַּרְא וַיָּרָץ לִקְרָאתָם מִפֶּתַח הָאֹהֶל וַיִּשְׁתַּחוּ אָרְצָה.

And [Avraham] lifted his eyes and saw, and behold, three men were standing over him; he saw and ran toward them from the entrance of the tent, and he bowed to the ground.

(Bereishis 18:2)

God made the day too hot for traveling, so no guests would trouble Avraham after his painful circumcision. Yet the absence of visitors pained Avraham even more, so God sent him angels, appearing as nomads.

What precisely upset Avraham? The absence of wayfarers suffering from the heat should have pleased a man who always sought to bring comfort to others!

The Midrash records that Avraham complained, "Prior to my circumcision, travelers came my way, but now they have stopped." As Rabbi **Elchanan Sorotzkin** explains, our forefather worried that his *bris milah* would render him a less desirable individual and as word of it got around, passersby would be put off, thus denying him the opportunity to influence them to serve God.

Thus on the third day after his circumcision, when he felt ready to resume his "outreach" activities, he was distressed to see no visitors and concluded that the fact of his circumcision had indeed created a barrier between him and potential converts.

God therefore sent angels disguised as men to assure Avraham that he need not fear, for he would yet continue his mission.

This phase was the most difficult one of Rabbi Nison Alpert's existence, but not only for the obvious reasons. When, earlier, Rabbi Alpert had been compelled to regularly undergo excruciating radiology treatments, his usually jovial spirits began to sag. His close friend Reb Dov Wallowitz, who had escorted him to Boston for the treatments, had implored Reb Nison to unburden himself. Rabbi Alpert had always been such a happy, friendly individual — it seemed strange that after all he had gone through with his illness and still had carried on as if nothing was wrong, that suddenly he should appear so despondent.

"Dov," Reb Nison had said, fighting back the tears, "it is not the illness but the *bitul Torah* which is killing me."

Foresight

וַיִּקְרָא אַבְרָהָם שֵׁם הַמָּקוֹם הַהוּא ה' יִרְאֶה אֲשֶׁר יֵאָמֵר הַיּוֹם בְּהַר ה' יֵרָאֶה.

And Avraham named that site Hashem Yireh, as it is said this day, "On the mount, the Lord is seen."

(Bereishis 22:14)

The Midrash elucidates this passage, observing that Avraham referred to the location of the Temple as a "mountain," while Yitzchak called it a "field" *(Bereishis 24:63)*, and Yaakov spoke of a "house" *(28:17)*.

Rabbi **Yissachar Frand** relates this Midrash to the prayers that the Patriarchs instituted. Avraham originated the prayers of the morning, which symbolize brightness, security and hope. Avraham lived a morning-like existence, so his prayer reminds us to supplicate when times are good.

Yaakov, however, began the prayers of the evening, which symbolize darkness and travail. Yaakov's life was filled with suffering, so he taught us to pray when times are rough.

Like his father and his grandfather, Yaakov prayed on the site of the Temple. In his time — as in ours — the spot was desolate, yet he perceived the light at the end of the tunnel. Yaakov realized that that lonely, lifeless plot, bereft of any light, would one day become a "House." It would be blessed in the future with the Holy Temple. Yaakov's perspective did not allow him to be discouraged by the present; he focused on the potential of the future.

"The Coastal Plain extends along the eastern United States from Massachusetts on the Atlantic coast to Texas on the shores of the Gulf of Mexico..."

That was the unmistakable Mrs. Klonsky, this time entertaining her avid students with fascinating geography tidbits. "The Coastal Plain varies in width from 75 to 300 miles. Along the Atlantic coast the surface is low, but then the land rises gradually to the west until it meets the Piedmont Plateau — i.e. the foothills of the Appalachian Highlands..."

Some of these vital details admittedly were lost on the students, who were busy writing copious letters, discussing fashion trends, cramming for an upcoming test, or simply relaxing (read: dozing) to the extremely conducive muzak of Coastal Plainology.

That is, until Rabbi Binyamin Steinberg made one of his famous surprise invasions. These unexpected forays in the middle of class were actually cherished by teachers and students alike. The teachers knew that they would benefit from their principal's sagacious advice regarding the material and their teaching methodology. He always had a tactful and upbeat way of presenting suggestions that were never off the mark. Furthermore, his liable-to-materialize-at-any-time presence did wonders for curbing potential trouble-makers within the class.

The students appreciated the diversion and relief their

principal's unannounced visits afforded. Even if the class wasn't bogged down with the intricacies of the Piedmont Plateau, the Appalachian Highlands, or the Allegheny Mountains, the Rabbi's good cheer and infectious sense of humor always livened up the lesson and actually transformed the boring into almost interesting.

Amazingly, Rabbi Steinberg, renowned principal of Bais Yaakov of Baltimore, was able to drop in on any class, be it *limudei Kodesh*, the sciences, literature, mathematics, history — you name it — and not only offer an intelligent comment, but just as easily substitute for the regular teacher, as he often did, whenever a teacher of any grade was absent.

On rare occasions, his surprise visits were viewed as "search and destroy" missions. Although his purpose in entering the classroom was actually to monitor and gauge the students' as well as the teachers' performance, he sometimes appeared just in time to nip a disciplinary problem in the bud.

Needless to say, Rabbi Steinberg's arrival in class was always greeted by expedient activation of "paying attention/keen interest" mode. Students who otherwise displayed at most mild interest in the estuaries of the northern coastline, or the low elevation around the Mississippi River, were suddenly intrigued by the subject. Utensils, amusements and artifacts that might otherwise have diverted the girls' attention from Mrs. Klonsky's instruction, instantly vanished. Writing implements assiduously engaged in extracurricular activities were swiftly reassigned to the scheduled subject matter. And all forms of literature not directly related to the topic evaporated like the morning mist. The more courageous among the student body greeted Rabbi Steinberg's arrival with raised hands in a valiant semblance of interest and participation.

Shira Markowitz, however, was caught off guard. Rabbi Steinberg swung around to the back of the room, a position which offered him a panoramic, uninterrupted view of how Incident Sheet* Shira integrated the lessons of the Intermountain Plateau's landforms.

Actually, at the time, Shira was engaged in some earthworks of her own as she double-handedly scooped chocolate pudding from a cup into her mouth, without benefit of a spoon. Great Plains and Central Lowland aside, this was definitely grounds for a weighty report on her already crowded incident sheet. One look at her mud-colored fingers made Shira realize that her name was mud, and that her ignoble nickname would cling to her like the viscous pudding clung to her skin.

Up to this point, Shira's incident sheet was decorated with an inordinate but otherwise unremarkable number of infractions, including tardiness, incomplete assignments, and being caught in the hall without permission. Today's report was sure to add plenty of color to her otherwise drab violations.

Color was indeed the operative word. Both of Shira's hands were dripping and coated in dark, rich, creamy chocolate pudding. There was nowhere to hide them, no way to clean them. To raise one of them under the guise of participating in the classroom discussion would have been suicidal, or at least self-incriminating. To try and conceal the evidence by sitting on her hands would have left telltale signs of her crime all over her clothes and created a dry cleaner's nightmare.

Keen-eyed Rabbi Steinberg resolved her dilemma by informing the perpetrator that her crime had not gone unnoticed. "Miss Markowitz, would you kindly step into my office?" Shira's moment of reckoning had arrived.

Shira had but one long hallway to dream up a justification. The time that this afforded was little enough; trying to keep pace with Rabbi Steinberg's ground-eating stride rendered the distance and Shira's alibi-planning time insignificant. En route, she licked and sucked her fingers madly in an attempt to purge them of the damning evidence while simultaneously searching — futilely — for a garbage pail where she could stow the pudding cup.

Things just weren't working out for Incident Sheet Shira Markowitz. In moments she was seated in the principal's office with her still chocolate-covered hands in plain view. Rabbi Steinberg tactfully handed her some paper towels and busied himself with the papers on his desk while she commenced her clean-up operation.

With swift, purposeful strokes Shira attempted to make quick work of her mopping up to demonstrate that there really wasn't such a mess after all. But this was not to be. The pudding was everywhere, and every swipe of the paper towel merely transferred it from one part of her hand to the next.

Patient Rabbi Steinberg, whose eyes remained fixed on his desk the entire time, detected that Shira hadn't yet succeeded in ridding herself of the slimy goop. Without looking up he handed her some extra towels, and fervently hoped for a speedy conclusion. The end, unfortunately, was nowhere in sight.

Shira could have been auditioning for a vaudeville slapstick routine. The industrious seventh-grader ringed each of her fingers and then proceeded to dab at her face as if she were playing a samba on her cheeks. The amount of paper toweling at her disposal was unequal to the task.

She realized that to ask for more would be tantamount to a confession of guilt. Thus, by default, she kept folding the paper in halves and quarters and eighths, trying to locate a still-absorbent section. To no avail. She discovered, to her frustration, that wherever she rubbed, she was applying more pudding than she was removing.

At this juncture Rabbi Steinberg handed the entire roll to

the poor girl and bided his time a few more seconds before addressing the matter at hand. Then, in a stern, yet friendly tone, the principal began. "I should really suspend you for behavior unbecoming a Bais Yaakov student," he told her. "Indeed, for behavior unbecoming a *tzelem Elokim*. I should, but I'm afraid that if I do you'll misconstrue the true nature and magnitude of the crime."

"You mean that I shouldn't have been eating pudding in class?"

Rabbi Steinberg shook his head no.

"You mean that I shouldn't have eaten pudding in class with my fingers?"

Rabbi Steinberg shook his head again.

"You mean that I shouldn't have eaten pudding in class with my fingers and gotten caught?"

"Astute deduction," Rabbi Steinberg remarked dryly, "but I'm afraid that you are still missing the point.

"The actual crime here was that you did not eat a good breakfast this morning. Eating the pudding, even if it was intended to rectify this wrong, is proof of that, putting aside for the moment — and I mean, just for the moment — the undeniable fact that it was consumed during class. The appropriate thing would have been at least to eat something nutritious." He allowed that thought to sink into Shira's nutrient-starved brain before passing sentence.

"And so," Rabbi Steinberg declared, "for the foreseeable future, I am going to monitor you to make sure that every morning you eat a proper breakfast..."

"You mean you're not going to write a report on my incident sheet?!"

"...I mean I shall check on you daily to verify that you have eaten a good breakfast, *before* coming to school. Miss Markowitz, are you familiar with the expression 'The proof of the pudding is in the eating'? In your case, the proof that you are eating a proper breakfast will be the *absence* of pudding — in your classroom, on your hands, on your face, or in my office!"

"No report on my incident sheet?" Shira reiterated in disbelief.

"No pudding, Miss Markowitz. No more pudding!"

* A student's record of unfavorable incidents which, when tallied, could result in a host of punishments including lowering of grades, demotion, or suspension.

Time-Honored Tradition

וַיִּהְיוּ חַיֵּי שָׂרָה מֵאָה שָׁנָה וְעֶשְׂרִים שָׁנָה וְשֶׁבַע שָׁנִים שְׁנֵי חַיֵּי שָׂרָה.

One hundred years and twenty years and seven years, these were the years of Sarah's life.
(Bereishis 23:1)

The Midrash relates that, in mid-sermon, Rabbi Akiva once saw that his audience was dozing off, so he expounded, "Why was Queen Esther privileged to reign over 127 provinces? Because she descended from Sarah, who lived 127 years."

What was it about this interpretation that could rouse drowsing students?

Rabbi **Yitzchak Meir of Gur** explains that Rabbi Akiva wished to stress the value of time. How was Esther able to rule over 127 states? Because Sarah's years were entirely free of sin! Sarah's well-spent time meant that every moment of her existence earned a reward: each second, a farm; each minute, another district; each hour, another village.

We all have been given the gift of time — to employ wisely or abuse. Who can fathom the reward for time well spent? This very thought snapped Rabbi Akiva's listeners to attention.

When his dentist informed him that one of his teeth required root canal work, Reb Nison Alpert was appalled — but not for the usual reasons. He inquired as to what the procedure entailed and when he learned that several lengthy sessions were necessary, he asked the dentist to just pull the tooth and be done with it. He simply could not spare the time. For the very same reason he never became a United States citizen: the naturalization process was too time-consuming. Reb Nison had no time to spare from his heavy schedule of learning and teaching Torah.

No Illusions

וָאֹמַר אֶל אֲדֹנִי אֻלַי לֹא תֵלֵךְ הָאִשָּׁה אַחֲרָי.

And I said to my master, "Perhaps the woman will not follow me."

(Bereishis 24:39)

"As for the merchant the balances of deceit are in his hand, he loves to oppress" *(Hoshea 12:8)*. The Midrash equates this merchant with Eliezer, who sought to marry his own daughter off to Yitzchak — the "loved one who is oppressed."

Why such criticism of Eliezer, accusing him of ignoble intent when — although he did hope for Yitzchak to be his own son-in-law — he never acted dishonestly or engaged in fraud?

Rabbi **Zvi Hirsh Wolk** explains that "deceitful balances" does not imply an absolute falsehood, but rather truthful, yet deceptive behavior. Although Eliezer behaved with seeming propriety, the act of concealing his true intentions fell within the realm of deceit. Giving a false impression, even when no actual falsehoods are uttered, is categorized by the Rabbis as deceit.

When the *chassan* of one of Reb Shlomo Zalman Auerbach's granddaughters was invited to meet his illustrious future grandfather-in-law, Reb Shlomo Zalman was surprised to find the table laid with fine china. Unlike his own dishes, this set was perfectly intact and all the many pieces matched. It was apparent that the Rebbetzin, knowing that the young man came from a well-to-do family, had borrowed her neighbor's lovely china for this special occasion, and had prepared a lavish array of food to present thereon.

Reb Shlomo Zalman was swift to dispel any illusions of grandeur which this sumptuous spread might have created, and explained that normally, on a *Motza'ei Shabbos*, the Auerbachs were "just regular," nothing fancy. He went on to mention Rashi's comment on the verse where Avraham *Avinu* enjoins Sarah to serve their guests lavishly, saying: מהרי שלש סאים קמח סלת — "Quick! [bring] three measures of flour..." Rashi explains that the reason Avraham had to expedite Sarah was because "A woman is not [by nature] generous with guests."

"The behavior of my Rebbetzin tonight," the Rav continued, "seems to contradict Rashi's observation, but I believe I can suggest a resolution: If a woman wishes to entertain her guests in a lavish fashion, she will do so but once a year, and the rest of the time she will be less generous. However, if she were to receive her guests in her regular, normal way, she would be pleased and able to do so all the time."

Awed as the young *chassan* must have been to find himself in the presence of the *Gaon*, he probably paid no attention whatsoever to the dinnerware. Just sitting at Reb Shlomo Zalman's table — not to mention, marrying the *Gadol*'s granddaughter — was fancy enough for anyone.

Hypocritic Oath

וַיְהִי עֵשָׂו בֶּן אַרְבָּעִים שָׁנָה וַיִּקַּח אִשָּׁה....

And Eisav was forty years old, and he took a wife....

(Bereishis 26:34)

Two characteristics distinguish a kosher animal: it must have split hooves and it must chew its cud. The pig has only one of these characteristics — split hooves. However, when a pig crouches down, its outstretched hooves seem to say, "Look how kosher I am," though it is not a ruminant.

The Midrash compares Eisav to a pig, for he maintained a promiscuous lifestyle and consorted with heathen women, yet at the age of 40 he made a show of settling down and marrying. Although this act might have signaled a dramatic change in his lifestyle, he continued to engage in abominable behavior; his marriage was no more than a porcine display of purity.

Rabbi **Yeruchem Levovitz** points out that hypocrisy is not unique to Eisav. Some people lead evil lives, but once they perform a single good deed — or introduce one altruistic component into an otherwise immoral act — they proclaim themselves to be righteous.

Fritz, you mind I see dat plizz?" Goldie asked. He held the *Jerusalem Post* to his chest possessively. "Come on, Fritz, I giff it right beck, don' vorry." Fritz surrendered his precious periodical, looking hopelessly lost without it.

"Here, Frieda, you are readink der best Enklich fun all uf us," she said, handing over the newspaper.

Frieda was obviously flattered. She preened and basked in the compliment, then shot Fritz a snide smirk, cleared her throat, and began to read:

> Dozens of Yemenites who immigrated between 1949 and 1951 claim that during their stay in the Transit Camps (*ma'abarot*) they were compelled to place their youngsters and newborns in the communal nursery. Later on, when they visited their children, the mothers were informed that the babies had taken ill and had been transferred to hospital.
>
> The mothers were all in agreement that news of their babies' illnesses had come as a shock. "Only the night before," said Mrs. Miriam Sharaby, "when I went to nurse my daughter, she appeared to be in the best of health." Her eyes filled with tears as she added: "How could a baby born on holy soil be anything but healthy?"
>
> Although the families were quartered in different temporary housing facilities for varying periods of time, their experiences were strikingly similar. Bracha Gamliel of the Rosh Ha'ayin camp related the following: "The people in charge of the nursery at first would not tell me where my son was, only that he was in hospital. I became hysterical. Finally they revealed the name of the hospital. My oldest daughter and I hitchhiked to the hospital

to see the baby, but when we arrived we were told that he had died."

Subsequent investigations revealed numerous discrepancies. The burial plot indicated as the site of her son's interment turned out to be nonexistent; the attending physician who had issued the death certificate was not registered in the hospital's staff roster.

Bracha Gamliel, Miriam Sharaby and over thirty other Yemenite mothers refuse to believe their children are deceased.

"Tsk, tsk, tsk, tsk, tsk," Goldie clucked sympathetically. Her eyes glistened with shared emotion. "I don' know vat's voise — to know der kit is det, or not to know vone vay or ah nudder."

"It's all just a bureaucratic mishmash," Fritz derided. "So they didn't write down the right place they buried the kids. Big deal. So the hospital records are a mess — this is news? It doesn't mean the kids are alive, or that they were stolen, or that there was any kind of conspiracy."

"Shem on you, Fritz," Goldie chastised him. "You should know betta. If de kitz vas tiny bebbies, so, sure, dey mebbe buried dem in ah nunmarked grev. Bot if dey vas olter — some uf dem vas two years, eefen four years — der mamas an' papas gotta know vhere is de grev."

"Of course," Frieda agreed, more than pleased to have an ally against her perpetual adversary. "But there were so many of them — you think they all died? It *had* to be a plot to steal the babies. They figured these women would never notice one more or one less when they had so many. Then they gave the babies to childless couples — or sold them!"

"Frieda, dahlink, it's not nice you should say 'dey' like

det whole govemend vas bed. Efter all, der govemend safed ah lots pipple. Bot in efery berrel dere's vone, two bleck sheeps. If dere vas soch ah conspiritzy, mebbe ah coupl'a bleck sheeps vas in it."

They tossed Goldie's idea around a little while longer, but came to no conclusion. Fritz remained adamantly skeptical of the entire affair. "Ach, you two old yentas are making a mountain out of a molehill," he insisted. "The whole business is just a figment of overactive imaginations."

The geriatric threesome lunched on cream cheese and olive sandwiches and sweet tea which Goldie doled out from her voluminous shopping bag and lingered on the bench until an unseasonably cool breeze began to blow.

"Plizz excuse me, lady an' gentlesman. I kent stend ah *tzuk* in mine *kraitz*." She bid her bench friends "Shalom" and headed for her apartment on Rechov Ruth, just off Tel Aviv's Dizengoff Circle. Faigaleh's replacement, Faigaleh II, was due for an airing in any case — that is, the cage would be suspended from a hook on the balcony for several hours while Goldie took her afternoon nap. Unlike his tone-deaf predecessor and namesake, Faigaleh was a warbler of some note, and a very contrary-minded one at that. Only when he was certain his mistress was asleep did he burst into song, hence the need to put the canary out during "siesta" hour.

With thoughts of Faigalehs I and II flitting through her mind and snatches of the morning's rambling conversation competing for her attention, Goldie was more than normally preoccupied when she stepped off the curb. A rusty-blue pockmarked "tender" swerved sharply and screeched to a halt mere inches from her Dr. Scholl's lace-ups, and as it did so, a cream and tan Mercedes plowed into its rear end.

The swarthy van driver jumped out screaming unintelligibly in fluent polyglot. *"Ya chamor!"* [Fool!] he bellowed at Goldie, at the driver of the Mercedes, at his van's posterior, and at the street at large. He slammed his palms down on the accordion-pleated, sprung hood of the late-model Mercedes and shouted, *"Ayn lechah breksim*?! *Harasta li bek-ex*!" [Don't you know how to stop? You've destroyed my rear-axle!]

Goldie stood frozen like Lot's wife, visions of her own plump body pleated like the hood numbing her senses. The passenger door of the van creaked open and out hopped a tiny, middle-aged woman with a bright-colored scarf wrapped around her head. She scurried to Goldie's side on slippered feet, chattering incessantly in a gutteral tongue, and then, to Goldie's added astonishment, grasped her hand and kissed it. Still chattering and making signs heavenward, she lifted the hem of Goldie's skirt and kissed that too, as one might kiss a Torah mantle.

All the while, Goldie remained transfixed. The woman, who Goldie reasoned was the driver's mother, scuttled over to the Mercedes and repeated her performance with the shaky teenager behind the wheel. Trembling, and with tears pouring from her eyes, the girl-driver placed her hands on her sun-tanned cheeks and shook her head from side to side in dismay.

Goldie roused herself from her stupor and poked her head through the passenger-side window of the Mercedes. "You spick Enklich, dahlink?"

The teenager turned towards her, shock and terror vying for first place in her eyes. "Ditchoo got a beng?" Goldie asked solicitously. "You vant I should call ah docteh?"

"N-no, no calling doctor," the girl stammered in high-school English almost as atrocious as Goldie's. "I-I not hurt. But auto — is bad, very bad. My parents... my parents be so angry!" A fresh wave of tears burst the floodgates.

"Vat for you cryink abot ah hunk uf teen? Tenks God you got your helt!"

The driver and his mother were still carrying on, he handling the ranting and gesticulating, she the osculating. Soon a clutch of rubberneckers had gathered and, in typical Israeli fashion, enthusiastically joined the fray. Traffic in Dizengoff Circle came to a standstill as scores of drivers piled out of their vehicles. There was much vociferous dispute over where to place the blame, the estimated cost of the repair, and, in particular, the best way to disengage the locked bumpers without inflicting even greater damage.

Six beefy bystanders had already hoisted the Mercedes clear of the tender-fender and were just about to march the cream leviathan backwards along the asphalt when two of Tel Aviv's Finest appeared on the scene.

"Alright, drop that car!" one of the officers demanded and the sextet of human hydraulic elevators promptly complied. The Mercedes came down with a crash that made its driver swoon into Goldie's welcoming arms.

The second patrolman was engaged in a shoving/shouting match with the van driver, whose mother was kissing anything that moved, and Goldie seized the opportunity to slip away to a quieter piece of sidewalk with her semi-conscious charge in tow. She sat the teenager down on the curb and, with a lace handkerchief, dusted off a square of pavement for herself.

"Vat's your name, dahlink?"

"Z-Zehava. Zehava Perlmutter."

"Dat's ver' nice, I em also Zehava, bot you ken call me Goldie. Now tell me efreytink."

Through tears and hiccups, Zehava reported that her parents were abroad and that they had denied her permission to drive the Mercedes in their absence. She had disobeyed their orders. "Is very terrible! They will to kill me!

They will to kill me!"

"Sha! Don' talk nontzense. I em sure your perentz luff you an' perentz vat luffs der kitz don' keel dem. Mebbe, dell scream etchoo, mebbe brek ah coupl'a bones — I'm just choking!"

"It is not joke! They *will* be breaking for sure my bones!"

"Nah," Goldie tried again. "Pipple is not brekkink der bones fun der own blud. Dat fella dere" — she pointed at the van-driver who was still going strong — "dat fella dere dey mide brek der bones from, bot not der own blud."

"That is what... oh, is no important." Zehava fell silent, her shoulders slumped in despair.

The swift-thinking patrolman (who earlier had ordered the release of the Mercedes) finished collecting all the loose car parts into an upturned hubcap and began taking down everyone's particulars on a grimy notepad. From her curbside perch, Goldie could see the van driver being handcuffed and shoved into the back seat of a police cruiser. His hands immobilized, he had become speechless, but his mother had turned ever more voluble.

"Excuse me, dahlink. I gotta do mine tzivic dooty..."

In the courtroom a week later, Goldie found herself seated next to Mrs. Tanami, of the colored scarf and carpet slippers. Alongside this tiny, fine-boned woman, Goldie, barely scraping four feet, eleven inches in her wedgies, felt like an Amazon. Mrs. Tanami had apparently resigned from active osculation and was now conscientiously shredding her straw pocketbook while reciting a sotto voce litany of tribulation. Although Goldie's comprehension of Hebrew was fairly extensive, her fluency was limited to "*ken,*" "*lo,*" and "*kamah,*"

[Yes, no, and how much?] and these she tried to insert appropriately into Mrs. Tanami's soliloquy.

"God is Great," the woman chanted without irony. "First my Moshe breaks his hip in '51 and has to walk with a cane, then my Avraham gets dysentery in the *ma'abarah*..."

"*Lo!*" whispered Goldie in feigned disbelief.

"*Ken!*" Mrs. Tanami rebutted. "Then my Mazal she disappears, then my Batya marries that no good..."

"*Lo!*" exclaimed Goldie.

"*Ken!*" the woman asserted. "But God is Great and they get divorced. And then Rachamim refuses to finish high school..."

"*Ken*?" Goldie interposed.

"*Lo!*" Mrs. Tanami reiterated. "And then my Tzion goes to America and drives a taxi..."

"*Kamah*?" Goldie tried for variety.

"A lot, but God is Great, he comes home every summer. Then my Herzl buys the van to deliver eggs from the moshav, and he has an accident with that pretty little girl and now he goes to jail!"

"*Lo!*" Goldie summed up emphatically and turned her attention to the court proceedings. Zehava was pale under her coffee-colored tan, her wavy hair pulled back tightly from her face. Above prominent cheekbones, her dark eyes swam with tears. Goldie waggled her fingers encouragingly at the girl, but received only a wan smile in response.

A tall, distinguished, fair-skinned gentlemen of fifty or so was giving testimony. It was Zehava's father, returned from abroad. "... and the beige Mercedes is registered in your name, sir?" he was asked.

"That is correct," Mr. Perlmutter replied.

"Would you tell the court, please, where you were at the

time of the accident?"

"Yes. My wife Berta —" He indicated a pleasant-faced redhead in the observers' gallery. "— and I were vacationing in..."

Goldie looked around the crowded courtroom. She recognized the faces of the car-lifting sextet, the police officers and several of the Dizengoff rubberneckers. "Poor leedle Zehavaleh," she thought. "She's only a tin-etcher — ah kit — bot mebbe she'll learn fun dis ah lessin to lissen ven papa sez no is no."

Herzl was called to the witness stand, unhandcuffed now and consequently garrulous. His testimony invoked all of the parties to the collision, Goldie herself included, and the audience obediently followed his pointing finger like spectators at a doubles tennis championship: Goldie — Zahava — Herzl — Mrs. Tanami — Zehava — Herzl — Zehava — Goldie — Mrs. Tanami — Herzl.

The affect was dizzying, but the twinkle in Goldie's blue eyes signified anything but confusion. She could hardly contain herself until she was called upon to testify. At last, it was her turn.

"Jutch, Your Honner, you vould mind ve not spicking Hibrew?" Lower court sessions in Israel were never noted for exaggerated formality and her request was easily granted.

"That will be fine, Mrs. Sokolow. What language would you prefer?"

She stared at him with wonderment. "Vhy, Enklich, uf course. I spick ah verra goot Enklich."

"Er, yes. Of course."

"I ken esk mebbe ah few qvestions, Jutch? Just to shuckle mine memries ah leedle. I em not soch ah sprink chicken, already."

"Very well, Mrs. Sokolow."

"Tenks, Jutch. Zehavaleh, dahlink, how olt are you?"

The girl looked up at Goldie in surprise. "I-I have seventeen years," she answered.

"Goot. An' how come you don' got no broken bones?"

The judge fairly leaped over his bench. "Mrs. Sokolow! I must protest..."

"It's hokay, Jutch. I vill vidraw de qvestion. Herzl, I hear you got ah lot sistehs an' bruddehs, *kineh hara.* Yes?"

The question was translated for Herzl's benefit and now it was his turn to look surprised. "Six," he replied through an interpreter, "*bli ayin hara,* may the Almighty bless them." He hesitated a moment and again the judge interrupted.

"Mrs. Sokolow, I fail to see the relevance of these questions. If you cannot demonstrate their relevance, I shall be compelled to call a halt to your cross-examination."

"Plizz, Jutch, Your Honner. It is mine folt ve're all siddink here today instead of mebbe svimmink in der helt clop fun Kink Doovid Hottel. If I vas not so bizzy tinkink about mine Faigaleh, I vas mebbe vatchink vhere I vas goink."

"Faigaleh is your daughter, then?"

Goldie peered at the magistrate through her bifocals as though examining him for signs of latent dementia.

"Faigaleh," she enunciated patiently, as one would instruct a slightly backward child, "is mine dahlink canerry. Ah boit. You know — 'tvit, tvit'?"

The spectators all laughed uproariously and the judge banged his gavel with more force than he'd intended. "Mrs. Sokolow, I still fail..."

"Plizz, ah few more minutes and you vill succeed. Ven I came to *Eretz Yisruel,* I had to liff mine dahlink leedle Faigaleh home in Ball-tee-more — it's a lonk story, I'll tell you mebbe vone day you come to mine house far ah *gluz tay.*"

"Please, Mrs. Sokolow..."

"Hokay. Ven Clara mine neighborkeh told Faigaleh I vas not comink beck, mine leedle *tzippaleh* drops det fun griff. So I vent an' bought ah nudder boit, vone dat looks just like mine Faigaleh..."

In spite of himself, the magistrate had become absorbed in her verbal meanderings. "Excuse me, Mrs. Sokolow, but don't all canaries look alike, more or less?"

"Dat's de point. Faigaleh Nomber Vone vas yella mit ah bleck byooty mark right here —" She pointed to her throat. "— an' Faigaleh Nomber Two is also got ah bleck byooty mark on der trote. Dat's how I em knowink dey vas sisteh an' bruddeh. Just like Herzl mit Zehavaleh."

The courtroom fell utterly silent. All eyes shifted from plaintiff to defendant and back again. A low-gauge rumble surged from the crowd of spectators, rising quickly in volume to a roar as the members of the audience translated the proceedings to one another in countless tongues.

"Order! Order in the court!" The gavel-head went flying across the room, wrenched from its handle by the force of impact with the gavel-rest, and struck the bailiff a stunning blow. No one paid him the slightest attention.

"Order! Order in the court!" The judge shouted ineffectually, tapping on his bench with the decapitated gavel-handle. Goldie imperturbably polished her eyeglass lenses with a snowy handkerchief.

It took a full ten minutes to restore a semblance of order and another hour after that for Goldie to clarify the convoluted thought process which had led to her astounding conclusion. She explained that her first clue had been Zehava's terror over her parents' anticipated reaction to the damaged Mercedes. It had aroused Goldie's suspicions that Zehava was not the Perlmutters' "blud" relative. The extraordinary dissimilarity of her coloring and features with those of her "parents" had been all the confirmation Goldie had needed.

"On de udder hend," Goldie continued, "you pud ah mustach on Zehavaleh an' she mit Herzl is tvins!" The gallery gasped in unison. Indeed, the resemblance was uncanny.

"Mr. Perlmutter," the magistrate said, addressing Zehava's father, "is it true that Zehava is adopted?"

Dov Perlmutter's fair complexion had turned an unhealthy, mottled grey. "Y-yes, Your Honor," he stammered. "We-we adopted her when she was a baby. But we were told she was an orphan!"

His wife suddenly found her voice. She rose from her seat and exclaimed, "What is all this idiocy! Zehava is our legally adopted child and we have always been good parents to her. I resent the implication that because we're not her biological mother and father we would have reacted to her disobedience any differently — or more violently — than natural parents would."

"Uf course, Meesis Perlmoota. I em verra sorry. I did not min soch ah tink. It vas just ah clue vat made me tink who Zehavaleh rilly vas." At this juncture the judge lost all hope of regaining command of his courtroom. Clearly, the gavel had passed to the lady in the elastic stockings.

"Dis kit Zehavaleh is rilly Mazal Tanami, der sisteh fun Herzl vat disappeared fun der Trensit Kemp in ninetin-hundret-an'-fiftivone!" The tumult in the room became deafening.

"I don't believe a word of this!" Mrs. Perlmutter railed. "How could you determine from a handful of jumbled facts that she's in any way related to these people!? It's all speculation and conjecture, and utter nonsense!"

Throughout this exchange, Zehava and Herzl stared at

each other across the room, their deep-chocolate eyes locked in seemingly telepathic communication.

"Mrs. Sokolow," the judge interposed, "despite the truly striking resemblance between the plaintiff and the defendant, you must admit the likelihood of Zehava Perlmutter being Herzl Tanami's long-lost sister is infinitesimal. Are you asking this court to believe that by the most incredible coincidence the Tanamis have been reunited?"

"Dit I say cointzidentz? Nah. It vas *bashert*, it vas *min ha-Shomayim...*"

"I can't stand another second of this!" Mrs. Perlmutter shrieked. "It's ridiculous, I tell you..."

"Sit down, Berta," her husband instructed in a defeated voice. "I-I think the lady is right." Again a collective gasp rose from the audience.

"Your Honor," Perlmutter continued, "when the social worker gave Zehava to me, the baby was wearing a silver bracelet."

"Yes?" the judge encouraged.

"The name 'Mazal' was etched in the metal."

All eyes turned to the bracelet which encircled Herzl's wrist, a bracelet not unlike the one Perlmutter had described. It, too, bore the name of its wearer.

"And where is this bracelet now, sir?"

"I-I threw it away." Perlmutter lifted a trembling hand to his forehead. "I wanted to eliminate any trace of her past, so that she would be ours and ours alone."

"That is understandable, Mr. Perlmutter," the judge said gently, "but when she achieves majority in a few months' time, Zehava will be entitled to know all the facts concerning her parentage." Perlmutter nodded mutely. "She will not necessarily choose to abandon you and your wife in favor of her natural family, you know. But regardless of her decision, you are morally bound to provide her with the information."

"I understand, Your Honor."

Mrs. Tanami was virtually jumping out of her skin with ignorance of the goings-on. At last, a spectator explained and the woman flew from her seat with a jubilant cry. She bestowed a multitude of moist kisses on all and sundry, and then ululated joyfully from atop the witness stand. Goldie rested her swollen ankles on a vacant chair, a blissful smile on her lips.

"Veydl I tell Fritz," she chuckled to herself. "I'll show dat Meester *Vays-Alles* dat 'Goldie Sokolow' is neffer makink Montana fun mole's heels!"

Latent Detriment

וַתִּהְיֶיןָ מֹרַת רוּחַ לְיִצְחָק וּלְרִבְקָה.

And [Eisav's Hittite wives] were a source of profound grief to Yitzchak and to Rivkah.

(Bereishis 26:35)

Since these Hittite idolaters brought "profound grief to Yitzchak and *to* Rivkah" [not just "to Yitzchak and Rivkah"], the Midrash infers that Yitzchak was the first to anguish over the situation. Raised among pagans, Rivkah was less readily repulsed.

Although Rivkah despised idolatry and had been separated from her heathen family for over sixty years, her childhood exposure still tainted her outlook. Yitzchak's upbringing was free of such dominion.

From this we learn that a detrimental influence can affect even a righteous person, and the impact can be felt even many years later.

A senior member of Israel's secret service (Mossad) became religious at precisely the same time that he was recommended for an extended espionage mission in an Arab country. The clandestine mission was potentially of enormous value for Israel's security and could theoretically save countless lives.

The newly religious agent found himself impaled on the horns of a dilemma. On the one hand, if he were to accept this mission it would be the high point of his career and perhaps his greatest contribution to his people. On the other hand, embarking on such a mission would inevitably entail violating virtually every religious precept and tenet that he had come to value.

The agent brought his *she'elah* to Reb Shlomo Zalman, and explained that for the duration of his mission abroad he would have to live as a gentile. There would be no observing Shabbos and *kashrus*, no laying of *tefillin* — in fact nothing that would so much as hint at his Jewish identity.

The Gaon began by saying that for such a mission, it was an obligation to accept the assignment. The inevitable violation of mitzvos was an unfortunate but unavoidable consequence, the price one must pay for the privilege and obligation of protecting one's brethren. This was no different, he said, from what Esther had done. She too had to sacrifice her religious observances in order to save her people.

"Furthermore," the Rav continued, "I do not believe that this would have a detrimental effect upon one's religiosity. Once the mission is accomplished, God willing, one would return home and resume a lifestyle that is religious and pure.

"However, despite all these compelling reasons, I do not recommend that *you* accept this mission, for I am afraid of one thing: Any man who accepts such an assignment and is willing to live at such peril, must also be prepared to kill in an instant, without compunction. This is the nature of espionage, and the likely by-product will be that the act of shedding blood will become 'insignificant in your eyes.' Once a person sheds another human being's blood, his value system begins to erode and becomes corrupted, and he becomes able to follow up an assassination with a leisurely cup of coffee. *You* will not be able to rectify such damage to your soul."

Caution: Jewish Minds at Work

וַיַּגֵּד יַעֲקֹב לְרָחֵל כִּי אֲחִי אָבִיהָ הוּא וְכִי בֶן רִבְקָה הוּא וַתָּרָץ וַתַּגֵּד לְאָבִיהָ.

And Yaakov told Rachel that he was her father's brother and that he was Rivkah's son, and [Rachel] ran and told her father.

(Bereishis 29:12)

Why does the verse refer to Yaakov as "her father's brother" when in fact he was Rachel's father's nephew? The Midrash replies that Yaakov warned Lavan: "If you intend to defraud me, I can retaliate with the same weapons."

Regarding this declaration, the Talmud asks, "May a righteous person act deceitfully?" The Talmud *(Bava Basra 153)* vindicates Yaakov's deception with the verse: "With the pure You act in purity, and with the perverse You are subtle" *(Shmuel II 22:27)*. Deception is despicable, but the only true antidote for perversity is subtlety. Clever manipulation of the deceitful brings about their downfall, thereby fortifying truth.

Berel Kasachkoff, like thousands of his brethren at the time of the Russian Revolution, knew that freedom to live as a Jew *and* as a human being mandated escaping from the Soviet Union. The Russians knew this as well and accordingly stationed sentries all along their borders.

A problem, Berel conceded, but nothing a *Yiddishe kop* could not overcome. One might say this was a rather flippant attitude, considering that the border guards were heavily armed and instructed to shoot on sight. Berel, however, had big plans and was not about to let a technicality — no matter how formidable — stand in his way. Thus, armed only with his wit and a prayer on his lips, Berel headed for the Polish frontier.

When Berel arrived at the most secluded spot he could find close to the border, he discovered that even there the border crossing was heavily guarded, and he was forced to scuttle his first plan. As he considered his options, he noticed that not only was the area well-patrolled, but the sentries were in a state of high alert.

It was only four months since the Revolution had erupted and whereas every citizen feared his own neighbor, Red Army soldiers were afraid of their own shadow. Not an especially auspicious climate for breaking the law... until Berel concocted a way to use it to his advantage.

Bravely and defiantly he made a beeline for the guard house and marched off toward his destiny. He strode right past the few merchants lined up at the border crossing, each of them displaying their papers and travel permits. Berel did not have a legitimate document to his name. The only identification papers he possessed had been forged to enable him to avoid the draft; an amateurish job, but the best he had been able to afford, it was the last thing he would present to guards who had instructions to refer all questions directly to jail.

"Halt!" ordered one of the soldiers.

Berel kept marching.

"I said, 'HALT!'"

Berel kept right on marching.

A second soldier aimed his rifle at Berel's heart. Berel could hear the cartridge slide into the breech. But still he continued marching toward Poland, on a collision course with the soldiers and their itchy trigger fingers.

"Papers!" the guard commanded.

Berel looked at him unbelievingly. "What did you say?" he asked.

"Papers! Let me see your identification papers!"

"My papers? You want to see MY papers? Do you mean you're asking to see MY PAPERS? Why, I should have all of you shot! Don't you know who I am?"

For a moment there was silence. Berel's eyes blazed with anger, fury, wrath and righteous indignation. By this time, he was fairly shouting. "WELL?" he roared. "DO YOU KNOW WHO I AM?"

The soldiers looked at one another. Before they could answer, Berel snarled, "Let me see *your* papers!" and then screamed "NOW!"

Stunned by the ferocity of his manner and the authority of his voice, the soldiers began fumbling through their pockets.

Berel continued shouting. "I ought to have you shot, and then drawn and quartered for good measure. The absolute insolence! The ultimate impudence! The outrageous audacity! And you call yourselves soldiers?!"

"We didn't know—"

"SILENCE!" Berel ordered. The guards meekly passed him their papers. He gave them a quick inspection, then threw them on the ground. "Fools! Imbeciles! You can be sure that when I return from my official mission across the border, I will have your HEADS!" he bellowed. Then Berel spat in disgust at their feet, and proceeded to cross the Russian checkpoint into freedom.

As he entered Poland, he couldn't resist a parting shot. When he estimated that he was beyond the range of their rifles, he turned and shouted at the top of his lungs, "*NOW DO YOU KNOW WHO I AM?*"

"N-n-no," they shouted back.

"Berel Kasachkoff, at your service!" He tipped his hat, gave the stunned guardsmen a brief but polite bow, and then ran for his life.

Fiscal Fidelity

זֶה עֶשְׂרִים שָׁנָה אָנֹכִי עִמָּךְ...וְאֵילֵי צֹאנְךָ לֹא אָכָלְתִּי.

These twenty years I have been with you ...the rams of your flock I have not eaten.

(Bereishis 31:38)

The Midrash comments:

> *A laborer customarily works diligently for two or three hours, then slackens. But just as Yaakov's first seven years were steadfast, so were his second seven years. Just as the first were faithful, so were the last.*

Yaakov was the paragon of morality in fiscal matters. Even in a situation in which goldbricking, laxity, and other forms of exploitative behavior are the norm, his integrity remained perfect.

Home of the Shlah and the Pnei Yehoshua, Frankfurt am Main was, until the beginning of the nineteenth century, a city abounding in Torah learning and fear of Heaven. But just one decade later, the stench of the so-called "Enlightenment" began to drift west from Berlin. Taking their cue from the French Revolution, Enlightenment agitators worked with the government to tear down the Jewish ghetto's figurative walls.

By 1818, the Jews were granted so much equality that German law forbade the public dissemination of Torah knowledge. All religious teachers were banished from the city along with the local phrenologists and all the other Neanderthals, and a fifty-gulden fine was levied against anyone superstitious enough to support Torah study. The *chevra kadisha*, which insisted on perpetuating archaic Jewish burial ritual, was dissolved, synagogue upkeep was curtailed, and the local *mikvaos* were either destroyed or drained. All the funds donated by the Rothschild family for religious institutions were summarily transferred to the silk-gloved hands of the Reform.

As in the days of Rabi Akiva, the Torah faithful had to go underground. Indeed, the lot of religious Jewry in Frankfurt am Main had become so bleak that desperate measures were called for. The community acted wisely in beseeching the Chief Rabbi of Moravia to leave his prestigious position in Nikolsberg. They could never match the honor, acclaim, or salary that Rabbi Samson Raphael Hirsch enjoyed there, but they presented the Rabbi with a mission that he — and the entire generation — could not afford to refuse.

From the day he arrived, Rav Samson Raphael Hirsch became a champion of the Orthodox cause. On every issue, he provided a dauntless and eloquent challenge to the Reform authorities and their government supporters who threatened religious life in the area. Rav Samson Raphael was able to nab the wily foxes and torch them by their tails.

Playing on the country's preference for a separation of church and state — which Bismark had just accomplished regarding the Catholic Church — Rabbi Hirsch fought tirelessly to emancipate the Orthodox from the shackles of the tyrannically secular Jewish governing body.

Autonomy was ultimately achieved, and Rabbi Samson Raphael Hirsch wasted no time establishing a new school system under his personal direction, based on the dictum of "*Torah im derech eretz.*" Perceiving the needs of the hour, Rav Hirsch boldly constructed a curriculum steeped in Torah but nonetheless acceptable to those seeking a secular education for their children. This left him with the enormous task of convincing the embattled community to send their children to his brave new school, and to support it financially.

Since his arrival in Frankfurt am Main Rabbi Samson Raphael had been under tight public scrutiny, but that paled alongside the inquisitions he was now subjected to. Rabbi Hirsch weathered the suspicious probes, however, and not a stitch of *shaatnez* was found when he was slid under the microscope.

Frankfurt Jewry found him knowledgeable in every area of Torah. And just as he was able to analyze esoteric matters with scientists and secular scholars, he was equally comfortable allaying the concerns of the laymen.

People were taken by the Torah giant's gentle manner. He never scolded any of his *baalei battim* or reproached a pupil in public. He was a fighter and a revolutionary, yet he had the demeanor of a gentleman. Every day he could be seen spreading crumbs outside his window for the hungry sparrows of the Rhineland.

Above all, the community was impressed by the scholar's integrity. Some initially wondered why this foreign-born upstart had insisted on personally collecting the funds for his projects. Their theories were not especially complimentary to the Rabbi. But once the townsfolk had occasion to meet Rabbi Hirsch and to attend his classes, they realized how baseless their accusations were.

Nonetheless, Rabbi Hirsch was forever concerned about

his appearance in the public eye. His personal conduct and manner were a *kiddush Hashem* of grand proportions. In his interpersonal relations as well as in his performance of *mitzvos* between man and his Creator, every action was considered and calculated. Rav Samson Raphael's salary was paid by the Orthodox community and he considered himself wholly accountable to them. Accountants were stunned by his meticulous recording of every expense and outlay from what he deemed communal funds.

As the venerable rabbi grew older, one financial concern was particularly on his mind. His annual salary was paid in full on the first of the secular year. In his typical piety, Rabbi Hirsch feared that he might die during the course of the year, leaving "unearned" communal money in his family's hands. He therefore took several measures to ensure that his passing would not result in what he considered unfair gains for his heirs.

From Rav Samson Raphael Hirsch's perspective, this anxiety was understandable. Despite his incredible humility, he realized what he had accomplished during his lifetime. He had single-handedly effected a revolution and a renaissance of religious Jewry in Frankfurt and throughout Germany. As the father of neo-Orthodoxy his commentaries and Responsa would be studied reverently for generations to come. After bringing so much *nachas* to his Maker and so much good to his People, he did not want his good name sullied by the slightest tarnish.

His sincerity did not go unrewarded. On the 27th of Teves, his holy soul was summoned to the Heavenly assembly. It was December 31, 1888 — the final day of the secular calendar.

In Him Will I Trust

וַיִּשְׁלַח יַעֲקֹב מַלְאָכִים לְפָנָיו אֶל עֵשָׂו אָחִיו אַרְצָה שֵׂעִיר שְׂדֵה אֱדוֹם.

And Yaakov sent messengers ahead of him to Eisav his brother to the land of Seir, the field of Edom.

(Bereishis 32:4)

Commenting on this verse, the Midrash cites the verse "He who passes by and meddles with strife not his own is like one who takes a dog by its ears" *(Mishlei 25:17)*. Such a person, continues the Midrash, resembles one who awakens a robber to inform him that he was sleeping in a dangerous area, whereupon the criminal pounces upon him. The good citizen would have no cause to be surprised. After all, declares the Midrash, "the bandit did not awaken himself — you woke him!"

How can Yaakov's dispatching messengers compare with meddling in an affair that was not his own or to rousing a sleeping thief along the road? Yaakov had fled because of Eisav's hatred and upon his return he had very good reason to fear his brother's revenge.

Rabbi **Chaim Shmuelevitz** explains the Midrash's analogy as a lesson relating to the extent of one's obligation to trust in the Almighty. As long as an affliction has not befallen oneself it is forbidden to dread it. God can always save a person at the last minute, so until then, intervention is akin to meddling in an affair that is not one's own.

True, one may not blind himself to imminent danger, but as long as it has not yet struck, it approximates a sleeping thief. Yaakov, however, did "take the dog by its ears," for had he not roused Eisav from his slumber, this incident might have been avoided.

On a Snowy winter evening a nineteen-year-old student from the Novardhok Yeshivah was assigned to guard duty. Like all of the other Jewish men drafted into the Russian Army, he had no choice but to obey orders, regardless of personal objections or religious conflicts. And this Friday night was no exception. He had been ordered to stand guard with his rifle, and he had to do so even though it was Shabbos. To disobey orders could mean death by firing squad.

The sub-zero temperatures of the Russian winter made it clear beyond a doubt that the young man needed a heavy overcoat, but he did not own one of his own, and the Russian Army had no extra overcoats to give out in 1918 (5678). He asked the guard he was to relieve to lend him his warm coat when his shift was over. It was normal for soldiers to share equipment or clothing, and the guard was happy to lend the coat to him. However, when the guard was ready to go off duty, he saw that his replacement was concentrating on his studies, and so, rather than disturb him, the guard hung the bulky army coat on a nearby tree and left.

For a while the yeshivah student was so involved in his learning that he did not even notice the cold. But a sudden frigid gust of wind interrupted his concentration and he became aware of the numbness in his hands and feet and the chill at his back. He was surprised to find himself manning the post alone and dismayed to discover that the coat, so kindly left for him by his predecessor, was hanging tantalizingly from the outstretched branch of a nearby tree.

There was no doubt that the weather posed a very real risk to his life, a condition which required him to violate the rabbinic prohibition of removing something which has been placed on a tree on the Sabbath. Nonetheless, he decided with the fullest conviction that his life was not yet in peril. "...I shall wait but another two minutes before protecting my health by transgressing the rabbinic prohibition," he thought to himself. And so he passed the entire Friday night in sub-zero weather, waiting and debating: "Another two minutes... Just two more minutes," until he was relieved by the next guard. Thus was the young Jewish soldier spared from violating the Sabbath.

The soldier's name was Yaakov Yisrael Kanievsky, and when he passed away over sixty-five years after his Red Army service, more than two hundred thousand Jews accompanied this great Torah leader to his final resting place. That incident in the Russian winter was typical of the path he was to follow. A life filled with "Another two minutes... Just two more minutes" of learning and teaching Torah made him so great that he became a legend in his own lifetime.

The Fearing and the God-Fearing

וַיִּירָא יַעֲקֹב מְאֹד....

[When Yaakov heard that Eisav was marching toward him with an army of 400 men,] Yaakov was greatly afraid....

(Bereishis 32:8)

For fearing Haman and not trusting God, the Midrash notes, the Jews should have been severely punished. But they justified their behavior, citing Yaakov's fear despite God's assurance to Yaakov "And behold, I am with you; I will guard you wherever you go, and I will return you to this land; for I will not forsake you until I have done what I have spoken about you" *(Bereishis 28:15)*.

In the Midrash, Yeshayahu rejects this justification and charges, "You forget God, your Maker" *(Yeshayahu 51:13)*.

Yaakov's fear differed from his descendants' generations later, explains Rabbi **Henoch Leibowitz**, for his evoked repentance and hope, while theirs resulted in gloom and despair. The first was commendable for it generated positive action, whereas the latter caused despondent passivity.

"It was a tempestuous storm..." This is how Chedva Silverfarb often began her *shiur* and it was not uncommon for her to seem to be talking to herself as much as to her audience. "...and the wind howled, heaving the flimsy bridge to and fro. High above the churning waters stood a terrified woman, clutching the rail for dear life. All she wanted, her solitary wish, was to traverse the narrow bridge to her home. But now, as the storm's fury peaked and the wind's velocity increased, the frightened woman realized that beyond all doubt, in seconds nature would have its way and she would plunge to her death in the raging, icy waters below. In desperation she began to offer every spiritual commitment imaginable. 'I shall refrain from *lashon hara*!' she vowed. I will never get angry again, I shall extend myself for *chessed*, I will pray with fervor...'

"After pledging to pursue a life of piety and spiritual endeavor, she felt secure enough to continue to make her way across the swaying bridge. With each precarious step, the storm subsided more, until it dissipated into a gentle breeze. Instead of feeling relieved, however, the woman was overwhelmed with consternation. 'How could I have made such foolish commitments?' she reproached herself. 'Everyone engages in *lashon hara*. How can I be expected to contain my anger when so many things upset me? It is unrealistic for me to devote my energy to others when I do not even have sufficient time for myself. And if I had enough time, I would pray, but surely not with such concentration.'

"In a few brief seconds, the woman had released herself from every obligation. At that very moment, however, the storm began to rear its ugly head yet again and a mighty gust heaved her against the railing of the bridge. Quivering with fear and trembling with remorse, she turned her face heavenward and declared, 'Oh God, I was only joking! I take my pledges seriously. I will even increase my commitments! Dear Lord, let me just return home safely!'

"We often find ourselves in situations like this," Chedva explained. "During childbirth, in hard times, on the *Yamim Noraim* we too feel as though we are crossing a narrow, teetering bridge, and we will pledge anything in return for safe passage.

"Inevitably, however, once the difficult times are over, we swiftly forget every single one of our commitments. Is this woman not you? I know in heart my of hearts that she is *me*."

Unending Gratitude

וַיִּשְׁמַע רְאוּבֵן וַיַּצִּלֵהוּ מִיָּדָם וַיֹּאמֶר לֹא נַכֶּנּוּ נָפֶשׁ.

And Reuven heard and rescued [Yosef] from their hand and said, "Let us not kill him."

(Bereishis 37:21)

What motivated Reuven to save his brother? The Midrash explains that when Yosef related his dream — "...behold, the sun, the moon and eleven stars bowed down to me" *(Bereishis 37:9)*, — Reuven reasoned that the stars corresponded to Yaakov's sons [minus Yosef], so if they numbered eleven, he was still counted among them.

This vision was a source of great consolation for Reuven, who had feared that, having presumptuously transferred his father's bed from Bilhah's tent to his mother Leah's *(35:22)*, he had lost his place in the family.

Hence the phrase "and Reuven *heard*." He heard the same thing that his brothers did, but from a different perspective — one of gratitude, which made him feel compelled to rescue Yosef from their hands.

Although Reuven knew that Yosef had not intended to do him a favor by recounting the dream, his appreciation was undiminished. The very fact that Reuven had benefited from

Yosef's [self-serving] dream moved him to rescue his ostensible benefactor.

Mordechai Amster washed up on the shores of America at the conclusion of World War II. An orphan without relatives or friends in the United States, Mordechai soon found a home in Brooklyn's Torah Vodaas Yeshivah. The administration of the Yeshivah, noting his fine character and keen sense of responsibility, promptly appointed him dormitory counselor.

Mordechai became very popular among the students when he opened a "canteen" — a snack bar selling various food items — on the Yeshivah premises. Rather than squandering his profits on potato chips, soda, and licorice, he saved up for a real treat: a visit to Eretz Yisrael.

By 1964, the year of the fifth *Knessiyah Gedolah* (a convention of great Torah authorities, held in Jerusalem), Mordechai had amassed enough pennies, nickels, and dimes to afford the trip.

In those days, most people sailed to Israel; very few aside from businessmen flew. But Mordechai had made a reservation aboard a nonstop propeller flight. Because of the uniqueness of this mode of travel, every passenger drove to the airport in a car full of relatives bearing bags filled with cookies, cakes, fruit, and other snacks to tide him over on the long journey.

When Mordechai saw all the families fussing over their Israel-bound relatives, he couldn't help but feel lonely. There was no one there to see him off.

Back in Brooklyn, however, a Torah Vodaas student was thinking to himself, "Our dorm counselor is flying to Israel and no one even went with him to the airport!" A moment later, Hirsh Goldberg was out on the street hailing a taxi.

Since this was before the days of terrorists and tight security, Hirsh was able to walk right up to the boarding gate and catch Mordechai just as he was about to leave the terminal. "Mordy! Mordy!" Hirsh cried out, and Mordechai stopped in his tracks to see who was calling his name. As soon as he saw Hirsh running towards him, his heart filled with joy. The two friends embraced and their tears mingled.

Hirsh Goldberg had been a true friend and Mordechai Amster never forgot it.

Not long after Mordechai returned from Israel, Hirsh became engaged. The wedding was to take place the following year but something happened in the middle. Hirsh suddenly became very ill and rumors spread that his engagement had been called off. With each passing month, Hirsh's condition deteriorated and eventually he was hospitalized.

Everyone at Torah Vodaas was horrified to learn that Hirsh Goldberg had contracted multiple sclerosis (MS), an incurable disease of the nervous system. Although Hirsh was now bedridden, his mind remained as sharp and clear as ever. This was the hardest part of the disease for him to bear. A diligent student, he had always loved attending classes in yeshivah. Once he was hospitalized, it was as if his lifeline had been cut.

One day, Mordechai Amster, eager to repay Hirsh for his thoughtful gesture at the airport, had an idea. With the cassette industry just beginning to develop, Mordechai became one of its earliest supporters. First he purchased two tape recorders and dozens of blank cassettes. Then he enlisted distinguished scholars to record their classes.

Those cassettes were the greatest gift Hirsh could have received. Not only did they give him a new lease on life, they also guaranteed him constant company, for his fellow Jewish patients flocked to his bedside to share in his learning.

Meanwhile Mordechai continued to upgrade his recording equipment, but Hirsh and the other patients in the hospital were not the only ones to profit from this instance of one mitzvah causing another. It was in Hirsh's humble hospital room that "Torah Tapes" was born, a project from which so many of us benefit.

And to this very day, it is "Mordechai Amster" who runs the American end of the operation.

Keep the Faith

כִּי אִם זְכַרְתַּנִי אִתְּךָ כַּאֲשֶׁר יִיטַב לָךְ וְעָשִׂיתָ נָּא עִמָּדִי חָסֶד וְהִזְכַּרְתַּנִי אֶל פַּרְעֹה וְהוֹצֵאתַנִי מִן הַבַּיִת הַזֶּה.

But think of me when all is well with you, and do me the kindness of mentioning me to Pharaoh, and bring me out of this house.

(Bereishis 40:14)

According to the Midrash, because Yosef requested that the royal butler remember him, he remained incarcerated an extra two years. As it is written about Yosef, "Happy is the man who makes the Lord his trust and turns not to the arrogant..." *(Tehillim 40:5)*. Yosef trusted in God, yet he also "turned to the arrogant" by requesting the butler's assistance rather than relying entirely on direct Divine salvation.

This Midrash appears contradictory, praising Yosef for trusting in the Almighty but faulting his trusting in man.

The **Sefas Emes** resolves this apparent discrepancy with the principle that, if someone devotes himself to a mitzvah, Heaven will help him uphold his commitment.

Had Yosef genuinely believed the butler could rescue him, he would have indeed become the conduit of salvation. However since

Yosef was "the man who makes the Lord his trust," he never thought that anything other than Divine intervention could free him. He simply went through the motions of seeking release, in keeping with his interpretation of the butler's dream.

The Almighty doomed these efforts just so Yosef could retain his exclusive trust in God.

The Alpert family always said that Rabbi Nison Alpert "lived for his *talmidim.*" Never was that more apparent than at the end of his days. It was to be the last Friday of his life, and his agony and torment were registered clearly on his withered countenance. The previous night had been a most demanding one for the HATZOLOH volunteers and *Tehillim* reciters alike, as the thin thread by which Rav Alpert clung to life unraveled. Suddenly, a *talmid* who had just arrived from Eretz Yisrael entered the Rav's room, bringing tidings and good wishes from the Holy Land.

To the utter amazement of all those present, Rav Alpert somehow raised himself up in his bed. An electrifying smile lit up his face and he greeted the young man with a hearty "*Shalom Aleichem*" such as had not been heard from the Rav in many months. Family and friends rushed into the room to witness this precious scene: a Rebbe in his final hour deriving *nachas* from a *talmid.*

Later that day, a friend and congregant whose son was to be married the following week was allowed entrance in order to receive the Rav's blessing. Rav Alpert clasped his hand and uttered seven words: "*Bitachon*, Reb Shimon! *Bitachon*, Reb Shimon! *Bitachon.*"

Rav Alpert's use of the term "*bitachon*" did not mean, simply, "trust in God that all will go well." He was alluding rather to the explanation of the Chazon Ish for "*bitachon,*" an explanation he had cited often: "Trust in God, for all that he does is good."

And in the last hours of Rav Alpert's life, when he was too weak to speak or even to move his limbs, Rabbi Menachem Genack tried to communicate with his esteemed mentor by reciting the *alef-beis* and watching for a reaction to any particular letter. His loving family, his students, congregants and Jews the world over longed for one final message, one word to help them carry on in a world that would be so empty and bleak after his departure. The Rav found the strength to comply.

At the letter "*beis*" he gave a sign; again at the letter "*tes.*" There was no reaction to any other letter, but Rabbi Genack felt certain that the Rav wanted to convey something of import, so he did not give up. He went through the alphabet one more time. Now at "*ches*" another flutter was perceived, and at "*nun*" Rav Alpert made his final voluntary movement.

"בטחן" — "*bitachon,*" have faith, for everything — even suffering — is God's will and is therefore good. He had once explained suffering, referring to our subjugation in Egypt, as a form of preparation for a spiritual experience. Suffering, Rav Alpert had said, strips away any haughtiness, any ego or feelings of self-importance which may stand in the way of God's message entering the heart.

Clearly Rav Alpert suffered sufficiently to entitle him to the spiritual experience and delight of resuming to learn with his father, his son Shaya and his revered Rebbe, Reb Moshe Feinstein. No doubt they, and the Chafetz Chaim (to whom he was related) and the Meiri (whose manuscript he had published) and the Raavad (whose manuscript he had prepared for publication) were all in the Heavenly Beis Midrash, waiting to greet him with joy, deference and love.

Expedience is the Name of the Game

וַיֹּאמֶר פַּרְעֹה אֶל יוֹסֵף חֲלוֹם חָלַמְתִּי וּפֹתֵר אֵין אֹתוֹ
וַאֲנִי שָׁמַעְתִּי עָלֶיךָ לֵאמֹר תִּשְׁמַע חֲלוֹם לִפְתֹּר אֹתוֹ.

And Pharaoh said to Yosef, "I dreamt a dream, and no one can interpret it, and I heard [that] you can comprehend a dream to interpret it.

(Bereishis 41:15)

According to the Midrash, Yosef was asked to interpret Pharaoh's dream only if it was in his favor. Otherwise, the tyrant wasn't interested in the interpretation.

The **Maggid of Dubno** explained this phenomenon with the following analogy:

A particular businessman customarily studied in the synagogue for several hours after the services. One morning a tradesman called on him at home but did not find him and departed. When his wife related what had happened, the businessman was outraged. "I could have made a fortune from that fellow! The next time someone comes to see me, I wish to be summoned at once!"

The following morning, an alms collector knocked at the businessman's door. His wife hurried to fetch him, and he returned home with great anticipation, only to discover a beggar waiting for him.

"For this you summoned me from the synagogue?!" he demanded.

"But I was merely following your instructions," his wife protested meekly.

The businessman rephrased his instructions: "Only if a merchant comes by, someone from whom I can profit, notify me. For a *meshulach*, who seeks to profit from me, I cannot be bothered."

This, concludes the Dubno Maggid, is how the wicked conduct themselves. They worship their god as long as they feel they can gain thereby. But if they stand to lose something, they change their policy.

Chester Davis let his eyes flicker over the letter he had just written. Heaving a sigh, he crumpled it and sent it to join its companions in the waste basket next to his desk.

He looked out the window of his fourth-floor office for inspiration. The reversed letters of the name "Interstate Rock Insurance Inc." emblazoned across the glass obscured his view. Had his seven months of working for the company similarly clouded his vision of the outside world? Another sigh escaped him as he went back to his troublesome letter for the sixth time. He read the finished product with ambivalence.

Mrs. Silvia Carpenter
7751 N. Fernwell Drive
Wichita, Kansas 67202

June 6, 1988

Dear Mrs. Carpenter,

We are sorry to inform you that the loss of your necklace was not reported to us within the required six-week period. Accordingly, we cannot process your claim for $400.

We understand that you were visiting your grandchildren in West Virginia at the time, and were unaware of the lapse of the notification period. Nonetheless, our regulations do not give us discretion to waive the reporting requirements.

We regret this unfortunate occurrence, but we trust you will continue to place your confidence in us in the future.

Yours faithfully,

Chester Davis

Interstate Rock Insurance Inc.
cc: Todd Nichols, Collections V.P.

Poor woman, Chester mused, but rules were rules. Maybe they could've made an exception just this once for this elderly woman with — judging by her policy — so few worldly goods. But his supervisor wouldn't hear of it, and nearly went through the roof when he had suggested it.

That will have to do, thought Chester, reaching for the next letter in his in-tray. As he read it, disbelief widened his eyes and furrowed his brow. He scratched his head and began to read it through again, trying to ignore the banter coming from the other side of the office.

"Oh no, Charlie, don't tell me you're measuring the symphonic fidelity of your Walkman again."

"Pardon me, but this is no Walkman! This is my WMD6C with quartz lock and disc drive! With this portable deck the Monteverdi Choir no longer sounds like the Sax Kittens, a guitar reclaims its missing midsection, and the bass builds a floor you can walk on. Here Mike, listen to Siouxsie and the Banshees — the sound is breathtaking. Hills and mesas and Andes arising from an ocean of silence..."

"Gentlemen, I hate to interrupt what sounds like a discussion of earth-shattering importance," cried Chester, looking up from his letter, "but wait till you hear this. A client in Denver has refunded us, I repeat, *refunded* us $1,000!"

"Give me a break, Chet," Charlie muttered, "I'm trying to teach Mike the finer points of technological development and you have to butt in with science fiction?"

"I don't think it's science fiction. It sounds to me like the real McCoy. If you two can tear yourselves away from your techno-toys for a minute, I'll give you a dramatic reading."

The guys dutifully sat up and looked attentive while Chester cleared his throat and began:

בס"ד

June 2, 1988

Interstate Rock, Insurance Inc.
422 Bloomfield Dr.
Hartford, Conn. 06002

Dear Sirs:

On February 12, 1988, I filed a claim for the loss of my silver Chanukah candelabra, valued at one thousand dollars. As I am sure you recall, I enclosed its evaluation by a local jeweler and a xerox of its detailed inclusion in my coverage.

Now, three and a half months later, I have discovered that the candelabra was not stolen after all, but has been sitting at my silversmith all this time. I had taken it in for repair, and, I'm afraid, completely forgotten about it.

I feel terrible for having caused you the trouble of issuing my coverage and embarrassed that I made such an outrageous error.

I enclose a check for one thousand dollars, please accept my most sincere apologies.

Yours truly
Chaim Stern

"This is a first: there's no doubt about that," Mike said in a mixture of amazement and relief — amazement over the content of the letter, and relief over the termination of Charlie's litany regarding the intricacies of high fidelity.

"Now what am I supposed to do?" Chet continued. "In the seven months I've been working for the Rock, we have never received a *refund.*"

"You got a point there," Charlie noted. "This company is designed to receive money for policies and send out money for claims — but that's it."

"This is a real doozy," Mike contemplated, rubbing his troubled temples. "You know, before I made it up here to Hartford, I was all over. I even sold policies door-to-door, and nothing like this ever happened. This is not only a first, it's history in the making!"

"Why don't you take the letter to the Marketing Department," Charlie suggested, "and find out where this account came from?"

"I've been there already," Chet said with a note of desperation. "They didn't know what to do with it either so they passed it on to the Underwriters Department. Underwriters kicked it over to the Accounting Department, and Accounting brought it back to the Claims Department, and Claims — you guessed it — dropped it on the desk of Chet Davis, with an inter-office memo that looks like a scorecard from a Ping-Pong match.

"So fellas, what do I do with this weirdo and his thousand bucks?"

"Hey, c'mon," Mike said defensively, "how're we supposed to know? We ain't executives. We ain't even 'suits' — we're just a bunch of yuppies."

"Pardon me," Charlie interrupted, "but the most recent survey has indicated that a 'yuppie' is anyone and everyone who eats out more than once a week, carries a MasterCard, knows that wine comes from California, and owns, or has owned, a yellow necktie. Therefore I do not qualify."

"Charlie, will you cut it out already?" Mike interjected as his colleague started fiddling with his Walkman once again.

He shrugged and turned back to Chet. "This one's over our heads; even Mr. Stereophonic Sound doesn't have the technology to deal with it. You better take this to the top, to the 'Boss' himself, and you're in luck because the board is in session."

"Are you serious?" Chet wheezed in exasperation. "You expect *me* to go to the *board* with this? They're probably deciding what premiums the President should pay on the White House. They're probably deciding what..."

Before he could finish his sentence, Chet was escorted, or more accurately *hoisted*, by two human forklifts named Charlie and Mike and deposited in the boardroom right in the middle of a heated argument:

"I propose we travel to the Hillcrest Course — it's just 25 miles out of Phoenix and has hosted the Ladies' PGA Tour for the last four years."

"Month after month we pass up going to Ojai Valley. Where else can you find a 6,100-yard course surrounded by mountains?"

"We are not going to Ojai! Just last week all the regional CEOs went to Maui and that's enough exotic courses for this season. As president of this company I am entitled to make some decisions!"

"Sorry, Boss."

"Hey, what are those guys doing in here?" Around the room a dozen or so fleshy faces looked up from their leather-bound desk pads to stare at the intruders. "Don't they know we're busy deciding important company matters and cannot be disturbed? What's the matter with you — can't you read English? There's a big sign hanging outside the door that reads, 'Board in Session.'"

Mike jabbed Chet to make him speak up, but he was intimidated into nervous silence. Charlie took the initiative:

"Excuse him, Boss, he's got this problem, but it's better if he explains it."

"Okay, let's hear," the Boss said, his curiosity piqued. "What in the world could be so important that you decided to interrupt the board?"

"Well, eh... you see we got this letter here," Chet fumbled, holding up the document to provide an air of authenticity, "and it has baffled the entire staff of the company. We simply have no idea what to do, and in desperation I was advised, er, to come to you, sir."

"Well, what is it? A government decision to downgrade all policies?"

"No."

"Aetna went ahead with its plan to undercut SBLI?"

"No, it's... kind of different."

"Oh, I know: no one is issuing life insurance without compulsory blood tests. And we better adopt the same policy before we're stuck with all the goners. No, no, you don't have to make any more gesticulations. We were just about to tackle that problem after we finished attending to some other pressing matters at hand."

"But..."

"But what? I told you we're in the middle of important business."

"I'm trying to explain that the letter is about an entirely different matter."

"It is?"

"Yes, Boss. It's from a client who returned money."

"Who *what*?!" the entire board chimed in unison.

"He filed a claim for something he thought was stolen, but a few months later he found it and immediately returned what we paid him."

A palpable silence wedged itself between the paneled

walls of the boardroom.

"I understand," Chester's Boss finally pronounced, as his deputies chorused murmurs of assent. "Just leave it with us, and we'll put it on our agenda."

Chet hurriedly placed the letter and the enclosed check on the enormous mahogany table and then darted out of the room with an audible sigh of relief.

The head of the Accounting Department picked up the letter and his eyes began to dilate. "Hey, Boss," he gasped in shock, "we really have a problem here. This guy is right out of them fairy tales. If we don't cash his check immediately he'll probably call us, or launch a letter campaign to find out why."

"Don't worry," the Boss replied with a wave of his hand. "There has got to be some easy way to bury the money. How much is it?"

"A thousand dollars."

"A thousand bucks?! Is this guy normal? It doesn't pay to be moral for that kind of money."

"The way he writes, I bet he would have returned a larger sum, too."

"Tell Pat to have the check endorsed," the Boss ordered. "Then hand it over to our regular dealer in exchange for $1,000 worth of office supplies."

The head of Purchasing removed his glasses and shook his head. "Sorry, Boss, we just completed our order for this year and our storerooms are full."

"All right," the Boss responded, "take the money and have the reception rooms painted."

Now the Services Manager started shaking his head. "They've been wallpapered for the last eight months, sir."

"Why can't we just enter the money," the head of the Underwriters Department put forward, "as coverage returned due to improper filing?"

"What?!" several Board members demanded. "We can do no such thing! The paperwork alone would run us over a thousand bucks!" The stuffed shirts were stumped, but not for long.

"I know how to bury the money," the Boss said with a gleam in his enterprising eye. "Where's this client from?"

"Denver."

"Great," the Boss fairly beamed with ebullience. "Let's get that junior fellow, you know, the one who burst in here, to go and investigate the case. We'll tell him he's going to adjust a claim. There aren't any direct flights out of Hartford so it will be an expensive ticket, and he'll have to kill a night or two there before he can catch a flight back. Best of all, the time he'll waste on this ridiculous mission talking to this 'straight nut' will teach him that next time he gets a letter like this, he should accidentally-on-purpose lose it instead of wasting valuable executive time."

The entire Board sat in awe of their boss' brilliant idea. At times like these, they realized it was more than being the son of the founder that made him the "Boss."

"As a matter of fact," the object of their sincere admiration added, settling back into his chair, "get that kid back in here. I'll assign him the mission myself. That'll really make him feel like hot stuff."

The Boss' secretary punched out a number on the intercom and issued a directive for Chet Davis to report immediately to the executive conference room. In a matter of minutes a trembling, quivering, speechless young recruit from the Claims Department was brought back before the Chief Executive.

"Junior, er... I mean, young man," the Boss began, "I admire your initiative. You really know how to sense a problem and bring it to the attention of the appropriate authorities right away."

Chet managed a half-smile.

"Therefore, I think you are just the man to investigate this matter. After all, it is rather out of the ordinary for a client to return a payment, so maybe there are some details here that require checking. Who knows? Maybe this client is hiding something; perhaps it's all a smokescreen to conceal coverage he has collected illegally."

All the exec veeps present nodded gravely in agreement and muttered similar suspicions. The Boss eyed his Board and then fixed a solemn gaze on his company's greenhorn. "Junior," he declared, "the Rock is entrusting a major mission to you." He then began to pour forth a dizzying array of insurancese:

"Keep your eye out for individual variable annuity contracts, fiduciary capacity, antedating, indemnities relating to flexible premium payments, and most particularly, master contracts with a noncontributory group."

Chester's hand raced across his pad, struggling to catch each vital phrase.

"Don't forget disclosure to MIB and riders relating to the beneficiary," cut in the high-pitched voice of the Services Manager, getting caught up in the torrent of jargon.

"Guaranteed insurability options are often problematic," added the head of Marketing, "not to mention disability premium waivers."

"Double indemnities," cried Sales.

"Deferment clauses," shouted Underwriters.

Chet's face turned chalky and he began hyperventilating. He gave up on note-taking and resorted to nodding wildly in all directions as the Board members competed simultaneously in offering increasingly obscure proofs of their expertise.

"Fifth-dividend options..."

"...current conversion..."

"...automatic premium loans..."

"...multiple-line coverage..."

As the crescendo peaked, Chet's jaw dropped low in gaping incredulity. Meanwhile, the bigwigs clutched their stomachs and tried their hardest to refrain from laughing.

"Now listen here, Junior," the Boss continued, struggling to regain his composure. "I have selected you for this mission because I know that you are a shrewd, keenly observant, perspicacious, judicious young man. Don't be taken in by any of this guy's honest, goody-goody talk. You better examine everything very well before you return with your report."

Still in shock, Chet barely noticed the compliment, but he tried to feign a Sherlock Holmes expression.

"I expect you back next week," the Boss concluded. "We will anxiously await your findings. So godspeed, and don't be concerned about the expenses. Money's no object when a company man is on an important mission."

The smirking executives all affirmed that statement and rose to pat the tyro on the back and shake his hand.

The Boss slung a solicitous arm around Chester and escorted him to the door. "Go down the corridor to the end," he instructed, "take a left and ask for Chris, the company's in-house travel agent. Just tell her you need an itinerary immediately and that I have approved it."

Chet fiddled nervously with the handle of his attaché case as he stood outside the Stern residence. In view of the board's warnings he had decided not to call in advance. If this Stern character was really a sly snake, he wanted to take him by surprise. Chet was determined to do Hartford proud.

The fellow who answered the door was not exactly Chester's stereotypical conception of a Midwesterner. Or a snake. He wore a large skullcap and sported a long, brown beard and spaghetti-like fringes dangling from under his shirt.

"Eh... Hello," the Hartford emissary managed, extending his sweaty hand. "My name is Chester Davis and I represent Interstate Rock Insurance and, well, that sure was a mighty nice gesture of yours to return your coverage, and we just wanted to show you how much we appreciated it. I hope you don't mind if I ask you a few questions."

"Why, of course not," Rabbi Stern answered, motioning the insurance man into his house.

"Yeah, so like I was saying, it was so unusual of you to return the money — you see, that doesn't happen too much in our company. So I was wondering if you wouldn't mind repeating exactly what happened."

Rabbi Stern sat his guest down, brought him a tall, cold drink, and began to recollect:

"About four months ago, I noticed that our old silver candelabra was missing. This was no ordinary candelabra, or *menorah* as it is called in Hebrew. I purchased it years ago in Israel and our festival of Chanukah wouldn't be the same without it.

"Naturally, this isn't the sort of item we would misplace. So we informed the police, but they failed to come up with any leads.

"Much as we hated to do it, we began to suspect our maid, Juanita. We wanted to give the girl a fair hearing, but since she barely speaks English and we don't know Spanish, it was an exercise in bilingual futility:

"Juanita, did you clean the breakfront? *Sí, Señor.*

Did you dust the *menorah? No se, Señor.*

Didn't you clean everything inside? *Sí, Señor.*

So why is one of the items missing? *No se, Señor.*

Maybe you took it out and forgot to put it back? *Nunca, Señor.*

Maybe you wanted to show it to someone and now you want to return it? *Nunca, Señor.*

Are you sure? *Sí, Señor.*

Who else do you think might have removed it? No *se, Señor.*

Do you want to think about it? *Sí, no se, Señor.*

Do you want to forget about it? *Sí, Señor.*

What should we do? *No se, Señor."*

Chet found himself smiling at the Rabbi's unexpected flair for dramatization. "Go on," he said.

Rabbi Stern continued his tale: "Although we couldn't be sure Juanita was responsible, we reluctantly let her go. This didn't help us find our *menorah* of course, but at least we hoped we wouldn't have to worry that more things would disappear. In the meantime we filed a claim with your company, and eventually your payment came through.

"Four months later, however — that is, two weeks ago — I noticed that my wife's candlesticks were cracked. I immediately brought them to the silversmith, who promptly asked me where I'd been all this time. Before I could figure out what he meant, he went to the back of his shop and brought out our *menorah*. 'Do you know how long this has been sitting here?' he inquired.

"Suddenly I knew very well. In my terrible absentmindedness, I had totally forgotten that I had brought the *menorah* in for repair right after Chanukah. And the silversmith couldn't even get in touch with me since he didn't have my telephone number and wasn't sure of my name. I can assure you that he was careful to take down all my particulars when he accepted the candlesticks.

"As happy as I was to have our *menorah* back, I felt terrible over having dismissed Juanita and very much wished to apologize to her. Both my wife and I made numerous attempts to locate her, but she had apparently moved out of state.

"In any event, since we had our *menorah* back, I had to return the coverage."

Chet was taken aback by the story. He had little reason to doubt Stern's sincerity, aside from the Boss' warnings. The last thing he wanted, however, was to return to Hartford a laughingstock and stand accused of being naïve and gullible. He would have to find some kind of guarantee that Stern was legit.

"Rabbi Stern," Chet began, "I'm not sure I fully understand why you felt that you had to return the money."

"Because it wasn't mine."

"Of course it's yours. The check was made out to you."

"But you only issued the coverage on the assumption that my *menorah* was missing."

"All right, but no one is asking you to give it back now."

"I repeat, the money isn't mine. If I don't pay it back now, I will have to pay it back later."

Chet nodded wisely and whispered, "You were afraid that we would launch a criminal investigation and accuse you of fraud?"

"No, nothing like that. It's just that everyone is accountable for his actions."

"Accountable?"

"To Heaven, to God."

Chet shifted awkwardly in his seat. "Oh, oh, I'm sorry."

"You don't have to be sorry, but you should be aware. Let me explain: according to Judaism, stealing involves far more than just putting your hand into someone else's purse. Shortchanging, making a call from the office without permission, pocketing paper clips, and even misleading someone or disturbing a person's sleep all fall under the biblical interdiction of 'Thou shalt not steal.' "

"Yeah,... well, I mean, I knew that," Chet stammered, his mind racing to find a more comfortable topic of conversation. "By the way, while I'm here, maybe I could interest you in one of our other policies?"

"Look around you," Rabbi Stern said. "Does it look like we need insurance on anything other than our few pieces of silver?" Scanning his surroundings Chet realized he had a point.

"You see, the silver has religious value for us; otherwise why should we squander our money on such luxuries?'

"Lots of people do... er, I mean lots of people buy valuables."

"True, but we believe that the more you have, the more you worry, and once you have this you'll always want that. I think it's more important that we look after what we already have."

"I don't follow."

"You know, our children, our health, our virtues. For example, since your company is probably paying for your trip here, I assume you are being very careful to watch your expenses. You wouldn't want to bill them for money you didn't spend, would you?"

"Huh?... I mean of course, I guess... As a matter of fact, I agree with you that — how'd you put it? — 'If you don't pay it back now, you'll have to pay it back later.' "

Rabbi Stern pumped Chester's hand and led him to the door. "I hope I've been of some help."

"Oh yes, you most certainly have. You really straightened me, I mean, this matter out. Goodbye, now."

The next day Chet was back at the Rock and eager to file his report. He made it just in time, as the Board was reportedly just about to depart for an important conference somewhere outside of Phoenix.

Chet was ushered into the Boss' office and planted his feet in the shag with newfound confidence.

"Okay, Junior, what's the scoop?" the Boss asked, looking forward to hearing about his flunky's fiasco.

"Well," Chet said breathlessly, "the bottom line is that the guy, I mean the Rabbi, honestly thought his candelabra was stolen, so he filed for theft. But by the time he'd discovered it at the silversmith's, Juanita had left town."

"Juanita?"

"Yeah. So he had to send us back the check. You see?"

"I think you'd better back up."

Chester dutifully shifted into reverse and explained the whole story, but afterward his Boss didn't seem to be any more enlightened.

"What is this guy, some kind of lunatic or something?"

"I'll tell you the truth," Chet conceded, "at first I thought he was really off the wall, like the kind of guy who takes nursery rhymes seriously. But after meeting him and being in his home a couple of minutes, I realized that he and his folk actually live it. Truth and honesty and ethics and all those kinds of things really mean something to them. No wonder you never see any rabbis running for office."

"All right, all right, I guess this case is finally closed. Just report your expenses to Accounting."

"No problem, I got it all written down here." Chet riffled through his date book until he found the appropriate page, which he ripped out and proudly presented to the Boss.

```
Expenses:   Week of June 11, 1988

Plane Ticket               $492.00
Car Rental                 $ 37.27
Gas                        $   6.50
Meals                      $ 26.00
     (Tips)                $   3.00
Motel                      $ 45.00
     (Video)               $   4.00
Shoeshine                  $   3.00
                           --------
                           $616.77
```

A look of incipient nausea came over the president. "Junior, did you fall on a rock while you were out in the Rockies? Your assignment was to lose that thousand bucks."

"Huh?" Chet gulped, all astonishment and stupefaction.

"How in the world could you come back with such a bill, for heaven's sake! I never heard of anything so preposterous in my life!"

"But Boss, these were my expenses, every one of them "

"Nobody with an ounce of sense, or a milligram for that matter, would turn in an expense record like this. This bill should have totaled $999.98 at least!"

"But what did you expect me to do?" Chet implored, still not understanding.

"Lose the grand."

All at once Chet grasped what his CEO, and all of corporate America, was promoting.

"But Boss, that's the whole point. That's what I learned from the Rabbi. You're not supposed to swindle, not even a penny, and certainly not $383.23."

"Ah, c'mon! Wake up to reality!"

"I did wake up — to integrity. We have no right to take money that doesn't belong to us."

"I'm not telling you to rob anyone," the Boss insisted.

"Do you think robbing only means holding a victim at gunpoint in a dark alley?" Junior countered, suddenly aware of the audacity in his tone.

The Boss flailed his arms to put an immediate end to the discussion. "Okay, Davis," he said, his patience depleted, "if that's the way you want to play it, then you find a way to work it into the Rock's ledger."

With a note of finality, he turned his back on his young employee and gripped an imaginary golf club. Then, arching his back, he teed off towards his vast picture window.

"Our customers out there trust us," Chester muttered. "I think we should be deserving of that trust." But his words fell on deaf ears.

Back at his desk, Chet took out his wallet, counted out $16.77, and added it to the check he had drawn from the Claims Department for $383.23. This time he had no need to look out his office window before writing his next letter.

```
Dear Mrs. Carpenter,
   In view of the unusual circumstances
of your case...
```

Watch and Learn

וַיְחַפֵּשׂ בַּגָּדוֹל הֵחֵל וּבַקָּטֹן כִּלָּה וַיִּמָּצֵא הַגָּבִיעַ
בְּאַמְתַּחַת בִּנְיָמִן.

And [Yosef's steward] searched, beginning with the eldest and ending with the youngest, and the goblet was found in Binyamin's sack.

(Bereishis 44:12)

The Midrash reports that, when the guards discovered Yosef's goblet in Binyamin's sack, his brothers castigated him as a "thief, son of a thieving woman," for his mother, Rachel, had stolen Lavan's idols *[see Bereishis 31:19]*. Binyamin could have countered, "You are the ones who sold your own brother!"

Rabbi **Avraham Twerski** adds that Binyamin could have also responded, "Wasn't your money returned to your sacks? Clearly the planting of the goblet is part of the same conspiracy."

But Binyamin did not protest this libel. Likewise, when Yosef's dreams came true, he did not taunt those who had accused him of being a self-centered dreamer.

Where did Yosef and Binyamin acquire this ability to resist the almost overwhelming temptation to defend themselves at the expense of another's dignity? From their mother.

When Lavan turned her wedding night into Leah's, Rachel did not object. Rachel even helped Leah convince Yaakov he'd married the right woman, by revealing the secret sign that she and Yaakov had prearranged, in order to spare her humiliation.

As Rabbi Twerski points out, Rachel did not have to lecture her sons about restraint, for she epitomized this virtue. The best way to impart true values to one's children is by exemplifying them. Parental self-sacrifice and other positive traits definitely influence children's behavior, especially in times of great stress.

The financial burden which Rabbi Chaim Yehudah Leib Auerbach bore was crippling. He needed to sustain his yeshivah, Shaar Ha-Shamayim, feed its pupils, and provide a monthly stipend for the married students. With the economy in Palestine at the time on the verge of collapse, and contact with the Jewish communities abroad at its nadir, the likelihood of Reb Chaim Yehudah Leib receiving a life-giving transfusion of funds from a generous philanthropist was virtually nil.

There was no alternative for the Rosh Yeshivah but to borrow large sums of money, with his family's belongings as collateral. And it was surprising to no one that, with no regular injections of capital, Rabbi Auerbach was consistently unable to meet his loan commitments. The debtors liquidated his collateral to cover the outstanding loans and in due time Rabbi Auerbach's home was bereft of any valuable possessions.

The situation went from bad to worse. With nothing remaining to back additional loans, the flow of money ceased entirely and Reb Chaim Yehudah Leib's family had no other resources at their disposal. They did not even have money for food.

Reb Chaim Yehudah Leib's righteous Rebbetzin, Tzivya, could not bear to see the suffering of her children and of the starving yeshivah students. She urged her husband to offer as collateral her last remaining piece of jewelry, a beautifully crafted gold brooch, the family heirloom she had inherited from her grandmother.

This gold brooch, with a large, lustrous pearl set in its center, had been bequeathed to the first granddaughter born after the grandmother's passing who would be named after her. Accordingly, its sentimental value far surpassed its significant monetary worth. It was the only legacy the family had from this grandmother.

Out of desperation, Reb Chaim Yehudah Leib reluctantly accepted his Rebbetzin's offer and provided this pin as collateral for a loan, and the money he received sustained them all for a while. When he managed to obtain some additional funds, the very first thing that Reb Chaim Yehudah Leib did was to rush out and try to redeem the pin from the creditor. But it was too late. By the time the Rabbi arrived, the pin had already been sold in lieu of repayment of the loan.

The loss of the gold and pearl brooch was a source of untold heartache in the Auerbach family. From that time on they were wont to relate with anguish in family circles that all that was left from the grandmother's pin was a hole in their heart.

The Auerbach household was now bereft of jewelry and furnishings, but the creditors did not stop coming. Up until this point the family had, somehow, managed to accept their lot with forbearance and restraint. Now, however, the creditors started removing the *sefarim* from the house, and this was too much for the family to bear.

They had witnessed the removal of their most cherished possessions and belongings with silent agony. But the *sef-*

arim, the holy books that were lovingly studied and pored over all hours of the day and night! These books were a part of their soul, and their wrenching cries of dismay and sorrow rent the Heavens. The family sobbed and shed bitter tears as their revered *sefarim* were carted away. One can manage in life without furniture, and even without a precious heirloom pin, but how could one manage without *sefarim*?

There is no nice way to put it: the Shaar Ha-Shamayim Yeshivah and its dean were bankrupt. Reb Chaim Yehudah Leib's financial situation had deteriorated to the point where he could not even borrow money, and he was no longer able to pay salaries or maintain his *kollel*. As if the situation and the shame of it were not enough, a perfidious rumor began to circulate that Rabbi Auerbach, who was pleading poverty and was unable to provide the stipend for the poor *avrechim* in his *kollel*, was in reality a man of ample means and in fact owned several flourishing orchards. One of the disgruntled rumormongers decided to take action and had Reb Chaim Yehudah Leib summoned to a *beis din*.

On the appointed day, Rabbi Auerbach appeared before the rabbinical court, with his Rebbetzin at his side. The head of the *beis din* looked at the two defendants standing before him with humble dignity. "Is it true that you own a number of orchards?" he demanded.

In an instant, Rebbetzin Tzivya responded, "Yes, honored *Rav*, I confess — it is true. Indeed we have four orchards, four beautiful orchards." Her words were greeted with surprise on the part of the *rabbanim*, and glee on the part of the plaintiff. "However," she continued, "none of them has yet borne fruit. Our orchards even have names, sir: Shlomo Zalman, Eliezer, Berel, and Dovid..."

Appease Process

וַיִּגַּשׁ אֵלָיו יְהוּדָה וַיֹּאמֶר בִּי אֲדֹנִי יְדַבֶּר נָא עַבְדְּךָ דָבָר בְּאָזְנֵי אֲדֹנִי וְאַל יִחַר אַפְּךָ בְּעַבְדֶּךָ כִּי כָמוֹךָ כְּפַרְעֹה.

Then Yehudah approached [Yosef] and said, "If you please, my lord, may your servant speak a word in my lord's ears, and let your anger not burn against your servant, for you are like Pharaoh."
(Bereishis 44:18)

The Midrash associates the term "approach" with battle, appeasement, and prayer.

Rabbi **Nison Alpert** explained that, just as battle requires an intimate knowledge of the enemy's strengths and weaknesses, conciliation demands thorough familiarity with the nature of the injured party, and prayer requires a genuine understanding of one's relationship to the Almighty.

Thus Yehudah prepared himself in all three realms, for appeasement succeeds only when the injured party sees that the offender will go to any lengths to make amends.

Dear Chatzkal,

I regret what I said and the way I behaved.

I know I caused you hurt, but I was only reacting to the statement you made...

Yossi crumpled up the letter, took a new sheet of paper, and began his fourth attempt to speak his mind.

Dear Chatzkal,

I really should have known better. I shouldn't have blamed you for...

This, too, was tossed into the circular file.

Yossi's wife could not help but notice her husband's intense concentration, and asked him what he was doing.

Yossi reflected for a moment and then stoically responded that he was writing a letter.

"So what's the big fuss?" she asked.

"Because I have to make sure it's perfect. There can't be any misunderstandings this time." Fortified with an even greater sense of purpose, he resumed his writing.

Dear Chatzkal,

I was wrong. If I had only realized...

This draft, too, joined its companions in the waste basket. Reduced to stony silence, Yossi buried his head in his arms and fixed his every thought on what was rapidly becoming a dead letter.

At last he sat up, grabbed another piece of paper, and began,

> ***Dear Chatzkal,***
>
> *I apologize with all my heart and with every fiber of my being. I love you.*
>
> *Your friend,*
>
> *Yossi*

Relieved that he had completed his mission, he got up from his desk. His wife asked if he could take some things along with him if he was headed for the mailbox. "I'm taking a different route," he explained. "I have to make this a personal delivery."

Unwilling to banish such a precious piece of paper to his pocket, Yossi clutched the letter in his hand. He boarded a bus to the outskirts of town and disembarked at the last stop. Somberly, Yossi made his way down the hill and his eyes began to swim.

Deliberately and determinedly, he made his way, until he finally reached Chatzkal and placed the letter on top of the fresh grave.

Mighty Oaks from Tiny Acorns Grow

וּבְנֵי דָן חֻשִׁים.

And the children of Dan [were] Chushim.
(Bereishis 46:23)

Dan had only one son, yet in *BeMidbar* we learn that Dan became the second most populous tribe. It says in the Midrash that in the *sefer Torah* of the *Tanna* Rabbi Meir, it was written, "And the *child* of Dan [was] Chushim."

The Midrash is not suggesting that Rabbi Meir actually had a different text in his *sefer Torah*. Rather, *Chazal* are symbolically conveying that Rabbi Meir was the Talmudic sage who was always *choshesh l'mi'ut*: he maintained that one should never discount a minority. After all, notes Rabbi **Eliyahu Munk**, a solitary son — a minority — evolved into the second most populous tribe.

Nothing small should ever be discounted: A single person, a solitary act, an insignificant gesture can bring about results that far exceed the effort expended.

Why Shmuel Bernstein was chosen to solicit funds for his yeshivah is a story in its own right, albeit a very short one. A somewhat naïve but nevertheless dedicated student, Shmuel never quite excelled in his studies. All right, let's call a spade a spade: Shmuel Bernstein's parents should have taught him a vocation. But nobody, *nobody* tried harder than Shmuel did. Avis could take a page from his book.

Shmuel was not so naïve as to be ignorant of his lack of success in learning. Still, he longed to make a lasting contribution to the field of Torah education. The dean of his suburban Jerusalem Yeshivah, sensitive to the needs of all the students, hit upon the idea of sending Shmuel abroad, where he might at least manage to collect some not-so-lasting contributions. But why quibble? One contribution might turn out to be as meaningful as the other. Such a mission, furthermore, would give Shmuel a sense of purpose and boost his self-esteem, and, with bountiful blessings of Providence, the yeshivah would not lose out on the deal.

Alas, for all the Rosh Yeshivah's good intentions, Shmuel Bernstein was simply not the man for the job. Remarkably, Bernstein did not come to that conclusion himself until he was already airborne, on his search-and-solicit mission to Toronto. Somewhere over the Atlantic, the awesomeness of his agency suddenly dawned on him and he was seized with a fit of schnorrophobia. Shmuel's youthful imagination conjured up a vision of dozens of creditors pounding down the doors of the yeshivah — many-tentacled creatures named *Arnona, Bezek and Pazgaz,* hurling *shtenders* and *sefarim* into trash dumpsters and herding *Rashei Yeshivah* and students away in humiliation and disgrace.

"If I fail to bring back enough money, the yeshivah may close!" he realized, now lathered in sweat. "If I fail to raise even enough to cover my trip, it definitely *will* close!" Shmuel began hyperventilating. His face turned chalky and he shivered with chills. His legs flailed in a nervous jig as his hands vise-clamped around the armrests. With anxiety contorting his features, he created something of a spectacle aboard the crowded plane.

"What's de matta?" asked an elderly gentleman seated on Shmuel's right. "Fear of flyin?"

"Er... no, I mean yes, I mean... I don't know."

The kindhearted, although not too subtle, neighbor saw that he had a case on his hands and placed a solicitous arm around Shmuel's twitching shoulders. "Ya got nuttin ta be scared of. My business takes me ta America nine times a year an I ain't falled out yet. Ha, ha! We're all in dis tugedder and dere's safety in numbers, so dere's nuttin ta worry 'bout."

But Shmuel was worried. The problem wasn't flying; it was landing. He had no training in soliciting funds and he lacked the necessary confidence to seek donations. Insecurity overwhelmed him, and the fear of returning to Israel penniless made his blood run cold.

"What, what?" his neighbor pressed. "Ya gonna keep dis *shvitzin* up de whole way, or what?"

"I-I'm afraid of collecting money," Shmuel blurted out. "That is, I'm afraid of *not* collecting money. Er, that is, I'm afraid of failing!"

"Ohhh," the neighbor said, a knowing look in his eye, "a *greener* headed for Toronta. I see dey're startin ya in de majors, huh?"

Shmuel nodded silently.

"No problem, pal. We'll get yer act tugedder; we're all old pros here." The man gestured to his cronies seated nearby. "Fresh meat," he proclaimed, hooking a thumb toward Shmuel. In milliseconds, fellow fund-raisers of every stripe began pouring out of every compartment of the plane, and an impromptu symposium on the do's, don'ts, and how-to's of fundraising was convened forthwith.

Everyone started offering advice on how to make it past the front door, how to counter "I gave already," how to conceal who sent you, etc., etc. Shmuel began scribbling copious notes, his head spinning dizzyingly as he tried to catch each and every tossed pearl of wisdom which might rescue his yeshivah from bankruptcy. But there was so *much* advice, flying in so many directions, that a tape recorder would not have been able to capture it all. One schnorrer after another graciously offered documentary proof of his expertise, with generous tips on the noble profession. The volume of voices reached a crescendo, and Shmuel's jaw gaped in incredulity.

Shmuel's neighbor, the ad hoc conference chairman, recognized the poor boy's dilemma and held up his hands for quiet. When calm was finally achieved, he informed the thirty or so delegates that, instead of imparting the secrets of the trade, they were only creating confusion. "We're all in dis tugedder," he reiterated in a voice of wizened authority, or at least seniority, "an it's only right we should help out dis newcomer ta our distinguished profession. But dis, dis racket, ain't helpin nobody. We gotta be whajacallit, systematic."

The senior schnorrer looked around until he was sure he had everyone's consent, and then, with the sonorous tone of someone swearing in a Supreme Court Justice, he addressed the novice. "Dere's five basic rules ta fund raisin; no more an no less. If ya stick ta dese simple rules, ya got it made. Ya'll be a whatjacallit, asset to yer yeshivah, an ya'll make a liddle *gelt* for yerself on de side. Got it? Good. Write dis down:

Rule #1: Dress neatly

Rule #2: Be polite

Rule #3: Compliment the host or hostess

Rule #4: Be brief

Rule #5: Speak the language of your patrons

"The rest is whajacallit, commentary. Take it from me, if ya stick ta dese rules, ya'll be a mitzvah magnet; ya can't lose." All of the delegates reverently nodded their heads and the meeting was summarily adjourned.

Shmuel dutifully copied the five rules on a fresh scrap of paper and stuffed it into his shirt pocket. Several times during the night he consulted the cardinal rules, and just having them on his person imbued him with a warm feeling of confidence.

At the Toronto terminal, Shmuel's comrades-in-alms arranged a ride for him to the *kollel* and secured a moonlighting taxi driver to take him to the Queen City's basic stops and attractions for *meshulachim*. As home visits were conducted only in the evenings, Shmuel had a whole day to rest up from his trip and prepare for his big debut.

Our hero slept fitfully, contemplating his upcoming appearance at the home of a local host. By early afternoon he despaired of getting any real sleep, so he hauled himself out of bed to begin his preparations. Suddenly, his mind was a blank. He quickly consulted his precious list.

Rule #1: Dress neatly

This seemingly simple rule would require a good deal of thought and effort on Shmuel's part. Neatness, like finesse, was not his forte, and he was wont to concoct his own original solutions to standard problems of grooming and attire. The fashion statement made by the young man's wardrobe was usually a resounding "*Nebach*!"

He stood in front of a mirror and looked critically at his dim reflection. Working his way down from the top, Shmuel noticed that his shirt was horribly wrinkled; in fact, all the shirts he'd brought were — a credit no doubt to his inimitable manner of packing. Not having changed out of his best shirt for the past day-and-a-half hadn't helped its condition, but he stuck with it (literally, I'm afraid) out of a sense of passive loyalty. The patrons he would visit would see only the front of the collar and the least creased fields between his tie and jacket. This comforting thought allowed Shmuel to consider the shirt an integral part of the shirt/tie/jacket segment of his ensemble. The ink stain from a leaky ballpoint could easily pass for an emblem on the pocket, he assured himself, and with that touch of class he could allow himself the luxury of disregarding a few wrinkle ranges here and there and a frayed cuff or two.

His tie, however, had no such redeeming invisibility. It wasn't merely stained; it was encrusted. Shmuel's method of cleaning it by rubbing a bar of soap over the globs of filth and lakes of soil only worsened the situation. *Post facto* he devised a rather unique solution, reversing his tie so that the stain-free inside was outside. Needless to say, the seam and lining were now clearly visible; but one had to admit that the tie at least looked clean.

Moving right along, Shmuel came to his belt, or actually his father's belt, which he had long ago cut down to his size. The simulated leather was a bit chapped — all right, missing in a few spots, and the loop was gone altogether, but when he rotated the buckle to the side, you couldn't tell that he'd punched the notches with a can opener.

His pants were not too bad, relatively speaking. Amazingly, there were no split seams, the few minor pizza-and-coke stains by now blended in more or less with the weave, and his jacket almost completely covered the shiny seat. His shoes, however, were in such a scuffed and dust-laden state that even Shmuel couldn't help but notice.

The would-be fund-raiser attempted to rectify that condition in the most expeditious way: Standing first on his left foot, he polished the uppers of his dusty right shoe against the back of his left trouser leg. Then he switched feet. There's no denying the effectiveness of the method, enhanced by some grease deposits formerly embedded in the fabric. However, the backs of Shmuel's pant-legs from the knees down (which he could not see) were now caked with all the grime that had previously sullied his shoes.

Looking his best — emphasis on the "his" — Shmuel was ready to embark on his mission to raise desperately needed funds for his yeshivah. Remembering that the other rules for successful solicitation, which he intended to fulfill with equal exactitude, applied to the actual encounter, he slipped his list into an unholey pocket for later reference, finger-combed his hair, and sat down to wait.

In the early evening Shmuel was picked up by a driver who asked if he wanted to be taken along the "regular route" or did Shmuel have some particular addresses in mind. Since he had been equipped by his yeshivah with a few leads to wealthy Torontonians, Shmuel fished around in his excuse-for-an-attaché case (i.e., plastic shopping bag with snap-close handles) until he found the crumpled document. He read the first entry to the driver.

"Huh?" the man behind the wheel asked. "I never heard of such a place; you sure it's in Ontario?"

"It's got to be," Shmuel replied. "My yeshivah gave it to me."

"Uh, uh," grunted the driver, who was beginning to realize just what he was in for with this raw recruit. "Let me hear what else you got."

Shmuel went over his entire list of leads with the driver, but only one address sounded familiar: 624 Prince Edward Drive. Unfortunately, the by now exasperated driver got his royalty confused and inadvertently delivered his unsuspecting passenger to 624 Prince Charles Drive.

Now, while Prince Charles did indeed reign in the Jewish part of town, his kingdom centered on the most assimilated section of the neighborhood. But assimilated by no means meant poor. In fact, the driver was enormously impressed with the residence that stood at his mistaken address, the most imposing edifice he'd ever encountered in a half-dozen years of motoring *meshulachim.*

The house was a stately three-story Victorian affair with an octagonal tower dominating the right front corner. A large porch, defined by a complicated gingerbread trim, started at the tower, extended along the front of the house, and swept around the left side. Above the double-doored front entrance and resting on the roof of the porch was a circular balcony, roofed with a cone that complemented the one on top of the tower. The mansion had obviously cost a fortune, although at present it was terribly run down and in a state of neglect.

Since the driver was unable to find parking in the driveway, which hosted three unusual vehicles — a beat-up Land Rover, a beat-up dune buggy, and a very beat-up Thunderbird — he parked far down the street to wait patiently for Shmuel to complete his business. By the look of things, he figured it was okay to leave the motor running.

"I usually work on percentages," he told the tyro *meshulach.* Shmuel had no idea what the driver meant. "But seeing as how this is your first time out," he continued, tactfully not mentioning the unlikelihood of there being a sum to take a percentage of, "I'll just take a flat fee. Good luck."

Shmuel got out of the car and checked the side mirror to see if his hat was on in the right direction. It looked all right, but he wasn't sure. For good measure he rotated it a half-turn, tucked his shirttails in, and rebuffed his shoes on his pants legs. Static electricity crackled as serge and sock united around calf level, but all in all Shmuel looked neater than he ever had before. Still, there was always room for improvement.

He scrutinized his reflection again, trying to think of an extra bit of dash that would render him debonair enough to attract sizeable donations to his cause. Shmuel's innovative mind soon hit upon just the right accessory for his outfit. In lieu of a handkerchief, he inserted a tissue in the breast pocket of his jacket and fluffed it out artfully. Of special note were the two paper-clips which from time immemorial had served as surrogate cufflinks.

Shmuel took a deep breath and strode up the walk to his very first house, hoping his lucky first knock would herald the first opportunity to help out his yeshivah. A most unusual aroma wafting from the window was inhaled along with his deep breath. The closer he came, the more pungent the odd smell became. Well, it couldn't be a sacrifice, he assured himself. Shmuel was at a loss to identify the bittersweet fragrance, but he wasn't about to allow a little thing like that to derail his mission.

When he reached up to knock on the door, he noticed the name engraved on the brass plate below the knocker: PEARLOWITZ. With his knuckled fist poised in mid-knock, he referred to his donor listing, where the name "Pearlman" appeared. "A typo," he figured. His knuckles continued their journey.

An aging hippie wearing a peasant dress with long billowing sleeves, granny glasses and earth shoes greeted him with a peace sign. She was wearing no less than thirteen necklaces, all constructed from decorative findings as diverse as telephone wire, Wrigley gum wrappers, and aluminum pop tops.

Her every movement tinkled, as she was adorned from head to toe with bells of various sizes, dimensions and resonances. Even her big hoop earrings had bells on them. Needless to say, she had several bangle bracelets that added to the cacophony. Every finger boasted at least one ring made from unidentifiable debris, except for the two rings that were salvaged cigar bands.

"Mrs. Pearlman... eh, er... owitz?" Shmuel asked. There was no answer. She looked him over, twice or thrice, registering but resisting comment on his attire, and then flashed the peace sign again. Shmuel understood this second communication to be an invitation for him to enter, so our hero gallantly stepped over the threshold.

It would be wrong to say that Shmuel was undaunted. In reality, Shmuel was daunted. Very daunted. He was caught so much by surprise that he quickly consulted his trusty instruction manual to see how to proceed. Staring right at him was

Rule #2: Be polite

which he immediately activated. He thrust out a peace sign with both hands, looking for all the world like a politician who has just won the primary, and solemnly intoned a polite "Thank you."

Bernstein didn't get very far before he was practically knocked off his feet by the unusual odor which permeated the whole house. He noticed the tiny pots that littered the floor, polluting the air with tiny puffs of smoke. Remarkably, these pots were about the most normal thing on the floor. But before he could take in the entire scene the hostess inquired, "How can I help you?"

Shmuel was again thrown off guard and quickly checked his list.

Rule #3: Compliment the hostess

Eager to oblige, Bernstein offered, "Nice-smelling house you have here."

"It's a special brand; it really blows your Karma."

"Thank you," Shmuel responded, remembering **Rule #2**

and at the same time reaching new heights in non sequiturology.

"Mrs. Pearl..."

"Hey, no one's called me that for years. That's, like, you know, so, like, *antique*! Call me Ginger, and have a seat. My planet is yours!"

Bernstein didn't know what to make of this invitation. He'd never been asked to share someone's planet before. He looked all over for a chair. He looked to the left; he looked to the right. He even looked up. But all he saw were oversized cushions strewn across the floor. The decor of the house did not seem to be highly prioritized.

A carillon symphony alerted Shmuel to the fact that Ginger was about to be seated herself, and sure enough, as he watched, his hostess folded her legs underneath her and sat down lotus-like on a woven Indian rug. "*Oy!*" Shmuel thought to himself. "I couldn't do that in a million years!"

He was still standing when Ginger waved him toward one of the giant floor pillows that were scattered about the room like fabric boulders. "Man, there's no need to, like, stand on ceremony," she said. "Pull up a pillow and plop!"

Shmuel nodded dumbly and tried to sit on one of the cushions. It was a mistake. He instantly sank up to his eyeballs in kapok. "*Gevald!*" he cried out as he struggled to find a secure, if not comfortable, position.

"Don't fight it, man!" Ginger advised. "Just go with the flow! Relax!"

Shmuel didn't have much choice: It was either stand tall or sprawl, and he desperately wanted to follow **Rule #2: Be polite**. So there he sat, or more precisely, lounged, in an overstuffed pillow, trying to make himself appear as presentable and professional as he could under the circumstances.

"Now," Ginger said, "let's rap."

"Pardon me?"

"Let's RAP! You know, like, tell me what's on your mind and I'll, like, *respond*!"

Shmuel glanced again at his *meshulach's* manual and again it did not fail him.

Rule #4: Be brief

Interpreting the instruction as literally as possible, he replied, "Charity."

Ginger pondered that for a moment. "I've got a goldfish named 'Faith' and a cat named 'Hope,' but there's no one here by the name of 'Charity.'" Then she brightened. "You must mean 'Chastity,' my daughter!" With that, the mistress of the house reached behind her back, deftly raised a ceremonial stick that looked like a Louisville Slugger, and whacked a massive Oriental gong that stood in a corner. The sound sent shivers up Bernstein's spine, but they quickly passed. Little did he know he'd soon be needing them again.

A beaded curtain clattered and from behind it a voice yelled, "Yeah, Ginger? Whaddayawant?"

"You have, like, company, dear!"

"I'll be right there."

Ginger turned to her guest. "My daughter's, like, a heavy metal freak, you know?"

"I do?" Shmuel asked incredulously.

"Yeah. Chastity can spend hours listening to punk rock, sometimes without even turning on her CD player. It drives me bananas. I mean, like, how can you live like that? All that violence. Things are meant to just *be*. Oh, I agree with her that order is really disorder and chaos is cosmic. But still, heavy metal is just *too* heavy for me. I think mellow is where it's at. You know, I mean, like, no one tells leaves on the trees where to fall; they just do their own thing. We should do the same, don't you think?"

Shmuel was stumped. Out of desperation, he simply replied, "R-r-r-right."

"Right *on*!" Ginger agreed, thrusting her clenched fist toward the sky. "Right *on*, brother!"

Before Shmuel could figure out what in heaven's name Ginger was saying, the beaded curtain parted. Bernstein thought it was a girl. But then he wasn't sure. It could have been a boy. She, or he, was dressed in black from head to toe. A long black shirt covered black jeans. A black leather jacket covered the long black shirt. Basic black motorcycle boots topped off the costume at the bottom.

The effect was enhanced by the person inside the outfit. Her skin was so pale, she could have done a minstrel show, like Al Jolson singing "Mammy." Except for the hair. The sides of her head were totally shaven. The hair on top stood straight up like chicken feathers. Half the feathers were green. The other half were pink. Deep black circles were painted around her eyes, and each ear was adorned with four safety pin earrings going up in a row. An enormous black leather belt with studs and rhinestones weighed down her waist. She was wearing a glove on each hand with holes for all ten fingers to show through. The nails matched the hair.

With a look of boredom coupled with sullen contempt, she entered the room. "Yeah?" she said.

"Chastity, dear, a friend of yours is, like, here to see you."

Chastity took one long glare at the *meshulach* fidgeting uncomfortably on the cushion beneath him. Her expression spoke volumes, all of them reading: "Ain't no friend o' *mine*."

Undermined but undeterred, Shmuel found inspiration and encouragement in **Rule #2: Be polite**. He rolled his eyes back in his best imitation of Chastity's greeting to him, and intoned sincerely, "Thank you."

Chastity's hands were on her hips. "Well?!" she snapped.

Shmuel feared to deviate from **Rule #4**, which demanded brevity, but he did feel that under the circumstances a little elaboration was in order.

"This, er, is not the Chastity, that is, *charity* I want, er, meant, um, *need,*" Shmuel stammered. The verbal advance in no way mitigated the young woman's unfriendly disposition, but her mother immediately grasped what he was driving at.

"I dig," she said. "You're not here to see Chastity. You want my son, Wounded Knee."

Before Shmuel could formulate a response to Ginger's latest misinterpretation and clarify that what he needed was a charitable contribution, she whacked the gong twice and yelled, "Knee-ee!" She then turned her attention back to her guest, making conversation to flll the gap.

"You know how Knee got his name, don't you?" she inquired. Bernstein shook his head, not trusting his tongue to utter even a monosyllable.

"His father was, like, shot during a Civil Rights demonstration at Wounded Knee, in South Dakota. His last great movement..." she explained, her voice cracking and a wistful tear falling from her eye, "was to save the Indians."

On this note Shmuel finally awoke to the fact that he was probably in the wrong house. The Last of the Mohicans wasn't exactly a likely donor for his Yeshivah. The problem now was how to extricate himself from the reservation without getting an arrow between his shoulder blades.

He didn't have much time to consider his dilemma, for before long the *Kaddish'l* arrived. Wounded Knee Pearlowitz was exceedingly tall, made even taller by the six-inch thatch of white mohawk bristles that ran down the center of his otherwise bald head. A rag of sorts was tied around his forehead like a sweatband and his jeans and T-shirt were ventilated with gaping holes. Unlike his sister, he was barefoot, but whereas she had shuffled zombie-like into the room, Knee came in with a flying leap, arms and legs assuming an aggressive martial-arts stance. "Hi-*ya*!" he shouted and Shmuel wondered if this was a variation on the more commonplace "Hiya, there," or if it had a more profound, esoteric meaning.

"Knee," Ginger opened with that same dazed look in her eyes, "there's someone, like, here to see you."

Knee's eyes did not roll heavenward in disgust but narrowed in suspicion. He began weaving around Shmuel in his lightfooted way, windmilling his stiffly held hands, chopping at the air and back-kicking a cushion or two. Shmuel, by now a real expert at returning weird salutations, mimicked Knee's gyrations, adding a polite "Thank you."

Escape was impossible, and probably inadvisable to attempt. Shmuel decided instead to make the most of the situation. If nothing else, it was a good chance to practice his *shpiel*. He consulted his little list, which again championed brevity, but this time Shmuel made an effort to include a subject and a predicate so as to make his intentions perfectly clear.

"I go to a yeshivah in Jerusalem. It's very poor; we need money."

"Far out!" Knee responded, pulling himself up a piece of floor. "That's Donovan's bag, too. The two of you should get along real good. This is totally awesome!"

"Of course!" Ginger agreed, gonging three times before Shmuel had a chance to brace himself. "Donovan's, like, my foster son."

From behind the beaded curtain, a boy of about eighteen emerged. "Yes, Ginger?"

"Care to join us? I thought you might offer our friend a little Colombian tea!"

Bernstein's eyes dilated as wide as Lenox soup bowls. Donovan — a true flower child if ever there was one — was wearing a dress. It wasn't really a dress; it was more like a saffron-colored robe. His hair was long and silky and tied back in a low ponytail with a piece of yarn. A small leather pouch dangled from his rope belt. Shmuel shook his head in disbelief as Donovan took his seat alongside him.

Ginger "formally" introduced them. "Donovan, make like an earthquake!"

Shmuel's curiosity got the better of him. "Make like an earthquake?" he echoed.

"Sure!" Ginger replied. "Make like an earthquake and SHAKE!"

Donovan gave him a soulful look and extended a hand. It drooped limply at his wrist. Going back to all important **Rule #2: Be polite**, Shmuel shook it. It was surprisingly smooth and smelled like the honeysuckle Shmuel knew back home in Jerusalem.

Donovan was the first to speak. "What's your sign? No, don't tell me. You must be a Libra."

"No," Shmuel said, "I'm a *meshulach*, and I'm collecting for a yeshivah..."

Ginger interrupted. "Donovan, dear, where are your manners?"

The saffron-robed boy thumped his forehead. "Sorry, Ginger," he apologized. "It was an oversight." He dumped out what looked like Tetley's tiniest little tea leaves mixed with oregano from his leather pouch.

"No thanks," Shmuel said politely. "I'm not thirsty."

The Pearlowitzes laughed at his little joke. Earth Mother rolled the tea in small squares of paper and the whole family lit up together.

There was no longer any doubt in Shmuel's mind: He was definitely in the wrong house. This family was not in any financial position to contribute anything. They didn't have enough money for furniture. They were obviously so poor they couldn't even afford dishes; they had to smoke their tea, instead of drinking it! The daughter wore her brother's hand-me-downs and had to cut her own hair, from the looks of it. One son wore torn rags and appeared to be handicapped, as evidenced by his stiff-limbed spastic movements. And the foster kid wore his *mother's* hand-me-downs. They didn't even have shoes, except for the girl, who had a pair of old boots on — in the summer, no less!

It was pathetic, and a waste of everybody's time, although the Pearlowitzes didn't seem to have anything special scheduled. Before he began the complex process of getting up off the floor, however, Shmuel furtively reached for his instruction sheet. As he perused the check list, he realized that he had been faithful to each and every one of the rules, and this gave him renewed confidence — especially as the sweet-smelling smoke that was wafting around the room began to have its effect on him.

Finally, his eyes focused on **Rule #5: Speak their language**. Bernstein unsprawled himself from his pillow. The room tilted strangely and he tried to tilt with it. As hopeless as the situation seemed, he felt it would be a mistake to omit even one of the tried-and-true directions given him by those men of vast experience. "All right," he told himself. "Give it your best shot." Then he cleared his throat importantly and began.

"Like, man," Shmuel said, "my yeshivah in *Yerushalayim* needs bread. If they don't get some, they're going to be, you know, like, nowhere! Dig?"

"We dig," the Pearlowitzes said in unison.

"That's why I'm here — to raise..."

"Our consciousness!" Donovan chimed in.

"*Right* on!" Shmuel exclaimed emphatically, hoping that what he had said made sense.

Ginger rolled her head. "How much dough has to go?"

Shmuel tried to translate. "Dough? Dough is like bread. And bread means... money!" The more the smoke filled the room, the easier it was for Shmuel to understand Ginger and Donovan. Luckily, Chastity and Wounded Knee were napping — or something; he was sure their rap would be too far out for him.

"What do you say to fifty?" he asked.

"That's heavy bread, man," she answered.

"The heavier the bread, the more earning for learning," Shmuel said. Then, for good measure, he added. "Dig?"

Ginger dug. Into one of the oversized floor cushions — which doubled as her handbag. The odd contents were soon arrayed on the Indian rug: dozens of powdered and pilled substances, a brass pipe of some sort, three or four strands of multi-colored love beads, a campaign button with the slogan "Draft Beer Not Students," followed by another one that said "Nixon's Only Platform Are His Shoes," a dog-eared pamphlet entitled "Growing Cannabis for Fun and Profit," some miscellaneous change and a few bills. At the very bottom she found a checkbook.

She retrieved a pen from the thick braid on top of her head, made out a check and handed it to Shmuel. "It's been real," she said.

"Peace unto you!" Donovan added.

"*Aleichem shalom,*" Shmuel automatically responded.

Still slightly whoozy, Shmuel made his way to the door. Although he had failed in his first attempt to be a big-time collector, he took solace in the fact that he had at least provided these people with an opportunity to do a mitzvah.

As he approached the car, he glanced at the check. Then he glanced again, exerting himself to retain his eyeballs in their rightful sockets. He counted the zeroes a second time, then a third. Shmuel again found himself hyperventilating and getting chalky in the face, only this time it wasn't from schnorrophobia. He expected the figure to change before his very eyes, but it didn't.

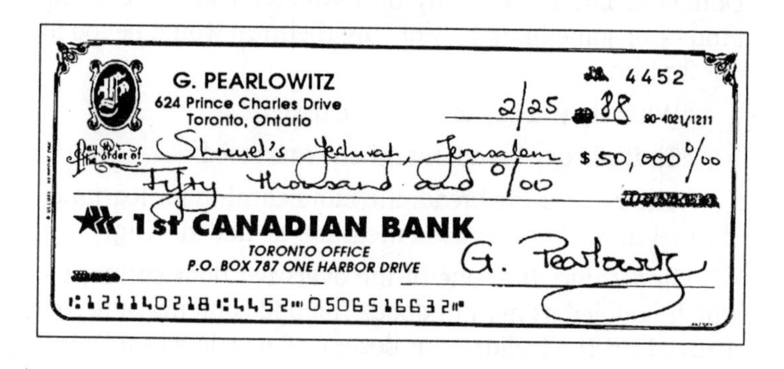
G. PEARLOWITZ
624 Prince Charles Drive
Toronto, Ontario

4452

2/25 88

90-4021/1211

Pay to the order of Shmuel's Yeshivah, Jerusalem $50,000 0/00

Fifty thousand and 0/00

1st CANADIAN BANK
TORONTO OFFICE
P.O. BOX 787 ONE HARBOR DRIVE

G. Pearlowitz

121140218 4452 0506516632

"Well, it sure took you long enough!" the driver said testily as Shmuel yanked the taxi door open. "A few more minutes and I would have called out the Mounties." His passenger appeared to be in a state of shock — or was it euphoria?

"Well, how was it?" he asked.

Shmuel shook his head. In a voice brimming with pride and self-confidence, he replied, "Heavy, man, heavy. Totally awesome."

Clarity and Courage

וַיִּשְׂאוּ אֹתוֹ בָנָיו אַרְצָה כְּנַעַן וַיִּקְבְּרוּ אֹתוֹ בִּמְעָרַת שְׂדֵה הַמַּכְפֵּלָה אֲשֶׁר קָנָה אַבְרָהָם אֶת הַשָּׂדֶה לַאֲחֻזַּת קֶבֶר מֵאֵת עֶפְרֹן הַחִתִּי עַל פְּנֵי מַמְרֵא.

His sons carried [Yaakov] to the Land of Canaan, and buried him in the cave of the Machpelah field, which Avraham had bought as a burial place from Efron the Hittite, facing Mamre.

(Bereishis 50:13)

The Midrash recounts that when the family approached the burial place, Eisav prevented their passage, asserting that the land was his. The brothers denied Eisav's claim and insisted that Yaakov had explicitly prepared this grave for himself *(Bereishis 50:5)*. Eisav demanded to see the land title.

While Naftali, the most fleet-footed brother, raced back to Egypt to fetch the document, Chushim, the son of Dan, could not comprehend what was happening because he was deaf. Once his brothers explained to him the nature of the dispute, he immediately grabbed a stick and cracked open Eisav's head.

Rabbi **Chaim Shmuelevitz** asks, "Why was Chushim the only one who defended Yaakov's honor?"

People naturally become inured to what

they hear and experience. Often their vision becomes distorted, as they concentrate on the matter at hand and lose sight of the big picture. As the brothers debated Eisav, they focused on the real estate and lost sight of the far greater issue of their father's honor. Only Chushim was oblivious to the argument, so his vision remained clear. He never turned his gaze from the disgrace Yaakov's remains were suffering.

Resigning yourself to a situation is the bane of a clear perception.

The Captain's instructions were clear: Goldie was not to remain on board after the *Padawer* set sail from Baltimore. True, the old lady had become a regular fixture aboard the ship during the previous weeks in dry dock, distributing homemade pastries to all the crewmen and generally behaving like everyone's grannie. But despite her assertion that he "vould see vhat ah nesset olt Goldie vill be durink de hard part uf de trip," the Captain remained adamant. His mission was to pick up war refugees and deliver them safely to Palestine — not to ferry sweet old American-Jewish grannies to "Eretz Yisruel."

To the Captain's thinking no asset could outweigh the presence of a sixty-year-old liability on a mission that required clockwork precision. The embarkation of the DPs would have to be carried out smoothly and swiftly. If the boat could not anchor close enough to shore for the refugees to board it across long planks, a wire would have to be strung from the ship to the dock; the DPs, in groups of forty or so would then board large rubber rescue dinghies and pull their lifeboats to the ship by way of the wire. A motor launch would also tow several dinghies over at one shot, and thus the transport of over a thousand passengers would be accomplished in under two hours. The carefully timed operation had to proceed without a hitch or else the *Padawer* would not be underway before dawn.

The pre-dawn sailing was crucial. While the various European governments were willing to turn a blind eye to the mass emigration of DPs, they could not afford to incur the wrath of the British, and a daylight departure would have revealed their complicity. But even if all went well during the transfer operation, the *Padawer* still had to evade the British Mediterranean Fleet, the RAF Mediterranean Patrol, and the Palestine Coastal Water Blockade.

"I'm sorry, Goldie, but your continuing with us to Palestine is out of the question," the Captain said firmly.

Goldie began to cry. "It's not enough de Britich von't let us into our homelend, but mine own grenchildrens are also goink to keep me out?" She pulled a lace handkerchief from her sleeve and mopped her streaming eyes. Several crewmen rolled their eyes heavenward in a helpless gesture of submission; the rest glared accusingly at the Captain.

The odds had suddenly shifted in Goldie's favor. She peeked over the edge of white lace and murmured, "Dis may be mine lest chance..." That was the clincher.

The loading operation proceeded rapidly and Goldie was on deck to welcome the 1,100 refugees aboard. The "illegals," shaken by their recent harrowing experience, seemed not to register the fact that a plump, snowy-haired figure straight out of a storybook occupied a place on the receiving line. Greeting them with blessings in Yiddish and Hebrew, Goldie distributed warm blankets, a little nosh, and plenty of cheer.

During the next four, difficult days, Goldie became well-acquainted with each and every one of the DPs. Even the most silent and sullen among them — those whose war experiences had been so horrid that they had sealed that part of their minds as if behind a brick wall — opened up to Goldie and poured their hearts out. They cried, and she wiped away their tears. They shouted angry words at a God Who they imagined had abandoned His people to such a fate, and she spoke soothingly of redemption and hope. By the fifth day, almost all of the passengers had joined Goldie's afternoon songfest-cum-*mussar shiur.* "*Chasdei Hashem ki lo samnu*" they sang, and each word struck a personal chord.

That Thursday afternoon, however, was to be the last of their pleasurable sessions on the *Padawer*, although when the youthful *chazzan* belted out the first notes of "*Yiboneh HaMikdash*" in his mellifluous tenor voice, none of them knew that.

He was only twenty-five or so, perhaps twenty-eight, but when he sang his eyes glistened and his brow creased. All who gazed upon his countenance and sat mesmerized by his heart-piercing voice knew that the young *chazzan* had seen more suffering than any twenty-five-year-old ever needed to see.

The voice broke off sharply in mid-note. For one fleeting moment, the crowd on the deck remained transfixed. Then they, too, heard the sound.

The Captain immediately ordered everyone below deck, but of course it was hopeless. A Naval Academy drill team would not have made it down those narrow ladders from a rolling deck in the three brief minutes they had before the patrol plane flew overhead.

The Captain knew to expect the worst. The plane continued to circle and soon two destroyer escorts were sighted on the horizon.

The appearance of the British fleet ships etched painfully sharp lines on the faces of all the crewmen. The Captain climbed down into the hold to apprise the passengers of the situation. It was unbearably hot and there was no longer any point in their remaining below: the "cargo vessel" had been identified. The Captain returned to the deck, lowered the Panamanian flag and hoisted in its place one bearing the word DROR [Freedom] in bold blue letters on a white field.

When the refugees emerged from the bowels of the ship and spotted the escorts, they fell silent. Even the youngsters, who normally chattered incessantly, became still, and a pall of terror descended on the decrepit scow.

The decks and armor of the towering destroyers gleamed smugly in the bright sun at the helpless, overcrowded immigrant boat. Sandwiched between those menacing Goliaths, the DROR defiantly continued on its course until it reached Palestine's territorial waters.

It was then that Goldie approached the Captain. "I vish to spick to der leader," she said, and the Captain for the first time lost his patience. "Which leader did you have in mind?" he retorted with some disdain. "The Prime Minister, Secretary Bevin, or will the Admiral of the British Fleet do?"

At that moment, a launch carrying a well-armed boarding party was rapidly nearing the DROR. The radio operator handed the Captain instructions just received from land: the DROR was to offer no resistance; the safety of the passengers — including many women and children — was paramount. The Captain reluctantly concurred.

When the British party boarded, Goldie elbowed her way through the crowd until she stood face to face with the English officer. Then, to the utter astonishment of the Captain and all assembled, she quietly removed her gold-rimmed spectacles and began polishing the lenses with the white lace handkerchief she always kept tucked up her sleeve, her eyes riveting his.

Seconds ticked away but no one moved. She replaced her glasses and then, drawing herself up to her full height of four feet, ten inches, she declared: "I just wanted to see for myself the officers of the invincible British Navy, the proudest Navy in the world, who require two destroyers and scores of crewmen to overpower an unarmed cargo boat filled with homeless war victims. The Almighty has a special place for brave little sailors such as you." Goldie's endearing accent had disappeared, to be replaced by one of which any Park Avenue matron would have been proud.

The jaw of the British naval officer dropped with an almost audible "thunk." Speechless, he slowly holstered his pistol. In the same moment, as though bolstered by Goldie's audacity, the engines of the DROR thudded to a halt, and the mood of the passengers shifted ever-so-subtly. Their silence was no longer one of despair and defeat, but of pride and defiance. The boarding party withdrew.

The DROR, wallowing on the rough sea, was unable — or unwilling — to get its engines going and the British were obliged to perform the distasteful task of piloting the scow to shore. With every bump, the sailors peered down in disgust at the ugly scrapes that the filthy refugee boat made on their gleaming hull — and the passengers of the DROR cheered.

As soon as the boat was in clear sight of land, Goldie hurled herself overboard. The ensuing British rescue operation was duly recorded for posterity, to the delight of the reporters assembled on the dock, and to the utter consternation of her rescuers.

Goldie had indeed proved to be an asset. The following day's world press would surely carry the story of a sixty-year-old lady challenging British destroyers and throwing herself into the sea rather than be captured alive. Of course, she had had no such suicidal intentions ["Ekshully, mine pocketbook fell in de vater," she later told a friend, "mit mine fency-shmency *siddur* inside. I should let dat drown?! Farget it."] but it was such stories about the heartless British monsters that destroyed the goodwill upon which the British mandate in Palestine rested.

The Benefit of the Doubt

וַיִּרְאוּ אֲחֵי יוֹסֵף כִּי מֵת אֲבִיהֶם וַיֹּאמְרוּ לוּ יִשְׂטְמֵנוּ יוֹסֵף וְהָשֵׁב יָשִׁיב לָנוּ אֵת כָּל הָרָעָה אֲשֶׁר גָּמַלְנוּ אֹתוֹ.

And when Yosef's brothers saw that their father was dead, they said, "Perhaps Yosef will hate us and surely pay us back all the evil that we did to him."

(Bereishis 50:15)

Why did the brothers suspect that Yosef — who had already declared that what had happened was clearly God's will — would harbor ill will against them after Yaakov's passing?

According to the Midrash, they "saw that their father was dead," because they were no longer invited to dine at Yosef's table, nor did he embrace them as he had during Yaakov's lifetime.

In fact, the change that took place was only a reflection of Yosef's piety and had nothing whatsoever to do with an old grudge finally aired after Yaakov's passing. On the contrary, the Midrash teaches:

Yosef's sole intention was for the sake of Heaven. In the past, Father seated me at the head of the table ahead of Yehudah, who is the king, and Reuven, who is the firstborn. Now it is no longer appropriate that I sit at the head.

Yosef feared that now; after his father's passing, he had no justification to sit at the head of the table. His dominion over Egypt, he felt, had no bearing on the fact that Yehudah was the king and Reuven the firstborn. Hence, dining at the same table could only create an uncomfortable situation, one which Yosef sought to avoid.

This, apparently, the brothers failed to consider.

Prior to the establishment of the State of Israel, the residents of the *Yishuv* lived in dire poverty. Combining money sent from abroad with the pitiful income from their simple jobs, they struggled to eke out an existence in the Holy Land. But as difficult as life was for Jerusalemites during this era, the fate of the city's many elderly was even more heartrending. There simply weren't the financial resources to provide the care and attention that these old people so desperately needed.

It was not uncommon for the aged to go hungry for long stretches, and quite frankly, many of the local residents were too preoccupied with their own existential hardships and wondering how they would feed their families to worry about the needs of senior citizens.

There was, however, one person who made the plight of the elderly his foremost concern. His name was Rabbi Eliyahu Reichman and he served as the secretary of Jerusalem's old age home. Reb Eliyahu had assumed a heavy responsibility, for the residents of the home were totally reliant upon him for their sustenance.

Reb Eliyahu's selfless acceptance of this duty earned him a reputation for being one of the righteous men of the old *Yishuv*. Such a reputation wasn't easily acquired at a time when even the simple tinsmiths and humble cobblers were pious, learned individuals.

The key to his success was his method of soliciting funds. His soft words and honest pleas melted hearts to the point that whomever he met actually looked forward to parting with their meager income in order to keep Jerusalem's old age home running. Whenever they saw the furrowed forehead, gaunt cheeks and silver-gray beard of Reb Eliyahu approaching, they knew that some sort of pledge, no matter how small, would be courteously elicited.

Providentially, Reb Eliyahu was joined in this line of work by his closest friend, Reb Shlomo Katz. Actually, raising funds for the infirm and elderly of Jerusalem was just one of the many interests these two shared. They had learned Torah together from the time they were children, and had grown up side by side in the *Yishuv* under the most austere conditions. Small wonder their friendship could not be accurately described with trite cliches like "brotherly love" and "genuine comradeship." For well over sixty years they intuited each other's thoughts and feelings, sharing life's joys and halving its sorrows. There was nothing one would not, or could not, do for the other.

Understandably, one of the greatest sorrows Reb Shlomo ever suffered was the passing of his friend and brother Reb Eliyahu. Reb Shlomo was joined in his mourning by countless residents of Jerusalem, who were heartbroken by the bitter news. Reb Eliyahu had touched and helped so many people, and they all came together to express their immense grief over the tragic loss.

It was a gloomy day; the sky was gray and bleak, and

there was a sharp nip in the air. It seemed as if even the weather had been tailored to reflect the mood of the people, for the atmosphere was thick with sadness. Nonetheless, inclement weather could not deter the untold hundreds of men and women from this final act of true *chessed* for Reb Eliyahu.

Streets began to swell with mobs blocks away from the site of the funeral. The crowd jammed the cramped, winding alleyways converging on the main thoroughfare along which Reb Eliyahu's bier was slowly carried. Groups of mourners desperately tried to join the funeral procession, a sea of black in which masses of people dressed in Jerusalem's traditional attire pressed tightly together, wherever they could. All along the route were scores of women, children, and those too infirm to walk. Peering through the arched windows of the single-story and double-story stone structures were many of the aged who had benefited directly from the deceased.

Shepherding this slow-moving flock was the bereft Rabbi Katz. Reb Shlomo had never looked more alone than he did on that day. Watching the grief-stricken figure trudge behind the body brought rivers of tears to the eyes of those participants keenly aware of the deep friendship that had existed between the two. The abundant sorrow over Reb Eliyahu aroused equal emotions of compassion and sympathy for Reb Shlomo's suffering. But these feelings were suddenly shattered and replaced by cries of indignation when Rabbi Katz abandoned the funeral procession to enter a flower shop.

It was the most bizarre and poorly-timed act imaginable! Many stopped in their tracks in disbelief, their eyes riveted to the flower shop, silently hoping for an explanation for such ignoble behavior. But Reb Shlomo was not to be exonerated, for a few minutes later he emerged with a potted plant in his arms, and headed off in the opposite direction of the Mount of Olives cemetery.

People from all walks of life had gathered to pay their final respects, and in some small way repay the kindness to the man who had graced their city with so much benevolence. But all at once the focus of the funeral shifted to murmurings about the deceased's supposed best friend. "Couldn't he have waited one more day before buying his plant?" the crowd grumbled reproachfully.

Reb Shlomo's behavior even disturbed the gentle, kindly soul of one of the most respected *tzaddikim* in Jerusalem, Rabbi Leib Levy. Instead of harboring his dismay, however, he realized that he was obliged to rebuke and correct the sinner. Does not the Torah instruct, "You shall not hate your brother in your heart; you shall surely admonish your neighbor..."? To avoid hard feelings, Reb Leib confronted Rabbi Katz right away.

"I simply cannot understand your behavior," he chided softly, clasping Reb Shlomo's hands. "Please correct me if I am wrong, but weren't you the *niftar*'s closest friend for over six decades? Where is your respect and honor for the deceased? How could you abandon him to purchase a flower pot?"

Reb Shlomo couldn't be offended by Reb Leib's question, for he was a good enough student of human nature to realize that there was bound to be strong criticism regarding his seemingly outrageous conduct. He gently took Reb Leib's arm and started to walk with him down the street.

"Reb Leib," he began, "I do not mean to detour you from the funeral but I cannot be delayed. You see, for years I have visited a certain leper in the hospital. Yesterday he passed away and his gentile doctors ordered that all of his possessions, and anything that had come in contact with him, be incinerated.

"I immediately feared for his *tefillin*. I knew that his doctors would not make any exception for them, but I had to try and spare them from being burned. After I explained the matter to one of the doctors, he agreed to allow me to bury the *tefillin*. He stipulated, however, that I must bring a flower pot to the ward today before noon if I had any intention of saving them.

"From the time that Reb Eliyahu was summoned to the Heavenly Court I have been guarding the body, and have had no other opportunity to take care of this matter. I hope you will trust me when I tell you that knowing Reb Eliyahu the way I did, I believe that had he been faced with the same situation — and you know that there was no limit to what he would do to help someone in distress — he would have acted in exactly the same way."

Reb Leib nodded his head and understood that no one would have preferred to escort the *niftar* to his final resting place more than his closest friend. Wiping away a wistful tear he commented, "May I resolve today to always give people the benefit of the doubt and may we all be comforted among the mourners of Jerusalem."

Reb Leib then turned to hurry back to the funeral. He was anxious to request that Rabbi Eliyahu Reichman beseech the Almighty to judge all of *Klal Yisrael* favorably.

Shemos

שְׁמוֹת

The Sign of a Spiritual Shepherd

וַיְהִי בַּיָּמִים הָהֵם וַיִּגְדַּל מֹשֶׁה וַיֵּצֵא אֶל אֶחָיו וַיַּרְא בְּסִבְלֹתָם...

When Moshe was grown, he went out to his brothers [and] saw their burdens...

(Shemos 2:11)

The Midrash relates, "He [Moshe] would weep and lament, 'Woe is me because of them! Would that I could die for them, for no labor is more arduous than [that of] bricks and masonry.' He used to shoulder their burdens and assist each and every Jew."

Chazal derive from Moshe *Rabbeinu's* behavior that every individual must empathize with his fellow human beings. Indeed, the Talmud states:

> *When the community is in trouble, let no man say, "I shall go to my house and eat and drink, and all will be well with me...." Rather, one must share the pain of the community. As it is said, "And Moshe's hands became heavy, [so Aharon and Chur] took a stone [and] placed it under him, [and] he sat upon it..."* (Shemos *17:12) — Didn't Moshe*

> *have a cushion on which to sit? [Yes, but] this is what he wished to convey: "Since the nation of Israel is in distress, I shall join it in distress" (*Taanis *11a).*

Whether one sits upon a stone or an easy chair in no way eases the plight of a suffering nation. Nevertheless, Moshe *Rabbeinu's* attitude was "Since they are in distress, I shall join them in distress."

The relationship between man and his fellow man — and between a leader and his followers — hinges on this point: Does one continue his routine while others suffer? If his people ache, yet he says, "I will go...and eat and drink, and all will be well with me," he has proven his disregard for the community.

Moshe *Rabbeinu* denied himself the simple creature comforts, for he could not endure his brethren suffering alone. This empathic quality has characterized every genuine leader of our people.

In less than an hour, the sun would set over Boston, and with the appearance of the first stars of the night of Shemini Atzeres, 1946, the Sukkos holiday would fade into cherished memory.

A row of old houses stood silhouetted against the darkening sky, looking solemn and vaguely sinister. But in one house the bleak exterior belied the unmistakable warmth of the lights that burned within its windows. It was the home of the Bostoner Rebbe.

While the Rebbe himself, in the *sukkah*, was savoring the

departing mitzvos of the holiday, the Rebbetzin was in the kitchen putting the final touches to the *Yom Tov* meal. Her preparations were always something of a mathematical feat: no matter how many guests were expected, she invariably seemed to produce three times the quantity required. And somehow, nothing ever went to waste.

The Rebbe's house was a veritable magnet for guests — those who were invited and those who invited themselves. Some were travellers unable to catch a connecting train or plane; others were strangers who had come to the area for medical treatment at one of Boston's renowned hospitals. And still others simply wanted to participate in a chassidic experience in the heart of New England.

How did they all find their way to the home of the Rebbe? Most had simply heard about him from others who had enjoyed his hospitality. The Bostoner Rebbe's reputation as a host extended nearly as far as his reputation as a charismatic leader.

Meanwhile, in the harbor at the other end of Boston, preparations of a different sort were being made. The longshoremen on the wharf, securing the thick ropes, cast long shadows as the sun dipped into the horizon and, with its last rays, poured buckets of light on the barges in the adjacent ferry basin. It was 4:05 in the afternoon and the *Thomas Edison* was about to dock at Pier 34.

Huddled aboard the overcrowded vessel were over 400 passengers from all over Europe. Of them, sixty-two were Jews, all survivors of the Nazi inferno. The rest were prospective immigrants who would first have to undergo medical examinations before an immigration official would determine their fate.

For the Jews, the United States would at last provide a haven from the murderous horrors they had endured in Europe. Alas, their relatives and friends would not share their new home. It was too late. And so, together with the haunting memories that were their constant companions, they joined the other passengers passing through the Reception Center, up the central stairs to the Great Hall. They had made it this far and now they were actually on American soil. But were they really home yet?

During the voyage they'd heard disheartening stories of people who had been turned back because of sickness. Heaven knew, none of them were strong. And after all they had endured, it seemed inconceivable that they would soon be granted the precious gift of a secure existence.

The Jews crowded together in the vast hall, one hundred and sixty feet long and eighty feet wide, with a ceiling so high that every step they took seemed to find an eerie echo way above them. This was the main center for immigrant registration, but all that registered with the disoriented new arrivals was the cacophony of clattering baggage-carts and touting money-changers, and the frightening sight of lines leading in all directions — to ticket offices, food counters and baggage depots. Even more alarming were the immigration officials, hoarsely shouting incomprehensible commands and wearing dark uniforms. For the Jewish immigrants, a uniform — any uniform — represented an army officer. And the sight of an army officer elicited an involuntary shudder.

They stood waiting, nervous and confused, monotony accentuated by the sight of the daunting bureaucracy ahead of them. It was an exceptionally busy day, for three other boats — from Liverpool, Piraeus, and Naples — had arrived earlier that morning. The Jews were separated from the others and directed to a side room where they would be checked and deloused. The very idea of such "selections" touched a raw nerve, awakening still-vivid memories of the painfully recent past in the unspeakable camps.

For the delousing process, the men and women were herded into small, separate rooms where uniformed personnel ordered them to strip. Their ragged, filthy garments were then handed over to be sprayed by an attendant sitting on the other side of a window. As though in a trance, the Jews slowly undressed and shuffled toward the window. While they stood around — naked, hungry and shivering — other attendants sprayed them with a foul-smelling substance. Now they were ready to shower.

Jewish immigrants who arrived in New England invariably travelled directly on to New York by train. Rarely, if ever, was there an acquaintance in New England to encourage them to stay. And while many who arrived on Fridays made the mistake of continuing their journey, not realizing that New York was six hours away, those who had arrived at this late hour of *Hoshanna Rabba* knew that no trip before *Yom Tov* was possible.

In fact, the Jews had talked of little else during the long voyage, for not one of them knew a soul anywhere near their vessel's destination. And yet, the most devoutly religious among them seemed to be the least concerned with the dilemma. Their apparent indifference was so striking that a group of fellow Jewish passengers had finally approached them and asked how they intended to spend the next two days of *Yom Tov* and the Shabbos which immediately followed them.

"Why, didn't you see the sign in Yiddish pinned up at the Hamburg port?" asked the oldest one, Abish Gottesman, a stooped, gray-bearded man with a smile of rare warmth.

"What sign?"

"The one about the Bostoner Rebbe."

"Bostoner Rebbe? What's that?"

"A 'Rebbe' is a Rebbe, and Boston is the town he comes

from... I guess."

"Where is Boston?"

"I never heard of it before either so I imagine it must be in Galicia," Abish ventured. "But that doesn't matter. The notice said that he takes guests and that the food is reliably kosher."

"How will you find him?"

"If there was a sign in Germany I'm sure that there will be signs in *America* telling us how to get to him."

"Are you really serious?" Isaac Hertz asked derisively. Isaac's father had been a tailor, and a pious Jew, but Isaac himself had long since discarded the traditions and was now the self-appointed chief cynic. "You don't even know what city he lives in."

"Don't worry," said Abish. "I saw the sign, and he takes guests and new arrivals."

And so news of the Bostoner Rebbe had swept quickly among the Jewish passengers, and in their state of anxiety, the image of the Rebbe was grasped enthusiastically as a sign of promise in the new and strange land they were entering. It did not matter that they had never heard of the town of Boston. It hadn't occurred to a single one that a "Rebbe" could get his title from an *American* town. All they knew was that the boat was docking at a city in New England, far from New York.

For the last two days of the voyage, the Jews had begun to wonder who this Bostoner Rebbe could be. A man who just picked up Displaced Persons from the piers and gave them food and lodging? A long-lost father who would be there to welcome them? Their imagination was heightened by the tedium of the voyage and the harrowing memories of the world they had left behind. Exhausted and close to despair, they had begun to think of little else but the Bostoner Rebbe. For some, he had taken on the dimensions of a Messianic figure; and even the non-religious among them were intrigued by this mysterious man from an unknown city.

There were, however, several men on board who had, somewhere in the ashes of Auschwitz, relinquished all their faith and hope. Scornfully, they called Abish and his friends the "wise men of Chelm," and accused them cynically of fantasizing about a mysterious "Chasidic Savior" with imagined agents all over Europe soliciting guests to his court.

"So, did you hear these learned men?" Isaac Hertz had mocked. "They will end up spending their so-called holiday in the streets!"

And now, in the stark, unfamiliar surroundings of the immigration building, the reality of the delousing and processing procedures did indeed shatter most of the illusions that the Jews had nurtured. As they gathered their meager possessions, the setting sun outside seemed to join in ridiculing their earlier fantasies. And the cynics clearly enjoyed the discomfort of the others, though some of them still appeared to expect the Bostoner Rebbe to magically emerge somehow from among the throng of officials.

"Maybe your Rebbe has a dark uniform," jeered Isaac, indicating a group of officials, "and plans to use this hall for the Simchas Torah celebration."

What could they say? In their pitiful imaginings, they had actually pictured the Rebbe greeting them at the docks and escorting them, all sixty-two of them, into his home. Now they stood outside, blinking in the sun's dying glare. Some children began to cry.

At that very moment two young men were walking down the docks to the immigration building. They walked briskly but their steps were heavy, as though they were reluctantly following instructions. And indeed they were. For Tuvia and Shabsai had instructions from the Bostoner Rebbe.

By the time the immigrants had cleared official registration and customs formalities, it was just one hour before *Yom Tov*. Those who had placed their frail hopes in the imagined hospitality of the Bostoner Rebbe felt so gullible and dejected that they hardly noticed the sarcastic comments of their cynical companions.

But then something happened that took everyone by surprise. Two chasidim appeared among the crowd of visitors outside the doors of the Arrivals Hall.

"*Shalom aleichem*, welcome to America, and *gutt Yontiff!* The Bostoner Rebbe would like to invite you for *Yom Tov* and Shabbos," said Tuvia mechanically, prepared for a blanket refusal of his invitation by the group.

All the members of the group froze. They simply could not believe their ears. Even the children stopped wailing for a moment and looked up wide-eyed. Tuvia and Shabsai drew back a few paces, glancing at each other in surprise as if to ask, "Did we say something wrong?" The skeptics slipped shamefacedly to the back of the group.

The sound of Abish's voice, quavering but clear, broke the silence: "We accept."

"'We?'" The question came simultaneously from both the chasidim and the cynics.

"Yes, *we*," he said firmly, "the whole group. We are extremely grateful. We had already decided to accept the Bostoner Rebbe's invitation."

The chasidim looked around at the tightly assembled group and saw the nodding heads. Their spokesman was indeed speaking for all of them. It suddenly dawned on Tuvia that somebody had finally accepted an invitation. Somebody? That *sixty* somebodies had accepted. He dashed over to a phone booth to make a call.

"Hello, Rebbe? We found some guests!" he blurted out excitedly. "A whole group of DPs have just got off the boat and they don't want to travel to New York before *Yontiff*."

"*Baruch Hashem*! But you must hurry. There isn't much time."

"But Rebbe, they wo... wo... won't fit in our car! The Rebbe doesn't understand, it's a group of over si... *sixty*!"

"All the better," replied the Rebbe calmly. "I can see we'll have a very joyful Simchas Torah."

"Some of them are not religious."

"Even better."

"Even better?"

"Yes, they need a proper *Yontiff* even more. Now hurry and help them into taxis. I will have someone waiting outside with money for the taxi fares and instructions as to which families will host them. I'll make the arrangements right away."

"But Rebbe, I don't know how to break this to you. We were speaking to the group, and they think, they think that they are all coming to you! As if you were expecting them! I told them that I hoped we would be able to place them with different families but they told me, I repeat THEY told me, that the Bostoner Rebbe was waiting for them. They won't go to anyone else. They trust only YOUR *kashrus*."

"*Be'ezer Hashem*," came the relaxed reply of the Rebbe, "we will think of something."

As soon as he put the phone down, the Bostoner Rebbe made a quick reckoning. It was now forty-five minutes until *Yom Tov* and all of the stores carrying kosher products were closed. Even if the Rebbetzin had enough food stocked in her kitchen, there would certainly not be enough time to cook as much as was needed for three days.

"Hello, a *gutten erev Yontiff*, this is the Bostoner Rebbe speaking..."

"... *She'ayris hapleitah* [Remnants of the Nation, referring to Holocaust survivors]! Of course, we'll do anything, send them right over."

"One last thing — we need food. Please bring over whatever you can spare right away, and don't come in the front entrance. Come around the back and bring the food directly to the kitchen."

Sleeping arrangements also presented a bit of a problem. Among the arrivals were families who should be housed together. The irreligious ones needed to be placed with extra care. And all of them had to be close to the Rebbe's house, where they would eat.

But the Rebbe was not unduly troubled. Despite all the problems, and the fact that many homes were already filled with *Yom Tov* guests, the issue at hand concerned the mitzvah of *hachnasas orchim* and so was certain to evoke Divine assistance. The Rebbe also had two factors working to his advantage — his charisma and his *kehillah*.

"Hello, this is the Bostoner Rebbe speaking..." In phonecall after phonecall, the Rebbe made the same appeal, pulling strings like a puppeteer and keeping a ledger of how many beds he had amassed. In less than twenty-five minutes, as the first taxis drove up to the entrance of his home, his work was done.

The group, exhausted after the seven-day ordeal of their voyage, also bore the indelible scars of a decade-long experience of horror. They were utterly drained and their tattered clothes hung loose from their shrunken frames.

In the few minutes it took for the group to emerge from the taxis and enter the house, the Rebbe braced himself for the extraordinary variety of temperaments and dispositions that he was about to host for *Yom Tov*. He knew that this group would require particular sensitivity and understanding. The very fact that they had all left the taxis even though his representative had asked them to remain inside so that they could be taken directly to their lodgings, was indication enough of what trouble might be in store. But the Rebbe was wrong.

Those who trooped into his house did not want food or sleep. It was twenty minutes to *Yom Tov,* and they were starving for mitzvos. The Rebbe was in the midst of bidding farewell to the *sukkah* and to the *lulav* and *esrog* when he heard them call, "Where is the *sukkah*?"

The Bostoner Rebbe was inside the *sukkah* waving his *lulav* to and fro in praise and deep supplication. The group had just a few minutes left to fulfill the mitzvos of the holiday and not a second to waste. Cake was hurriedly rushed into the *sukkah* for a blessing of *laishev basukkah* while the guests impatiently waited on line for their turn to bless the *lulav* and *esrog*.

At the same time, a veritable underground railroad was chugging its way into the kitchen. The Rebbe's wife had also been busy on the phone and women were soon bringing *kugels*, chickens, cakes, fruit, desserts, pastry — and whatever else they had in the house. Within minutes, the Rebbetzin's kitchen appeared to be equipped for a year-long siege.

Now, squeezing out of her packed kitchen, the Rebbetzin emerged to meet her guests. A more serene and courteous woman never graced New England. Moving effortlessly through the crowd, she smiled her "*Shalom aleichem*" and "Thank you for coming," lighting a spark of warmth and hope in everyone she greeted.

Noting the relatively humble surroundings, they wondered how she was able to prepare for such a huge crowd.

"I have help," answered the Rebbetzin sweetly, pointing to the steady stream of women coming and going outside the window.

Like the Rebbe, she was careful not to betray the fact that they had only just found out about the group's arrival. Had the newcomers known of the desperate flurry of activity preceding their arrival, they would surely have felt embarrassed at causing their hosts so much trouble. Instead they smiled in their blissful ignorance, believing that they were doing this Rebbe — who, *nebach,* lived so far from New York — a favor by joining his court for *Yom Tov.*

The members of the Rebbe's community played their roles with equal élan. In almost every home, the hosts willingly vacated their own bedrooms and gladly suffered discomforts to make room for their guests. They were only too eager to do whatever they could to help the *she'ayris hapleitah.* And whatever they gave up was well compensated for with the most moving and memorable Shemini Atzeres and Simchas Torah of their lives.

The singing that night seemed to resound for miles around. The city of Boston had not seen such celebration since its Tea Party. And the dancing was the dance of victory. The feverish intensity of the celebration continued until the small hours of the morning. Not *mir vellen zey iberlebben,* but *mir hot shoin...* We have not been defeated, we still have our Torah and our faith, we are blessed with fellow Jews who perform mitzvos and good deeds and love each other as themselves.

This lesson was not lost on the non-religious members of the group, all of whom received the same attention and even additional courtesy from the Rebbe. And the skeptics. Their skepticism was quickly melted away by the Rebbe's warmth. They soon forgot themselves and sang and danced no less heartily than the rest.

As crazy as it was, it all made sense. Even to the cynical immigrants who had thought they would never see their host, and the cynical young chasidim who had thought they would never greet these guests.

Concealed Weapon

וַיֹּאמֶר מִי שָׂמְךָ לְאִישׁ שַׂר וְשֹׁפֵט עָלֵינוּ הַלְהָרְגֵנִי אַתָּה אֹמֵר...וַיִּירָא מֹשֶׁה וַיֹּאמַר אָכֵן נוֹדַע הַדָּבָר.

[After seeing an Egyptian cruelly strike a Jew, Moshe killed the aggressor. The next day, as Moshe attempted to make peace between two of his brethren,] one retorted, "Who made you our prince and judge? Do you mean to kill me [as you killed the Egyptian?"] Moshe was frightened [and] said [to himself], "So the matter is known!"

(Shemos 2:14)

According to the simple interpretation, "the matter" is the slaying of the Egyptian. However, the Midrash offers a different explanation:

> *Moshe pondered, "What was Israel's sin, that it has earned the punishment of being oppressed more than any other nation?" But once he heard these words, he understood that the sin was talebearing. [When Moshe killed the Egyptian, the only witness was the Jew who was saved. Dasan and Aviram — the two quarreling Jews — must therefore have learned of the incident through gossip.] Thus he said, "The matter is known" — Now I know the reason for their bondage.*

Regarding this midrash, Rabbi **Yissocher Frand** cites the Zohar, which states that *lashon hara* sets in motion a dynamic that demands punishment. God can look at man's good actions or his bad actions. However, the mechanics of *lashon hara* are such that they cause God to focus on the bad [perhaps because when one speaks or gives credence to *lashon hara*, he himself essentially focuses on the bad].

Liberty, Monticello, Swan Lake, Ellenville. This is the buckle of the "borscht belt." For most of the year this area is comprised of a series of sleepy little villages strung out alongside the highways and byways of the Catskill Mountains region of upstate New York. Typically, these samples of Americana consist of a main street, several shops, a gas station, and a special corner where bored kids and unemployed adults hang out.

From June to September, however, the Catskills — better known as simply "The Mountains" — undergo a dramatic transformation. Quiet country lanes turn into clogged arteries. Prices for food, clothing and rent skyrocket. Noise levels become higher, tempers shorter. And chaos reigns supreme: the Jews are back!

Like the swallows returning to Capistrano, thousands of Jews from all over New York City make a yearly pilgrimage to the land of their forefathers and country cousins. In its heyday, the Catskills had dozens of exclusive and expensive resort hotels where the well-to-do invested as much energy in their relaxation as they ever did in their work.

Today, only a few of these "international resorts" remain, but in their place you'll find summer camps, vacation homes, and bungalow colonies by the hundreds. You'll also find scenes that are hard to imagine anywhere else: chasidic men and women hitchhiking (in separate groups, of course) along Route 42; little boys with long *peyos* and woolen *tzitzis* sharing the sidewalk with the redneck natives of Ferndale and South Fallsburgh; formerly vacant parking lots turning into impromptu flea markets and swarming with transplanted bargain-hunting matrons from Queens and Brooklyn.

Max Weiss was an exception to the avalanche of humanity that hit the Catskills every spring and summer. He lived there all year 'round in a colony known as "Weiss Acres." In its previous incarnation, Weiss Acres was called the Dairyland Hotel, a rambling country house that had its own peculiar clientele — people who wanted to be *near* those who could afford the best. The Dairyland advertised that all the "big names" in entertainment had played there. And they may have — when they were little kids, not show biz celebrities! At the Dairyland Hotel, the only "live" entertainment you could ever find was shuffleboard, pinochle, mah-jongg, bingo and other low-impact athletics. It was a low-budget vacation geared to a generation that knew how to pinch a penny until it cried "Ouch!"

Eventually, the men and women of that generation passed on, and the Dairyland Hotel was simply abandoned. Max Weiss bought the property from the heirs of the original owners, not for the hotel, but for the bungalows that used to house the staff. He felt that they would make a good investment. And they did. For years, he rented them out to his *landsleit*: people who hailed from his hometown in Hungary. The money he made during the summer provided him with enough to live on for the rest of the year.

Max was married to Miriam Herskowicz, but they had found each other very late in life and to their regret never had children. Throughout their years as the landlords of Weiss Acres, Max and Miriam kept to themselves. It's not that they were unsociable. It's just that they got along best with one another. In time, they became so close that they could practically dispense with language; a word, a glance, an inflection was enough to communicate volumes.

"Papa..." Miriam would say in a special tone of voice.

"Okay, Mama, okay. I'll go into town to do the shopping," he would reply, "and then I'll fix the leaky roof."

For more than thirty years, Max and Miriam appeared to be as inseparable as a couple could be, and when Miriam died, a part of Max died with her. He became withdrawn, silent, reclusive — alone with his thoughts and his memories. Even the people who stayed at his bungalow colony could tell the difference, as Max became progressively more bitter. Many of them left in mid-season, and did not return the following year.

After the "regulars" stopped coming, new groups of vacationers took their place, but with each passing year the groups grew smaller. There was virtually no repeat business, and vile, nasty rumors about Weiss began to circulate. Many spoke of "Max the Maniac" — the short-tempered, mean-spirited old codger who ran the colony. They said he would stalk the grounds after midnight, a haunted look in his eyes and mayhem in his heart. Soon the vacationers stopped coming altogether.

One spring day, a van drove up the winding road that ran off Route 42. It had been years since anyone had stopped by to inquire about renting a bungalow, and the whole place had a desolate feel to it. When Miriam was still alive, Max had always kept up the grounds, painting the exterior of the "big house" annually even though it was not in use. Miriam wouldn't have had it any other way. But Miriam was gone and Max had just let everything slide.

Max stepped out onto the old porch, scowling at the approaching vehicle. The van came to a halt in front of him. The doors opened and two young men stepped out. "*Shalom aleichem*," the taller of the two said cordially. "My name is

Yossie Schneider and this is Akiva Berg."

"Hmph. I'm Weiss. Whaddaya want?"

"Mr. Weiss, we're from Bnai Dovid — that's a yeshivah in Brooklyn. Our yeshivah is looking for a summer home. Mrs. Stein, the real estate agent in Woodbourne, told us about the Dairyland Hotel. Would you mind if we looked at it?"

"Suit yourself. But it's 'Weiss Acres' now, and the hotel is closed. Hasn't been used in years."

"That's okay," Kivi said. "We need a place for our *beis midrash* and most of the properties around here just aren't big enough for us."

"If we could get it into shape, I think this place might suit our yeshivah very well," Yossie added.

Max let Yossie and Kivi tour the grounds on their own. They began with the main house. After passing through the "suites" and the kitchen facilities, they came to the dining hall, a cavernous, high-ceilinged room large enough to hold 250 people. Empty chairs were scattered around, some positioned at the few remaining tables, to ghostly effect. "If you listen carefully, you can almost hear conversations still lingering in the air," Kivi said uncharacteristically. The place is really getting to him, Yossie thought, if he's hearing voices. Maybe it was just the wind and the echo of their footsteps. Then Yossie imagined the whispered sound of conversation too, but to him, it wasn't voices from the past, it was voices of the future — the future of Bnai Dovid.

No matter how hard they tried, Yossie and Kivi couldn't hide their enthusiasm. "Mr. Weiss," Yossie exclaimed, "this is perfect!"

Kivi agreed. "It sure is. In fact, it's ideal. I can't believe it! Is it available?"

Max Weiss looked at the two boys and something stirred inside him. A tiny spark of life seemed to flicker in his eyes.

"Maybe," he said gruffly. "Let's talk."

And so it happened that the Dairyland Hotel, that is, Weiss Acres, got a new lease on life as the summer home of Bnai Dovid Yeshivah. When Yossie Schneider said it was ideal, he had no idea *how* ideal, but he soon found out. Although the main house had been boarded up and looked a bit shabby inside and out, everything was in surprisingly good working order. A paint job and some minor repairs were all that was needed to render it habitable. The hotel's dining room was able to hold the *beis midrash,* while the rooms and suites would accommodate the students. The "Tea Room," which was adjacent to the dining room and kitchen, had a huge terrace which, when enclosed and incorporated with the Tea Room, would create a space that was ample for the entire yeshivah to eat their meals together. The *rebbeim* and their families would enjoy the relative privacy of the bungalows.

For the winter months, Max would serve as the "watchman," keeping an eye on the place, but during the summer, he would have no responsibilities whatsoever. In exchange for turning the property over to the yeshivah, he received a sizeable cash settlement, and would be entitled to free room and board for the rest of his life. The yeshivah undertook to see to his final arrangements, after 120 years.

From the moment the deal was done, Weiss Acres became a hive of activity as never before. Workmen assaulted the place and whipped it into shape. In a matter of days, the yeshivah moved in, settled in, and settled down to the business of learning Torah. But despite the dramatic changes, Max remained untouched and unmoved. He continued to keep to himself and avoided any social contact. If anything, his reclusiveness increased, his brusque manner intensified, and his isolation from humanity was total, or nearly so.

Yossie Schneider was the single impediment to Max's complete disengagement from the human race. When he wasn't learning or teaching some of the younger students,

Yossie would often seek the old man out. "Mr. Weiss, please come to a *shiur,*" he would say. "You'll enjoy it. You really will!"

Max's reply never varied. A grunt of scorn or a snort of disdain was the most Yossie ever got for his efforts.

"You can't fool me, Mr. Weiss, I've heard you *daven,*" Yossie said one day, trying a new approach. "Come on, you belong with us." Yossie expected the usual response, but as he turned to leave, he heard old Max clear his throat. Yossie froze in his tracks and dared not breathe, afraid any sudden sound or movement would deter the elderly Weiss from taking this first tentative step into the outside world.

Max cleared his throat again and said, "I appreciate all your invitations, but I'm... I don't want company. Since my wife passed away..." — he winced as he uttered the words — "it's hard for me to... to be in a crowd. We were very close, Mama and I and, it, well..." Max's eyes brimmed with tears, and his voice cracked as he blurted out, "It's not easy... you understand."

"I'm sorry for your loss," Schneider said with genuine feeling, "and I do understand, but please believe me, you are welcome to join us any time."

Max nodded his head, looked away, and shuffled off.

This conversation, and variations of it, were repeated for several years. When Yossie got married, Max didn't come to the wedding, but Yossie could tell that Max was happy for him in his own private way. When Yossie's son was born, he invited Max to the bris. Weiss didn't attend, but that was all right; Yossie had come to respect Max for his silent struggle. Although he had heard the "Max the Maniac" rumors, he himself had never seen Weiss angry — not even when some of the younger boys made a racket around his bungalow. And while the old man did take late-night strolls around the grounds, he never ever committed any "mayhem."

The passing years took their toll on Max, and Yossie was

keenly aware of it. Weiss became even more withdrawn, if possible, walking the property for hours on end, talking to himself. Yossie wanted to slow down the march of time and hold on to his silent friendship with the old man, but it was not to be. One evening as he was putting his younger children to bed, he received a call that he had known would one day come. The boys had found Max near his bungalow, slumped in his chair. A rebbe had called the HATZOLOH rescue service, and although they arrived in record time, it was too late. Max was gone.

Quite naturally, it fell to Yossie's lot to handle Max's funeral arrangements, but never having done this before, he took Kivi along for support. At the local Jewish funeral home they met Sanford J. Siegel, R.E. (Registered Embalmer to his professional associates; Rich Embezzler to those who were unfortunate enough to require his services).

A youthful overdose of comic books had painted a portrait in Yossie's mind of the tall, somber funeral director, attired in formal black tie and tails, with dull slicked-back hair, pursed lips and receding chin. This image was off by light-years. Sanford Siegel was a Catskill Mountain version of a used-car salesman.

The glitter of greed that lit up Siegel's grey eyes when he found the naïve-looking young men on his doorstep was all they needed to make them lose their innocence.

"Remember, you're not just buyin a box," Siegel began in a gravelly voice, "you're makin a statement about your love for the dearly departed. So lemme show you this here number." He had a way of imbuing the sad duty of choosing a casket with the atmosphere of Bingo Night in Brooklyn. "It's our top-of-the-line enamel job. Just look at this baby." He gestured with his rank-smelling cigar, showering ash all over his yellow-and-green plaid sports jacket. "Comes in four fashion colors: classic burgundy, which is the one everybody's buyin this year; indigo for a sophisticated look; fire-engine red for people who prefer something a little more ah, if you'll excuse the expression... lively; and my personal favorite, ten-mile orange — it glows in the dark. We got the matchin leather padding inside and a light that goes on when you lift the top."

"Please, please," Yossie begged. "We're only interested in a plain pine coffin, according to Jewish — "

"Or how about our nautical model," Siegel interrupted, clearly carried away by his own sales pitch.

"You have a *nautical model* casket?" Kivi asked, stunned at the thought that something like that could actually exist.

"Yeah — it's got portholes! The dear departed can look out and see all those who came to wish him *bon voyage* on his last journey! We call it the Titanic Ta-Ta." Siegel huffed on one of the round windows and polished it with his sleeve.

"That's a very comforting thought," Yossie said dryly.

"Comfort? You want comfort?" With sausage-like fingers he patted a stainless steel sarcophagus. "This here's your orthopedic model — Spinal Taps — specially designed to give the dear departed the rest of his life, for the rest of his li— "

"Mr. Siegel!" Yossie cut him off. "I want a plain wooden box. Do you understand? A plain wooden box."

"Okay, okay, wood. How's about the Bobby Fischer Bye-Bye, for chess enthusiasts. Made of wood, of course, and it comes in your basic black — African ebony — or basic white, from American birch."

"Stop! Please! No LeMans, no Titanic, no Bobby Fischer. Plain wood."

"Will that be Philippine mahogany, Indian teak or Brazilian rosewood? I can get you walnut, if you like. The pecan is nice, but it takes a couple weeks. As long as you're waitin, for just a few grand more, we can even have a biography of your loved one carved on the outside for future generations."

"How about a pine box. No handles. No power steering or power brakes. No wall-to-wall carpeting or fancy upholstery, or tinted glass. Just plain, simple pine — the kind that is kosher according to Jewish Law."

"Okay, okay. You win. Plain, simple, no scrollwork. The Woolworth Special. I can't guarantee that it'll hold up, you realize. Now, the fiberglass numbers..." he added, his voice rising with enthusiasm, "those things are made to last. Guaranteed to protect your loved one from fire, floods, earthquakes, hurricanes and other natural and man-made disasters for a period of seven hundred years or your money'll be cheerfully refunded to whoever is left to receive it."

"The discussion is closed. I've made my decision," Yossie stated sternly. "Now Mr. Weiss is making his: he wants to be buried next to his beloved wife Miriam."

"Yeah, yeah, his beloved wife," Sanford Siegel sneered, clearly put out at not being able to sell Yossie a $22,000 casket. "I know all about it. What I don't know is why she would want to be buried next to him. I mean, I've known Max Weiss for maybe a hundred years, and believe you me, that was no lovin spouse, if you get my drift. He didn't even come to her funeral. And far as I know, he never visited her grave. Now don't go givin me that 'you-shouldn't-speak-bad-about-the-dead' look. I knew Miriam when she was still single — Herskowicz, her name was — and she was a good woman. But since she died, Weiss forgot all about her."

"What are you talking about?" Yossie felt his face burn with anger. "There must be some mistake. He loved his wife. He told me so."

"If you ask me, he told you what you wanted to hear. He didn't even care enough about her to go to her funeral. He didn't visit afterwards. And he didn't even pay for perpetual care. See for yourself — the grave's Weed City."

"I don't believe you," Yossie said hotly, appalled at the slander Siegel was dumping on Max.

"So don't believe me. I was at her funeral. Max wasn't. You don't trust me? Ask Clara Shulman. She lived at Weiss Acres for years. She left because she couldn't stand the way he treated his wife."

"Mr. Siegel, I do not want to hear any more malicious gossip. The funeral will be tomorrow and you will do as Mr. Weiss instructed. Is that clear?"

"Yeah, sure, clear as a bell. But I'm gonna give you Clara's phone number anyway."

All that afternoon and on into the night, Yossie Schneider debated with himself. Why should he listen to that *lashon hara*, that scandalous, libelous talk? It was all a pack of lies. On the other hand, why would Siegel be willing to give out that lady's phone number, if it weren't true? And if it *was* true, why would Max Weiss pretend to have loved his wife if he hadn't?

Finally, Yossie decided that he would call Mrs. Shulman to let her know about Max's death and the time and place of the funeral, and if she had something to say about Max, this would give her a perfect opening.

"Mrs. Shulman?"

"Yes?"

"My name is Yossie Schneider. I am affiliated with the Bnai Dovid Yeshivah which took over the Weiss Acres hotel and bungalow colony from Mr. Weiss."

"I see," she said cautiously.

"Well, I'm calling to tell you that Mr. Weiss has passed away and the funeral will be at two o'clock tomorrow afternoon at the Beth Abraham Cemetery. As someone who once stayed at Weiss Acres, I thought you might want to know about it."

"Thank you, but I doubt you'll see me there. I was very close with Miriam, his wife, and I can tell you..."

Yossie didn't want to hear what she had to say next. He wanted to put the phone down and run away, but it was too late.

"Max Weiss never once visited his wife in the hospital when she was dying. He didn't show up to the funeral, either. So as far as I'm concerned, no one should show up for him. Good day."

Yossie slowly replaced the receiver, shaking his head from side to side. "For all these years, I thought he was a real *mentsch*," he murmured. "Now, the truth comes out. Max Weiss was simply using the memory of his wife to justify his antisocial behavior. Why couldn't I ever see that? How could I have respected the man so much? How could I have been so naïve?"

The next day, Yossie got up early to *daven*. The big round white-faced clock on the *beis midrash* wall threw minutes into the lonely hours of the morning. The clock seemed to be moving more slowly than usual. Eight o'clock. Nine o'clock. Ten. Ten-thirty. Yossie couldn't stand it. Eleven. Every time he looked up, the hands had moved, but just barely. By one o'clock, he was exhausted, irritable, and tense. "I don't *have* to go to the funeral," he thought. "I'm not related to the guy. I'm not his son. I've got better things to do with my time."

Akiva Berg burst into the room. "Yossie!" he called out. "Don't you know what time it is? The van is full and it's waiting in the parking lot. C'mon, quick!"

"Kivi, I'm not going. I don't feel very well."

"What? You're the only *mishpocheh* he has!"

"I'M NOT *MISHPOCHEH*!" Yossie yelled. "I didn't adopt

him and he didn't adopt me. Now, you heard what I said, so get in the van and go."

Kivi stared at him. Yossie glared back, perspiration beading his forehead like drops of rain. "Okay, okay, I hear you," Kivi said. As he walked out, he mumbled "*Refuah sheleimah*," and shut the door behind him.

Yossie felt his heart had turned to lead. He tried to convince himself that there was no reason for the heaviness he felt, but it was no use. After what seemed like hours, he heard the van return from the cemetery and Yossie tracked Akiva down. "What happened? Did anyone come to the funeral?" he asked.

"It was small — like you'd expect. Nothing unusual. A niece from Cleveland was there. Her husband made a little speech. Rabbi Levensohn said a *Kel malei* and Kaddish, and that was it."

"You say the niece's husband made a speech? What was it about?"

"I don't remember his exact words. But he mentioned that Mr. Weiss was a special man who had loved his wife very much. So much so that his doctor wouldn't let him visit her in the hospital, or even go to her funeral, because they were afraid the shock would kill him."

Yossie gaped at his friend, his face ashen. "He... he said that?!"

"Yeah, and he also said that even after Mrs. Weiss died, Max carried on like she was always there with him. He just couldn't accept the fact that she was gone. But you knew that."

Yes, Yossie did know that. What he didn't know was why he'd allowed himself to be misled about Max. Why hadn't he trusted his own instincts? Weiss had certainly never done him any harm — or anyone else, for that matter. So he was a little peculiar; so what? Was that a reason for Yossie to have turned his back on him?

"Okay, Kivi, tell me the rest."

"There's n-n-nothing else to tell. Really." Akiva turned away.

Yossie looked his friend in the eye. He could tell there was something more. "Spit it out, Akiva. What else did he say?"

Kivi's voice dropped to just above a whisper and he lowered his eyes. "He said that Weiss had told him how happy he was that the yeshivah took over his place. And, and... he mentioned you."

Yossie's knees felt weak. "Me?" he gasped.

"Yeah. He said that Mr. Weiss was especially fond of Rabbi Schneider. In fact, the niece wanted to meet you and thank you for all you had done over the years. But I told her you were sick."

If he wasn't sick before, Yossie Schneider sure was now. He closed his eyes against the pain. A wave of nausea swept over him. "Kivi! What can I do? I didn't mean to..."

"I know. It's not your fault. You just weren't feeling well, that's all."

It was almost sunset when Yossie Schneider finally found the strength to go to the Beth Abraham Cemetery. The gates were locked, but that wasn't about to stop him. It had been a long time since he had climbed a fence, or anything more strenuous than a flight of stairs, but he was determined to visit Max Weiss and beg his forgiveness.

After several false starts and a hard fall, he made his way up one side of the eight-foot-high chain-link fence. Slowly, he swung his right leg over the top. His pants ripped at the thigh. In seconds, he could feel a warm trickle of blood flow down toward his ankle, but it didn't matter. The pain in his leg couldn't match the pain in his heart. Yossie swung his body over and the other leg followed. Clutching the metal links with his fingers, he slowly let himself down a couple of feet, then dropped to the ground.

The Beth Abraham Cemetery was not large, but it took him quite a while to locate the Weiss plot. He scanned one headstone after another, quickly taking in the names: Kopleman, Shuster, Zveig, Stein, Lasky, Levy, Shapiro. Working his way down the rows, he finally came across the name Weiss: Miriam Weiss. Next to it was a fresh grave with a little brass marker that read

Max Weiss
5675-5750 (1914-1989)

Yossie stared at the grave. After a few minutes, he began to speak. "Max, Mr. Weiss. This is..." His voice left him. He tried again. "It's me. Yossie Schneider. I wanted you to know how sorry I am for not coming. It wasn't my fault... I didn't mean..." Yossie stopped. Tears filled his eyes. "Believe me, I valued our friendship. Please forgive me! Please forgive me!"

Yossie searched desperately for some sign, some indication that Max heard and forgave. But there was only silence. How long he stood there, Yossie didn't know. Finally, in the fading twilight, he realized he had to start back. The wind whipped at his torn pants. He made his way to the fence and began climbing.

When he reached the top, he looked out across the cemetery grounds and this time he had no trouble picking out the headstone that marked Miriam Weiss's grave. As he looked at the two graves side by side, a sense of peace came over him. It was comforting to know that Max and his wife were reunited at last.

Yossie Schneider thought that the wound in his heart would never heal. But that very night at *Maariv*, when he stood up in the Weiss Acres *beis midrash* and began to discharge his duty as Max's surrogate son, the pain of his guilt ebbed. At first his voice cracked and he felt he couldn't go on. Then the words of Kaddish rang out clear and strong:

"*Yisgadel v'yiskadesh...*"

What's Done Is Done

וַיְדַבֵּר אֱלֹקִים אֶל מֹשֶׁה וַיֹּאמֶר אֵלָיו אֲנִי ה'.

And God spoke to Moshe, and said to him, "I am the Lord."

(Shemos 6:2)

From this verse the Midrash deduces that man may not question actions which God has already taken.

Some explain this perplexing Midrash to refer to the two times Moshe approached the Almighty with the question, "Why?" First, in *VaEra*, he inquires, "Why have You dealt ill with this people?" *(5:22)*. Then, after the sin of the golden calf, he demands, "Why, O Lord, will Your wrath burn against Your people...?" *(32:11)*, and he is answered, "And the Lord said, 'I have pardoned according to your word'" *(BeMidbar 14:20)*.

Unlike Moshe's second question, his first is never answered, and, according to our sages, he is punished for posing it. His second "Why," however, does earn a reply. For unlike "Why, O Lord, will Your wrath burn against Your people...?" which is constructed in future tense, "Why have You dealt ill with

> *this people?" concerns the past. As such, it is more accusative than interrogative, challenging God's authority. To quote* Koheles *[as the Midrash does], "What is man that he should come after the King regarding what He has already done?" (*Koheles *2:12).*

To a child, thirteen years seems like an eternity. Once a boy begins to understand that he is a Jew and that at the age of thirteen he will become a bar mitzvah, the six or seven years that remain until he reaches his young life's second great milestone seem as if they will never pass. Yet the same boy's parents, who recall every detail of his birth as though it happened last week, awaken on the morning of the young man's entry into adulthood and wonder if the last thirteen years have merely been a dream.

For a parent, particularly a mother, every aspect of a child's birth is indelibly etched upon her mind. For the child, however, unless the events surrounding his birth are brought home to him in some unusually cogent manner, they are dismissed as prehistory. No matter how many times he hears about how Mommy said it was time, how Daddy called the ambulance, and how they laughed when they first saw him because he was all purple, and his eyes were crossed, and he didn't have any hair, etc., etc., etc., for him, it remains the story of someone with whom he is but vaguely familiar.

This is the story of thirteen years and a birth so unusual that for a handful of people, who were not even blood relations, every detail remains to this day vivid and unforgettable. The birth was unusual not in the clinical sense, but in the historical sense — unusual in that which preceded and followed it.

It is the story of Menasheleh, growing up under what

seemed to him to be perfectly normal conditions. For him, his entrance into the world and into our people's immortal Covenant remained more or less a mystery, over which he had never lost much sleep.

But mostly it is the story of the saintly Leah, Menasheleh's mother.

Leah had always been able to keep a secret. That's why on her wedding day, her father shared with her his own greatest secret: "Leah'leh," he began, "I have something I wish to reveal to you. I want it to remain a secret, at least during my lifetime, but someone else should know it, and I know that you, Leah, although you are only seventeen years old, will understand why. A number of years ago, after I had begun writing my *sefer* on the Maharsha, I actually saw him. I saw the *heiligeh* Maharsha in a dream. He came to me and thanked me. He told me that my work would help countless *lamdanim* understand his *perush* better. He told me that it was essential that I continue my work, and then he kissed me!"

For many years after her father's death, Leah did not reveal his secret to a living soul. But her father was right, she *had* understood it. She had understood it so well, in fact, that shortly after her wedding, she sold all her jewelry — that is, everything of value that she owned — in order to finance the publication of her father's *sefer*.

That, too, was a secret Leah kept, but there was nothing secret about the events surrounding the birth of Menasheleh, whom Leah had named for her missing husband's father. Nevertheless, Leah was one to hold her peace. It would never have occurred to her to boast, and besides, for the holiest and saintliest members of our People, *mesirus nefesh* hardly seems remarkable. Neither does evidence of God's guiding hand.

Thus, when Leah was miraculously reunited with her husband, the learned Reb Yitzchak Zev, and when she and her family made it to the land of the free and the home of the brave, she did not immediately contact some literary agent to help her negotiate the rights to her wartime memoirs. Nor did she seek out a screenwriter to sell and tell her astounding story to the world.

Instead, upon settling in Sommerville, New Jersey, and later in Williamsburg, Brooklyn, Leah dedicated herself to the fulfillment of the secret vow she had made during some of the darkest days our People have ever known. Only after her death did her husband find a yellowed slip of paper containing a short note, written in Hebrew, which she had dated 12 Menachem Av, 5704 (1944):

I have been here for three weeks. My husband, father, family, and klal Yisrael are in exile, I know not where, and I have heard nothing of them. Here in this camp, at three o'clock in the afternoon, I hereby make a neder that if HaKadosh Baruch Hu reunites me with my family and with klal Yisrael I will bring up my children to be dedicated to Yiddishkeit, and I will help them and their father learn Your Torah all their days.

And she did.

She, her family, and her husband's yeshivah settled first in Sommerville, remaining there for just one year before relocating to Mt. Kisco, New York. When the children became older and needed to attend school, the family resettled in Williamsburg, but the yeshivah remained in Mt. Kisco. Leah's husband, who was a Rosh Yeshivah, had little choice but to commute between Mt. Kisco and Williamsburg, leaving Leah and the children alone from Sunday through Thursday.

Five days out of seven, Leah was father and mother, maid, cook, administrator, confidante, nurse, psychologist, educator, and role model to her children. But she did not mind. In fact, during this time, she also gave *shiurim* to women, excelled in *bikur cholim* and other acts of *chessed,* and established a women's organization for the support of Torah institutions. Despite all of her accomplishments, she hardly thought herself extraordinary. For Torah is the life of the Jew, and where Torah is concerned, there are no limits to self-sacrifice.

Leah even found time to celebrate, and thirteen years after Menasheleh was born, in a place from which so many had not returned, it was time to make a bris. A *bris*?! Yes, *morai ve-rabbosai,* a bris. For Menasheleh. But don't worry. It was not his first.

Have you ever been to a bar mitzvah in Williamsburg? I mean *old* Williamsburg, ten or fifteen extremely short years after the liberation of Europe. Who better than the Jewish residents of Williamsburg knew how few had returned from the European inferno? And who better understood the meaning of a bris, bar mitzvah, or wedding?

A Williamsburg bar mitzvah. The surroundings, and even the fashions, may have been modest. The food was not. Do you like your gefilte fish sweet or spicy? Why choose? Have a little of each. Or why not a lot? How many kinds of herring can you imagine? Double that number and add five. Think of rafts of every type of *kugel* known to mankind, sliced into perfect squares. Think of steaming cholent measured not in pots but in washtubs, *kishke* measured not by the pound but by the mile, and *tzimmes* made from enough carrots to feed every rabbit on the eastern seaboard for a month. Think of armies of seltzer spritzers, brigades of beer bottles, and platoons of schnapps. And marvel at the scores of cows and chickens that made the supreme sacrifice to participate in the celebration of Menasheleh's bar mitzvah.

Imagine a symphony of loud, ebullient Yiddish, mostly spoken with a Hungarian dialect. Picture rows of tables covered with white tablecloths and adorned with dishes, glasses, and cutlery — all purely utilitarian but spotlessly clean. Picture two rooms, a bit overdue for a paint job, adjoined by a door and perhaps a small window. Picture one room packed with men in black coats and long beards and the other with women in long skirts, long sleeves, and *tichelach*.

Picture Menasheleh, with a slight downy growth about his upper lip and chin, looking just a bit bewildered in his ill-fitting first hat and *kapota*, sitting at the head table next to his *Rosh Yeshivah* father. Picture his father with more gray hair and wrinkles than a man his age should have, but looking self-assured and grateful. Picture him quietly accepting *mazel tovs* while his wife, whose cheeks had reclaimed their rosy hue and whose once-emaciated frame had regained its humanity, sneaks doting glances at the young apple of her eye.

And picture one more guest. A man. A bit shabbier than the rest, a bit more bent over. At the table, two vacant chairs separate him from the nearest celebrant. His salt-and-pepper beard is unkempt even by Williamsburg standards, and his mangy *shtreimel* reminds one of the theoretical possibility of substance without form. The sleeves of his *kapota* are frayed, and his shiny pants are a mite too short. He speaks with no one and hardly touches his food. His hands exhibit a slight tremor, but his eyes, his amazingly green eyes, *rabbosai*, glitter like two emeralds.

No one seems to recognize this strange figure. Yet no one is terribly concerned about his presence — if an indigent has crept in from the street, *nu*, there's not enough food to go around? Even Leah, if she has seen him, has no idea who he is, although she once knew him well.

Eventually the steaming platters cease their restless shuttling back and forth from table to table. The muted rattle of knives and forks against plates dies down. The Rav gives his *derashah* and before the father of the bar mitzvah is to give his, it is young Menasheleh's turn to present his laboriously studied *pilpul*. As he stands up and clears his throat, so does another figure, one with green eyes, who seems oblivious to the events transpiring at the head table. At the sound of his loud, raspy "ahem," all heads turn in his direction. Those quicker on the uptake are already shouting "*shah*" in a typically Williamsburgian stage whisper and none-too-subtly motioning for the interloper to sit down. One fast-thinking, enterprising guest pushes a bottle of schnapps towards the man; another, a plate of *kugel*. But the stranger's emerald eyes, as if chipped from agate, are fixed upon Menasheleh, who is by now quite at a loss as to whether to remain standing or take his seat.

As if no one has yet noticed him, the stranger takes a seltzer bottle and, in the time-honored tradition of Jewish gatherings, begins clinking his spoon against its side, calling for quiet and attention. The hand gestures and shouts of "*shah*" are emanating from all quarters now, and men are beginning to whisper all sorts of speculations concerning the identity of this nuisance.

But the man is incorrigible. This is without a doubt the loudest and most persistent seltzer-bottle clinker in the history of New York *simchahs*. With little choice, Menasheh's father touches the boy's shoulder, quietly signaling him to be seated, and raises his hand patiently for silence so that the uninvited eccentric can have his hearing. The room quickly hushes, and the figure, in a voice of surprising strength and clarity, calls out one word:

"Menasheleh."

The boy fixes a wide-eyed stare upon the man, and the

voice is heard again, but this time it is an octave or so higher, and it is singing. It is singing that tune so familiar to anyone who has studied in yeshivah and so unknown to the rest of the world. It is the tune that non-religious Jews hear perhaps once a year — when the Four Questions are asked at the Seder. This time, this yeshivah sing-song has just one word: "Menasheleh." And then, after a shorter pause, still in sing-song, "Menasheleh, *oy mein* Menasheleh."

And the song continues: "*Rabboisai, moirai ve-rabboisai.* You think this *kugel* is *geshmak*? Have I got news for you! I once tasted *kugel* many times better!" All the while singing: "*Moirai ve-rabboisai*, you think we are all here to celebrate Menasheleh's bar mitzvah? Well, I've got even bigger news for you! We're here to celebrate Menasheleh's *bris.*"

By now many of the guests are feeling quite indignant. First, this vagabond insults the food, and then he insults the... On the other hand, the hook is in, and everybody realizes that there is much more here than meets the eye. And so the stranger, feeling that he has his audience in the palm of his grizzled hand, continues his song: "A story, *rabboisai*; listen to a story. It happened not so long ago, and not so far away.

"It was already the summer of 1944. The Nazis, *yemach shemam ve-zichram*, were in a hurry. Their enemies were closing in fast. But by this time, *rabboisai*, half of Hungary's Jews were ashes. We did not know this, of course, but when they put us on that train, very few of us thought we'd ever come back.

"How many *heiligeh, chusheveh Yiddin* died on that train, *rabboisai*, don't ask. None of us ever counted. How many lost their minds? Who knows. But when we got there... when we got there, the first thing they did was throw out the bodies. The doors to that freight car opened wide, *rabboisai*, and before our eyes had even recovered from the sudden flash of sunlight, we could hear the thud of bodies hitting the pavement. It was fresh asphalt, and later, when they made us lug the bodies away from the train, most of them had stuck, *Rachmana litzlan.*

"But, you will ask, where were we? Believe it or not, *rabboisai,* we were in Vienna. Ah, Vienna. But believe me, *rabboisai,* we were not there to waltz or gaze at the Danube. Later, after the war, we found out that the Nazis made short work of generations of Jewish life in Hungary. We found out that every train loaded with Hungary's Jews went straight to Auschwitz. Every train except for five. About one of these trains, I would not like to talk, *rabboisai;* some things are better left unsaid. It is about the other four, I want to tell you.

Four trains, *rabboisai,* four trains, filled with precious, *heiligeh Yiddin.* Why? Only the *Aibishter* knows, *rabboisai,* that's for certain. The *Aibishter* is the only One Who will ever know. After the war, I tried to find out. Don't think I didn't. I asked everyone. Anyone who would listen. I was crazy," he begins to whisper as the sing-song fades. "I had to know why my train went to Vienna when all of Hungary's *Yiddin* went to the furnaces of Auschwitz. Finally I got to some professor. A former Jew, but don't get me wrong, *rabboisai,* a very nice man. He writes books, history; makes a living off the Second World War. But a very nice man all the same.

"He sits me down and makes me a cup of tea. I don't drink it, of course, but very nice. He asks me if he can turn on his tape recorder. 'Why not?' I say. He switches on his tape recorder and asks me about 'my wartime experiences.' I tell him my English it's not so good. He tells me I can answer in Yiddish. He's got a nice boy from Brooklyn translates for him.

"After about an hour of asking me questions, he answers mine. 'We don't know,' he says. 'We just don't know. It's too early to tell. It will take generations to comb through all of the Nazi archives. There are thousands, maybe millions of papers. Most of them are in Israel,' he tells me. 'That's where most of the research is going on, and that's where most of the survivors are. But it may be a hundred years before all those documents have been analyzed. And who knows if they will shed any light on those four trains? Yes, I know of those four trains. It's an interesting problem.'

"'An interesting problem?!' I think to myself.

"'I could write a paper on that, I certainly could,' he says, looking at the wall.

"'What does this mean, a paper?' I ask.

"'Oh, nothing, nothing at all,' he says, looking back at me. 'Anyway, those four trains are an interesting problem. One I've thought about myself. Look here, Mr. uh...'

"'Call me Yisruel.'

"'Yes, Mr. Yisruel. The best we can figure...'

'Who is this "we"?' I keep asking myself.

"'...is that by that stage of the hostilities, there was no slave labor remaining in Vienna.'

"'What does this word mean, "hostilities"?'

"'Hostilities means the war. The war. Anyway, by this stage of the war, the mayor of Vienna may have appealed to the SS for help. By that time, many of the slaves may have died in the bombardments; many more had probably died of starvation and disease. There was plenty of work. The Allied bombers had left the city in shambles, and tremendous manpower was required just to keep the streets clear. There are records of other such arrangements. The mayor would have had to pay the SS a fee for transporting and maintaining you. Out of that fee, the SS would have paid for your food and clothing, etc.'

"'What food?! What clothing?!' I shout.

"'Yes, I understand,' he tells me. 'Be that as it may, the city of Vienna would have transferred funds from its budget to that of the SS. The more economically the SS ran its operation, the more it would have profited from the service it provided. The SS officers may even have skimmed some off the top.'

"'What does this mean, "economically," and "skimmed some off the top"?' I ask, and I see his former Jewish eyes fill up. He can't answer me right away. Like I said, he's a nice man. Then he says, 'They tried to save money on your food.' He clears his throat.

"'But we don't know yet.' Again we. 'We do know that the camp where you were taken, Strasshof, was a transfer camp for slave labor.' This he knows without me telling him. 'And we know that until you arrived, there had never been any Jews there. It was manned by Germans and Ukrainians...' He knows his concentration camps, this professor. 'But you're right, Mr. uh... how do you pronounce that again?'

"'Yisruel.'

"'Ah, yes, Yisruel, thank you. It was very strange, those four trains. Very strange indeed, Mr. Yisruel.'

"'Thanks a lot, Professor Knows-Only-Facts,' I'm thinking. '*You* I need to tell me that it's strange? *You* I need to tell me about the Ukes with their clubs? *You* I need to tell me about the beatings and the starvation? *You* I need to tell me how everyone above the age of nine worked a minimum of thirteen hours a day? How they had little children shlepping debris from bombed out buildings? *You* I need to tell me how many *heiligeh Yiddin* died there?'

Nu, nu, it could have been worse. At least the Austrians didn't throw us out of the shelters when the bombers came. At least they slipped us food sometimes, on the sly. Compared to the rest of the Jews of Europe, we were in a country club! But why us? Why these four trains?'

"But like I said, he's a nice man, so instead of shouting, I say to him, 'Thank you very much, Herr Professor. Thank you for your time.'

"And he says to me, 'But you didn't even touch your tea.'

"'It's okay,' I tell him. 'I wasn't thirsty.'

"Four trains, *rabboisai*," the sing-song resumes. "Four trains, and on one of them a woman who's expecting. A woman, I said? She's really no more than a *maideleh*. Where's her husband? She doesn't know. Isn't she afraid to give birth? No, no. She already has two daughters; giving birth doesn't scare her, but something else does. What if it's a boy? How will she make a bris? *Rabboisai*, have you ever heard of a devout woman with two daughters pray for a girl?! But that's what she does. Better a girl than a boy without a *milah*. But she brings one clean diaper with her, so that if it is a boy, he will have a nice, clean diaper for his bris.

"Some would call it *mazel, rabboisai*; others would call it *Hashgucheh*. No matter. This woman, her name is Leah, gets an 'easy' job working in an office because she speaks so many languages. This is Tammuz, she's due in Tishrei, and all the time she's praying for a girl and trading rations for cigarettes. Why cigarettes, Leah'leh? You don't *smoke*?! Ah but this we all know, don't we, *rabboisai*? We all know that cigarettes were the currency of the camps. What will be when the baby is born, if she needs to buy something for him? If she needs some special favor? So all the time she's trading rations for cigarettes. Thank God, it's an easy pregnancy; at least she's not shlepping heavy loads and getting beaten every day.

"She's such a wonderful woman, always doing favors, always encouraging everyone, and a wonderful mother to her own little girls. They're too young yet to work. All day they're alone. 'If the bombers come,' she tells them, 'run into the woods. They don't drop bombs in the woods.' But at night, when she comes home to them, she sings to them, and tells them stories to strengthen their *emunah*. One of them gets sick, *Rachmana litzlan*. The child never comes back.

"Anyway, everybody loves our Leah'leh, and everybody

wants to help. And all the time, she's praying for a girl and trading rations for cigarettes.

"But the *Aibishter*, He plays a trick. First He sends our Leah'leh to Vienna instead of Auschwitz, then He gets her a 'good' job in an office, and then what does He do, *rabboisai*? A *broch*! He gives her a boy!

"'What will be?' she wonders. The day after the birth, she's already on her feet. She's talking to Dr. Tuchman. Tuchman wasn't a *tzaddik*, but even within a *Judenrat*-encased heart there is still a spark of a *Yiddisheh neshumeh*. Sometimes he's willing to help his fellow *Yiddin*. 'Dr. Tuchman,' she tells him, 'I want you should get me permission from the *lagerfuehrer* to make a bris.'

"'Young woman,' he tells her, 'what's the matter with you!? Amalek should give permission to have a bris? They're already asking when you'll be back at work. I don't even want to mention your name. Go hide and nurse your baby, and I'll try to get you as many days off as I can.'

"'But Dr. Tuchman,' she says, 'a boy must have a bris on his eighth day. It says in the Torah!' She's a learned woman, this Leah'leh.

"'But, young woman...

"But Leah'leh, she doesn't know from 'buts.' 'Dear Dr. Tuchman, when Hashem gave us the mitzvah of *milah*, He didn't say that we're exempted in a concentration camp. We still have to keep His *mitzvos*. If He decides that I can't make a bris, then I won't be able to make a bris. But until I know otherwise, I have no choice but to try. So if you won't speak to the *lagerfuehrer*, I'll do it myself.'

"*Nu, rabboisai*, how do you say no to such a *tzaddekes*? Even Tuchman couldn't.

"And so the next day, he's there bright and early. 'Young woman, I can't believe it. I spoke with Amalek himself, and he says you can make a bris! You must have had quite a father to earn this *zechus*!'

"But Leah'leh doesn't smile. She's got another worry on her mind. 'Who will be the *mohel*?' she asks.

"'Why, my dear, I'll do it myself,' says Tuchman. After all, he's an M.D.

"But Leah'leh looks away. 'Maybe I shouldn't make a bris. The baby seems so weak...

"Tuchman looks at her for a minute like this time she's really *meshugeh*. 'Cancel the bris after Amalek himself has agreed?!' But then he understands. 'All right, young woman. I'll see what I can do.'

"And the next day, *rabboisai*, he's back, all smiles. 'You're not going to believe this, young woman. A transport arrived yesterday, and there was a *mohel* on it!' But then, suddenly he gets very serious. 'Young woman,' he says, 'I don't know what kind of *zechus* you have, but Somebody wants that *yingel* of yours to have a bris. I met this man yesterday. He's not only a *mohel*; he's also a rav and a *shochet*.

"'Anyway, I tell him the story. He says he doesn't have his knife, his *mohel messer*. Before he left, he managed to pack only his *chalef*, his ritual-slaughtering knife. After all, he thinks, a Jew never knows where he might find himself and what he might need. So he packed his *chalef* before he left, but he didn't manage to pack his *mohel messer*. So I say to him that we have surgical instruments at the hospital, and surely he could..., and before I can finish, he says he just wants to check and make sure. So he opens up his bag, and nearly faints: there's no *chalef*, only a *mohel messer*!'

"So Leah, she doesn't answer for a minute, and then she says, 'Dr. Tuchman?'

"'Yes, young woman?'

"'Would you be *kvater*?'

"And that's how it was, *rabboisai*, not so long ago, and not so far away. Our Leah'leh, she named her son Menasheh for the father of her husband, and she davened that God should give her the strength to lead her pure little boy to *Toireh, chupah,* and *maissim toivim*. And when you cried, Menasheleh, when you cried at your first bris, do you know what your mother said to you? 'Don't cry,' she said. 'When you turn thirteen, I'll make you a real *simchah*. Your father and I together. We'll make you a bris like nobody ever saw.'"

And then the stranger whispers, "And you know what, Menasheleh? You stopped crying."

"Oy, Menasheleh, my Menasheleh," he sings, choking now on his own tears. "Do you see, Menasheleh? Do you understand that this is not only your bar mitzvah, but the *simchah* of those who never made it? The celebration of those whose mothers didn't have the strength yours did, and those not blessed with your good fortune. And Menasheleh, it is also the second bris your mother promised you. Do you understand what had to happen so that you could have your first bris at the proper time? Can you fathom what *mesirus nefesh* that was? Do you see what being a Jew means to your mother and meant to so many *heiligeh Yiddin* who did not come back? Do you understand your great *zechus* and your great obligations?"

Then, suddenly, he stops, this strange man. He looks slowly around the room. He coughs twice, removes a grimy handkerchief from his pocket, blows his nose loudly, and resumes talking. His voice becomes stronger. His green eyes begin to sparkle. His right thumb begins tracing great arcs in the air, and the sing-song becomes even more pronounced.

"And the cigarettes, *rabboisai*, what ever happened to all of Leah'leh's cigarettes? What's a bris without a *seudah*? She traded those cigarettes for enough bread that at least ten men could eat a few morsels. I know, because I had a couple of crumbs myself. And she traded for some wine, an onion, some half-rotten potatoes, a bit of salt, a couple of eggs — very expensive items, eggs — and who knows what else. And somehow — to this day I don't know where she baked it, she said it was her secret — she made a *kugel.* And believe me, *rabboisai,* if you think the *kugels* of Williamsburg are *geshmak* that *kugel, rabboisai,* that *kugel* that Leah'leh prepared for us there in that Nazi hell had *ta'am Gan Aiden."*

Blinded by Bias

וַיֹּאמֶר ה' אֶל מֹשֶׁה כָּבֵד לֵב פַּרְעֹה מֵאֵן לְשַׁלַּח הָעָם.

God said to Moshe, "Pharaoh's heart has hardened; he refuses to let the people go."

(Shemos 7:14)

Evoking a homonym of the Hebrew expression for hard-heartedness (*kaved lev*), the Midrash maintains that Pharaoh's heart (*lev*) turned into a liver (*kaved*), for anyone with a heart would not have enslaved the people.

Rabbi **Avigdor Nebanzahl** associates this Midrash with a popular parable about Pharaoh's heartlessness and illogical behavior.

A donkey had the gall to tax a lion, the king of beasts. The lion killed the donkey for his audacity and presented the carcass to the fox to prepare it for consumption. The fox did as he was told, but when he discovered the heart, he coveted it for himself and devoured it.

When the lion inspected the donkey's remains and discovered the heart missing, he demanded to know what had become of it. The fox unabashedly responded, "My master, had this donkey had a heart, it would *never have dared tax you!" (*Yalkut Shimoni, VaEra *182).*

So, too, Pharaoh's refusal to acknowledge the King of kings after each plague proved him to be heartless. Though Pharaoh clearly saw what he was up against, and even his own people pleaded with him to release the Israelites, he remained intransigent.

How does the heart affect man's reason? Rabbi Nebanzahl offers a modern analogy: Man's brain is indisputably the most sophisticated computer; it can solve intricate problems in nanoseconds. But like any computer, it requires correct data.

The heart supplies the brain with information. But if the heart is tempted [by greed, by pride, etc.], it misinforms the brain, which then reaches the wrong conclusion. For example: Smoking unquestionably poses a significant health hazard. Yet a smoker, even an observant Jew well aware of the mitzvah to "guard your [health] very carefully..." *(Devarim 4:15)*, continues to smoke because he wishes to. If the heart wants to smoke, it will provide the brain with such biased data as, "Plenty of smokers are perfectly healthy, whereas numerous horribly diseased individuals have never touched a cigarette. Furthermore, how dangerous could smoking be if doctors themselves indulge?" A brain fed such disinformation will undoubtedly err and sanction smoking.

Likewise, since Pharaoh did not wish to liberate the Jews, his heart enabled him to dismiss even what he saw with his eyes. A liver cleanses the blood of impurities, so a liver-like heart should cleanse one of half-truths, not manufacture them, unless you say that such a heart perversely "washes away" the truth. Such a heart relays distorted information to the brain, blinding Pharaoh — or anyone similarly afflicted — to the truth.

The Bronx. Once the respectable "uptown" address of successful Jewish immigrants of earlier years, it was, in the 1960s, still home to ninety thousand of them. The stately mansions all along the Grand Concourse had been subdivided and converted into three-, four- and five-room apartments where the Jewish population continued to live in relative harmony in that huge ethnic melting pot. They would stroll on Pelham Parkway, read the newspapers in the park or discuss the Workmen's Circle on the stoop. There were more *Forwards* delivered to the corner candy store than copies of *The Daily News*. Yes, the Bronx was Jewish, but it wasn't particularly religious.

In the middle of all this was the Wallace Avenue Shul, a little hideaway for old men who cherished the warmth of the cozy *shtibel*, a place where they could hold on to their past. The Rabbi was Yisrael Rabinowitz, a pudgy, good humored Jew from Lomza who had survived the Poles, the Germans and the Russians — which made it likely that he would survive the Americans too.

The Wallace Avenue Shul and its rabbi didn't look like much, but everyone knew they enjoyed the special Grace of God. For Rabbi Rabinowitz the shul was home, and there he would learn Torah from four-thirty in the morning until ten o'clock at night. One morning, his predawn entry into the shul foiled the plans of two thieves who were engaged at that moment in breaking a hole through the shul wall into the Orlinsky supermarket next door. More about that wall — and the supermarket — later.

Another wall of the synagogue, shared with an adjacent bakery, was known as the "*haise vant*" because of the oven mounted on the bakery side. One Friday afternoon, a large volume of gas had accumulated in the oven. When the pilot was lit later that night, the oven exploded with a force which ripped through the ceiling. It generated a blaze the likes of which the Bronx hadn't known for years.

Two city blocks of Wallace/Lydig Avenue were engulfed in a four-alarm fire that raged through nine stores. Looking down the street that night observers saw a hook-and-ladder truck every ten yards and scores of grim-faced firefighters directing hoses and opening hydrants. And there was Rabbi Rabinowitz, standing before his shul, *Tehillim* in hand, praying in the glow of the fire. The next morning every Italian, Black, Puerto Rican and who-knows-what from the neighborhood filed through the synagogue during Shabbos services, just to see with his own eyes the shul that hadn't burnt down.

Every Friday Rabbi Rabinowitz telephoned an employment agency to send someone to mop the shul's floor. By the late 'sixties the Bronx had already justly earned its reputation as a jungle, and it was the "natives of the wild" who were sent for the job. But Rabbi Rabinowitz was undaunted. Back in Lomza, and later in Siberia, he had lived through worse. Actually his background provided the necessary skills for dealing with indigenous populations: his offers of hot coffee and an occasional free meal were met with surprise and appreciation. His kind words in pidgin English brought out the best in all who passed through.

One Sunday afternoon on his way back from a *simchah* on the Lower East Side, Rabbi Rabinowitz was accosted by six thugs. "Hey," yelled one of the muggers, "ain't ya dat Ray-bye from up dere in de Bronx? Let him go, guys. He's ma Man." The group dissolved, and the astonished rabbi resumed breathing.

The rampant crime that pervaded the Bronx forced the Wallace Avenue Shul — per order of the Police Commissioner — to install a "buzzer lock." Soon after it was in operation, a member complained to the rabbi that he had knocked one evening but the door wasn't buzzed open. Rabbi Rabinowitz, reasoning that the shul and its rabbi were obligated above all to serve the community, decided to forget about the buzzer, and the door remained open from then on (a noble gesture, to be sure, but one fraught with hazard).

Hoodlums who frequented the Carvel Ice Cream store across the street liked to impress their girlfriends by throwing lit firecrackers and cherry bombs through the open door of the shul. On one occasion, two teenagers heaved a can of garbage inside. They had the misfortune of having it land on a policeman who had come in to pay "*yizkor* money." The officer chased after the "poipetratas," apprehended them, and administered a little justice of his own before he brought them before the due offices of the law to administer its own fair share. Word of this incident spread quickly through the neighborhood and quiet reigned for a while at the Wallace Avenue Shul.

In fact, the only major problem which plagued the shul was the neighboring supermarket's persistent drive to expand so as to house a meat department. Such an expansion was, in the eyes of many *baalei batim*, a godsend for the shul. According to Orlinsky's plan, the shul — which was too large to begin with — would be divided in half, thus cutting the rent, heating, cleaning and lighting bills. The landlord of both properties, aching to expand the supermarket because of the potential jump in revenue, even sweetened the pot by offering the shul a long-dreamed-of lease.

But Rabbi Rabinowitz wouldn't hear of it. "What! Turn a

shul into a *treifa* butcher shop, open on Shabbos?!"

He took his case everywhere but he didn't stand a chance. He even appealed to State Senator Samuel Bernstein and Borough President Robert Abrams, who offered their sympathy but explained that without a lease there was nothing that could be done.

In the meantime, the landlord resorted to other means of persuasion. He had a whole bag of dirty tricks: He paid welfare recipients to make threatening telephone calls, and when that failed, he arranged for a phony city inspector to examine the shul.

In marched the landlord and the inspector — actually a cashier from the supermarket next door disguised in a white cloak with a shiny, official-looking badge (bought for a dime in a toy store). To start with, he told the rabbi that the floor wasn't safe and called for his "assistants" who were waiting outside.

Instantly, a crew appeared hauling planks and demolition equipment. The "inspector" then turned his attention to the wall separating the supermarket from the shul. "This wall is no good," he declared and with the help of his eager workers started pulling away the sheetrock.

Rabbi Rabinowitz finally sensed that something wasn't kosher and telephoned Mr. Friedman, a congregant better versed in English and less naïve than himself. As soon as Mr. Friedman sized up the situation, he threatened to call the police. The "inspector" fled.

After this tactic had also failed, the landlord raised the rent from $200 to $1,000 a month, a sum way beyond the shul's meager means. The landlord wasted no time in filing a civil suit against the shul for "refusing" to pay the rent. As *mazel* and Rabbi Rabinowitz would have it, the judge was a devout Catholic: His Honor threw the landlord out of court for ruthless treatment of a house of worship.

But the landlord still was unwilling to forgo the higher rent of the supermarket, which threatened to relocate if it couldn't expand. He appealed the decision of the lower court to the New York Court of Appeals. This time it seemed hopeless for Rabbi Rabinowitz; even the shul members were on the side of the landlord who promised to lower the original rent and to give them "whatever they want" as long as the store could enlarge.

The court hearing was set for a Tuesday. The previous week Rabbi Rabinowitz visited all of the prominent rabbis and *Rashei Yeshivah* for blessings. Even some of the *rebbes* failed to see the significance of the issue — but Rabbi Rabinowitz was unshakeable.

That Sunday afternoon Lydig Avenue was suddenly startled by a loud crashing sound emanating from Orlinsky's supermarket. With no apparent cause, the store's roof had caved in. Since it was Sunday, no one was inside. Since it happened during the afternoon, half the Bronx was on hand to witness the omen.

The next morning, the Fire Commissioner was astonished to discover that the shul was intact. "Rabbi," he began, removing his cap, "er, excuse me for disturbing you while you're studying, but maybe you know what happened here? How could it be that the supermarket is totally demolished and your temple didn't lose a chip of paint? I hear they've been giving you some trouble...? Well, there you have it — an Act of God."

The only one unaffected by the miracle was the landlord. He informed the rabbi, in no uncertain terms, that he intended to pursue his case.

On Tuesday morning, the day of the court case, the

landlord received a phone call from the Emergency Ward at Jacobi Hospital informing him that his daughter had been injured in a car accident. Before he left for the hospital, he made one important call:

"All right, Rabbi Rabinowitz, I give up — you can keep your shul..."

A Chance to Change

וַיֹּאמֶר ה׳ אֶל מֹשֶׁה בֹּא אֶל פַּרְעֹה כִּי אֲנִי הִכְבַּדְתִּי אֶת לִבּוֹ וְאֶת לֵב עֲבָדָיו לְמַעַן שִׁתִי אֹתֹתַי אֵלֶּה בְּקִרְבּוֹ.

And the Lord said to Moshe, "Go in to Pharaoh, for I have hardened his heart and the heart of his servants in order that I may display these — My signs — among [them]."

(Shemos 10:1)

The Midrash comments:

> *Said Rabbi Yochanan: Does this [verse] not substantiate heretical claims that Pharaoh had no opportunity to repent? As it says, "for I have hardened his heart."*
>
> *Rabbi Shimon ben Lakish replied: Let the mouths of heretics be sealed, for, "He scorns the scorners..." (*Mishlei *3:34). God warns once, twice, and even thrice. If man still does not repent, God closes his heart to repentance, so He may exact vengeance from the sinner.*
>
> *Thus it was with wicked Pharaoh. Since God sent word to him five times, and he took no notice, He said, "You have stiffened your neck and hardened your heart; therefore, I*

will add to your defilement by further hardening your heart."

Rabbi **Eliyahu Lopian** explains that sinners rationalize their lifestyles — just as heretics defend Pharaoh — by insisting, "I cannot overcome my nature." Such a claim borders on heresy. God's hardening of Pharaoh's heart gives heretics an excuse to claim that he did not have the ability to repent, but clearly this was not the case: Pharaoh had more than fair warning and ample opportunity to repent.

Rabbi Shimon ben Lakish is firm in his reply. Like Pharaoh, a person is given fair warning, but ultimately he must pay for his transgressions. Man certainly is able to change, if only he heeds the warnings.

Hey, Gramps!" This was the second epithet to be hurled in the Bostoner Rebbe's direction. The first had been "Hey, Greybeard," but it was the second that made him pause in midstride. The Rebbe, it was well known, was a very modest man. He was also a venerable Torah authority and chasidic leader and unaccustomed to being addressed by that title — and certainly not in that tone.

He turned toward the source of the shouting to see two of New York's Finest frisking a hirsute youth in bleached-out jeans and a sloganed T-shirt diagonally across the street. The Rebbe crossed over to investigate.

The youth, in his late teens, lolled languidly against a brick wall, with apparent disdain for the patrolmen examining the contents of his pockets.

"Come to rescue me, Grandpa?" the boy challenged in a flippant tone.

"Do you need rescuing, my son?" the Rebbe countered, "and why do you call me 'Grampa'? If indeed we are related, then I would be happy to offer any assistance I can."

"Hey — I don't need no old coot to rescue me!" the teenager insisted with as much indignation as the circumstances allowed. "Beat it, old man. Go back to your temple!"

The Rebbe was only slightly taken aback by the youth's brash tone. A man renowned for his equanimity, the Bostoner Rebbe could not be unsettled, even by a young hood about to be taken into custody. On the contrary, the Rebbe's composure seemed to unsettle this tough teenager. The Rebbe knew that Providence had "invited" him to the site for a reason, and he was curious to know what it was.

"You still haven't told me why you called me 'Grampa,' young man."

"I don't owe you no explanations!" the boy replied, but could not restrain himself from answering the warm, gentle Rebbe's question. "You look like a picture I seen of my Grampa — alright?" The defiant final note, unwarranted by the circumstances, came out only through force of habit, the Rebbe thought, but he was far more interested in the boy's words than his tone.

"If I remind him of his grandfather," the Rebbe mused, "this youngster is in more trouble than meets the eye." Aloud he said, "Pardon me," addressing the police officer, "but are you taking this young man into custody? Has he committed a crime?"

"Well, Rabbi," the older of the two began, "we come here on this two-eleven, see? 'Robbery In Progress.' An' this here kid, he's in a darned awful rush to flee from the scene of the crime. So we start pursuin' him an' let me tell ya, this kid can run! Me an' Frankie, here, we ain't hada workout like that since we pursue that 'sneaker-boy' clear across the Brooklyn Bridge, am I right Frank or what?" Frank nodded in agreement.

The Rebbe waited patiently for a gap in the patrolman's recitation to inquire, "Is there any evidence that this boy was involved in the robbery?"

"Nah," Frank replied, "he's clean. But we're taking him downtown for questioning."

Throughout this exchange, the teenager maintained his apathetic stance, casually flipping a coin in the air to further demonstrate his total disinterest in the goings on. "What is your name, young man?" the Rebbe asked, but the boy only stared at him vacantly. Frank seized a fistful of the youth's shirtfront and demanded, "Don't you got no respect, punk? Answer the old man!"

"What if I don't," the teenager sneered, "I'll get another dose of 'police brutality'?" Frank released his shirt abruptly.

"The name's Goldberg," he said, confirming the Rebbe's suspicions, "Mark Goldberg. What's it to you?"

Turning to the patrolmen, the Rebbe said, "Officers, I am Moshe Horowitz from Forty-ninth Street. Your lieutenant and I are well acquainted. If you would be so kind as to release Mr. Goldberg to my custody, I shall take full responsibility and you gentlemen can get on with your vital work." The patrolmen shrugged their shoulders, aware that they had no hard evidence against the "punk," and handed him over to the softspoken Rabbi. Just then, the radio in their patrol car squawked to life. They climbed into the sedan and drove off without even a backward glance.

Mark thrust his hands into his pockets and said, "Good move, Rabbi. See ya around." He spun on his heel and headed down the block.

"Just one moment, young man," the Rebbe ordered in a stern tone. "Since I have assumed custody of you, you are obliged to come with me."

Mark, not one to obey orders, immediately backed down when he saw the Rebbe's adamant expression. "Okay," he surrendered, "that's cool," and with a mock-gallant sweep of his arm, stepped aside to allow the Rebbe to pass. "Like they say: 'Age before beauty,' man — so you lead the way." The Rebbe *krechtzed* a mighty "*oy*" and started for home with his charge in tow.

Along the way, the Rebbe asked Mark if he ever had a Jewish education. The youth simply rolled his eyes. Taking that for a "no," the Rebbe said, "Well, then, I have a great deal to teach you." Goldberg paled visibly. From the expression on the boy's face, the Rebbe could tell he was wondering if he might not have been better off "downtown" with Frank.

As they approached the steps of the Bostoner's home, the Rebbe announced, "First we'll eat supper."

"Now you're talking, man!" Mark said with genuine enthusiasm, certain this meant a reprieve. The Rebbe went over to a closet and returned with a large yarmulke. He extended it to Mark, who stared at it with revulsion. "That beanie's for *me*?"

"Of course," the Rebbe replied. "Now, our first lesson is how to wash our hands before we eat..."

"Gimme a break, old man! If I feel like washing my hands, I'll wash my hands and I don't need no wacko greybeard to show me how!"

The Rebbe, pretending he had not heard, led his guest into the kitchen where he instructed him how to wash and how to make the blessing. He went to great lengths to explain that one may not interrupt between washing and eating — even to speak, and the few seconds of silence between washing and breaking bread provided a welcome respite from Mark's incessant tirade, the thrust of which was that "this religion trip" was not for him.

It did not matter. The Bostoner Rebbe had every intention of showing Mark the sights on a "trip" the boy clearly preferred not to travel. An unappreciative Goldberg was to have greater exposure to the Rebbe than some of the Bostoner's closest chasidim.

After supper, the Bostoner Rebbe showed his ward — so recently detained by the police on suspicion of robbery — to a bedroom containing several valuable items. "This will be your room," he said, as if welcoming an honored guest. Mark was overwhelmed, not by the Rebbe's gracious hospitality and generosity, but by his naiveté. And the test proved too great for him.

His first night at the Rebbe's residence, he began to "case the joint," prowling out of his room when he was sure that everyone in the household was asleep. He had already emptied his bedroom of valuables and stashed them in a pillowcase under the bureau. But just when his gaze fell on some silver ornaments which he thought might bring him a tidy sum, he heard a sound that made his heart pound loudly in his chest. Mark peered into the room from where the noise emanated and discovered his host reading aloud in a strange language from an oversized book. The would-be thief could not have known that the Rebbe was merely engaged in Talmudic research, but the fear of being apprehended in mid-felony swiftly sent him tiptoeing back to bed to await a better opportunity.

Over the next few days Mark learned that this "Rabbi" whom he had stopped on the street was no ordinary cleric. His host was none other than "The Bostoner Rebbe," whatever that meant.

One thing it did mean, was that an incredible number of men in chasidic garb constantly swarmed all over Mark's newly-staked turf. There was always someone and his brother-in-law who wished to visit, consult, or seek the blessing of the Rebbe. All this interference placed a definite crimp in

Mark's style; still he found time to snatch almost anything that wasn't nailed down. The challenge he now faced was finding a way to abscond with the loot undetected.

After four days in the Rebbe's court, Goldberg had more than he could handle of piety and Jewish observance, but three square meals a day and a warm bed were certainly an improvement over cold pizza and a park bench. Furthermore, he had not yet solved the problem of his getaway since the Rebbe's nocturnal Talmudic research continued unabated. One other factor made him contemplate and recontemplate his decision to leave: as difficult as it was for Mark to admit it to himself, deep down he had taken a liking to his "Rabbi."

It was evident that the Rebbe liked him, too. Mark was well aware that many of the chasidim who entered the Bostoner's court did not share the Rebbe's feelings towards him. Although they always communicated in Yiddish, which he did not understand at all, certain nuances and gestures did not require translation.

As far as Mark could tell, the Rebbe was as oblivious to their protests as he was to Mark's own constant grousing regarding the dictates of religion. Mark was intrigued: was the Rebbe the absentminded type, the saintly type, or simply hopelessly naïve.

A lot of things were "missing" from the house, but the Rebbe refrained from leveling any accusations. Mark felt certain that, no matter how much time the Rebbe spent studying his old books, he had to know about the pilfering, if not through the comments of others then by empirical evidence. The Rebbe was "cool" all right, frustratingly cool. Is this some psychological ploy, Mark wondered, or is he just giving me enough rope to hang myself? Mark vowed not to underestimate the Rebbe or be taken in by his unassuming façade.

When the Rebbe received a cassette in the mail of a well-received lecture which he had delivered, all the members of the household were anxious to hear it. But the tape recorder could not be found. This time, the family felt, the situation had gone too far. They brought their grievance to the Rebbe, but all he had to say was: "There really isn't time now to listen to the tape. We can wait until later."

Mark began to get nervous. The Rebbe's absolute confidence made Mark suspect that a trap had been set for him and he'd walked right into it. He surreptitiously replaced the tape recorder and some of his more valuable "loot."

The Rebbe, for his part, had no such trap set. He simply intended to wait for Mark to turn around. He held long discussions with him and continued to cater to his needs — physical and spiritual — and to try and kindle the dormant spark within Mordechai Goldberg's soul.

And that spark, like the sparks of so many other Jews, was eventually ignited by the warmth and affection and infinite patience of the Bostoner Rebbe.

Darkness Is Also a State of Mind

...לֹא רָאוּ אִישׁ אֶת אָחִיו וְלֹא קָמוּ אִישׁ מִתַּחְתָּיו....

And the Lord said to Moshe, "Stretch out your hand towards heaven, that there may be darkness over the land of Egypt, darkness that may be felt. ... They did not see one another, nor did anyone rise from his place....

(Shemos 10:21, 23)

The Midrash says that the darkness which plagued Egypt was palpable, freezing everyone in their "place." The **Chiddushei HaRim** explains that the darkness reflected the Egyptians' selfishness. They did not see one another, because all that they ever saw was themselves. Since no one rose from his place, meaning no one rose to help others or was ever helped by an Egyptian to rise from his troubles, ultimately they could not even move themselves.

One of the most glorious chapters in our People's history is reserved for a solitary Englishman: Dr. Solomon Schonfeld. Known to some as the "Angel of Rescue" and to others simply as "Father," he was both to thousands of our brethren trapped by the Nazis and abandoned by the world at large.

Every Jew that Dr. Schonfeld saved was a story unto himself, a gripping tale filled with drama and heroics. Time and again, Dr. Schonfeld endangered his freedom and even his life to help the victims of war, placing the welfare of others above his own. No matter how great the risk or how improbable the odds, nothing could deter this outstanding statesman and rescue worker.

A rabbi by profession, Dr. Schonfeld somehow managed to acquire a British Army uniform, which he wore in order to provide himself with an aura of authority. In actuality, however, he needed no impressive regalia to win people's confidence. The rabbi's clear, bright eyes, his height and bearing, together with his forthright manner of speech, always earned him attention and respect.

When World War II finally ended in 1945, the battle to save Jewish lives — physically and spiritually — had hardly begun for Dr. Schonfeld. There were still thousands of Jews, primarily orphaned children, who had no home to return to and no family members left alive.

With faith, determination and originality as his only weapons, the rabbi fought for the emigration of every Jewish soul marooned on Europe's blood-drenched soil. Equally concerned that the orphans be raised in a warm, Jewish environment, Dr. Schonfeld invested unlimited time and energy in seeking loving families to adopt them.

One typical story from this period involves a fellow who sought Dr. Schonfeld's help in rescuing a young relative stranded in Europe. Because the rabbi was so incredibly busy, the only time he could schedule a meeting was at 3:00 in the morning. But at least at that hour, the petitioner was certain, he would have Rabbi Schonfeld's undivided attention.

Imagine his surprise when he found dozens of people ahead of him on line that morning! When his turn finally came, Dr. Schonfeld had his hair cut as he listened carefully and took notes. And when the fellow left, he saw someone preparing the rabbi's "supper."

As if this unparalleled selflessness were not enough, whenever Dr. Schonfeld was unable to find a suitable family to adopt an orphan, he would gather the refugee under his own protective wings.

During one of the rabbi's trips to Europe after the war, he received a message that the British ambassador in Prague was looking for him. Dr. Schonfeld reported to the embassy the next morning and was greeted by a very angry-looking official.

"Are you the Dr. Schonfeld who has been arranging the 'children's transports'?" he demanded.

"Yes, I am," Dr. Schonfeld replied.

"Are you not a member of the clergy?" the ambassador pressed.

"That is true," he nodded.

"Well, then, I'll have you know that yesterday a woman came to see me, requesting permission to visit her son in England. It soon became clear to me that her son had left for Britain in one of your transports.

"I will have you know, sir," the ambassador went on, "that the British government issues visas for the children on your transports on the assumption that they are orphans. But if a woman wishes to visit her son, then surely the child is not an orphan! You are therefore guilty of committing a disgraceful crime by deceiving us. A member of the clergy should know better than to lie!"

Dr. Schonfeld rose to his full height. "Mr. Ambassador," he countered forcefully, banging his hand down on the desk with a loud clap, "if there is one Jewish child left in all of Europe whose mother is still alive, will you hold it against all the others?"

The tragic truth of Dr. Schonfeld's words quickly registered with the British official and he immediately regretted his outburst. Indeed, his cold, blue eyes, which moments before had been filled with anger, now filled with tears.

According to Dr. Schonfeld, this very ambassador would yet compensate for his mistake. He ended up providing the Angel of Rescue with more visas for Jews than any other clerk in the British Foreign Office.

For God's Sake

וַיֵּט מֹשֶׁה אֶת יָדוֹ עַל הַיָּם וַיּוֹלֶךְ ה' אֶת הַיָּם בְּרוּחַ קָדִים עַזָּה כָּל הַלַּיְלָה וַיָּשֶׂם אֶת הַיָּם לֶחָרָבָה וַיִּבָּקְעוּ הַמָּיִם.

And Moshe stretched his hand over the sea, and the Lord caused the sea to go back by a strong east wind all that night, and made the sea dry land, and the waters were divided.

(Shemos 14:21)

What caused the sea to split? An amazing Midrash avers: "The sea beheld the Talmudic teaching of Rabbi Yishmael."

Rabbi **Yaakov Neiman** explains that the sea would have happily split at the Almighty's direct command, but the waters resisted taking orders from Moshe, for they considered themselves just as devoted a servant as he was. Why should the sea be compelled to alter its nature, if Moshe was not?

But then the sea "beheld the teaching of Rabbi Yishmael," which states, "The Torah is elucidated through thirteen principles," one of them being a *kal vachomer* [an a fortiori argument].

The waters immediately comprehended the difference between themselves and man. The sea [and all of nature] obeys God's explicit command, while man follows even His implicit instructions, making sacrifices even on the basis of a *kal vachomer*. For instance, Chananyah, Mishael, and Azaryah — the famous martyrs of the Book of Daniel — plunged into a fiery furnace because they derived a *kal vachomer* from the frogs that plagued Egypt: "Though the frogs were not commanded to do so, they flung themselves into the hot ovens of the Egyptians. Can we do no less?"

By dedicating ourselves to God's will even when He Himself does not articulate it, we glorify Him. Thus, the sea obeyed Moshe — who was doing God's bidding — and split in two.

The postal service in Tzivityan, Lithuania was computerized long before the high-tech age of automated bank tellers and electronic cash registers: it had Valinkov. Valinkov's brain was like a pocket calculator. He could add up a column of figures standing on his head and never make a mistake. Indeed, so accustomed were the townspeople to his unerring accuracy that they never even bothered to count their change.

Except once. On that fateful day Valinkov had had an argument with his wife and a Jewish customer benefited from the clerk's distraction. By chance he counted his change and discovered, to his amazement, that an error had been made in his favor.

He returned at once to the post office and said humbly to the clerk: "I'm afraid, sir, that your arithmetic was not correct."

Valinkov was irate, offended by the affront to his impeccable reputation, and quickly whipped out a fresh sheet of scrap paper to redo his calculations.

But no matter which way he added, the total differed from his original one. "You see?" the Jew said, "I was given fifteen kopecks extra," and he placed a handful of coins on the counter and left.

The clerk was speechless. *No one* — least of all a Jew — reimbursed the Government! Why, in those years (between the World Wars) Lithuania's Jewish population was sufficiently victimized by governmental agencies to justify grand larceny. But this? This insignificant overpayment didn't even qualify as pilfering; it was more like a gift, albeit a modest one. And who would reject a gift from the Government?

"Perhaps," thought the clerk, "that is the very reason he returned the money — it was too paltry a sum to be worth the risk of being caught." Valinkov decided to test the next Jew who entered the post office, this time with a more irresistible amount. True, he would have to make up the deficit from his own pocket, but it was worth it.

Later that afternoon, Valinkov went ahead with his plan. When the Jew discovered the discrepancy, he was tempted to remain silent and simply enjoy the Government's unexpected largesse. His conscience, however, gave him no rest. He brought his dilemma before Tzivityan's rabbi — Reb Yaakov Kamenetsky.

Reb Yaakov made his *psak* perfectly clear: a Jew is forbidden to possess even the smallest fraction of a coin that does not rightfully belong to him. Word spread swiftly throughout the town.

It was just before closing time and Valinkov had been congratulating himself on his perspicacity, when the Jew walked into the post office. The bewildered clerk could do nothing but accept the proffered bundle of notes. "Can they all be so naïve... or honest?" he wondered.

Again and again the clerk tested the honesty of the Jews of Tzivityan, but Reb Yaakov's firm ruling and his sterling example fortified the people and they withstood the trials.

When the Nazis marched into Tzivityan one year later, it was this Gentile clerk, and this Gentile alone who risked his own safety to rescue the Jews of the town. They had proven themselves to be a holy people, undeserving of such a dire fate.

Revenge

אָז יָשִׁיר מֹשֶׁה וּבְנֵי יִשְׂרָאֵל אֶת הַשִּׁירָה הַזֹּאת לַה'....

Then Moshe and the Children of Israel sang this song to the Lord....

(Shemos 15:1)

Why did *Bnei Yisrael* sing only "then," never before?

The Midrash explains that only after the crushing defeat of the Egyptians were the Children of Israel impelled to sing God's praises: "Although You are Eternal, Your throne was not firmly established, nor were You known in the world, until Your children sang [at the sea]. Thus, 'Your throne is established from then...' *(Tehillim 93:2).*"

Rabbi **Chaim Shmuelevitz** notes that God was not manifest as the Ruler and Judge of the world until Israel sang at the sea. Having witnessed Divine Justice visited upon the Egyptians, the People were awed, and God's Glory increased dramatically as He demonstrated that the wicked are eventually punished.

Unmotivated by petty vengeance, the promotion and acknowledgment of Divine retribution is extremely praiseworthy. Upon seeing the triumph of Justice, explained Rabbi Shmuelevitz, revenge should be celebrated.

Dr. Gisella Perl hurried into the labor room in Mt. Sinai Hospital. The patient, a woman well past her childbearing prime, lay listless on the bed, a large oxygen mask over her face. "It's only the thirty-second week, Doctor," the nurse reported, "and the mother's in bad condition. She was in one of those awful camps, I think. She has a number on her arm."

The doctor looked up sharply. "So have I," she replied gruffly as she felt for the patient's pulse. "Who is her physician?"

"Dr. Marcus, but he's on vacation."

"We will do a section," Dr. Perl announced, scanning the patient's chart. "Has the mother been told it might be necessary?"

"Yes, doctor," the nurse answered. "We'll start prepping her now."

"Wait!" Dr. Perl noticed for the first time the beautifully embroidered kerchief that was wrapped around the patient's head. She ran her fingers over the delicate stitching and the patient's eyes fluttered open. Doctor and patient stared at one another in stunned recognition.

"Gisi!" the woman exclaimed weakly, her voice muffled by the mask. "Is it really you?"

Dr. Perl nodded mutely, her eyes glistening with unshed tears. The patient drifted back into unconsciousness.

"God!" Gisella Perl cried aloud, "God, grant me a life for a life!"

While she donned a sterile cap and gown and scrubbed her hands with antiseptic soap, Gisella relived the terrors of her past and the occasion of her earlier encounter with the patient. Only three years had passed and yet the circumstances were so different it might have been a century ago. She pushed the bitter memories aside quickly and then, with her head held high, strode into the operating theater to seek revenge in the only way she knew.

The whistle blew, the dogs began to howl and the train doors opened with an ear-splitting crash. Another transport had arrived at Auschwitz.

The dark night was aglow with yellow billows of fire that spewed from huge smokestacks, sharp red tongues of flame licking the sky. Clouds of ash from the crematoria hung over the camp and the air was redolent with the nauseating smell of burning flesh, the flesh of thousands of Europe's Jews. A woman went mad on the spot, emitting a hackle-raising shriek that resembled nothing human. The single pistol shot that silenced her scream was followed by the dull thud of her falling body, and a dreadful silence fell over the new arrivals.

"Everyone out!" The shouted order was accompanied by a hail of kicks, lashes, clubbings and curses. An S.S. detachment, armed with instruments of death, brutally separated the men from their wives, the parents from their children, the old from the young. Then, suddenly, the prisoners were standing before the "master" himself, the master of the Kingdom of Death.

He waited for them as he had waited for so many others, a seductively handsome man exuding the fragrance of expensive cologne and fancy soap. He waited with arms folded and a cruel smile on his bloodless lips: Josef Mengele — the man whose orders no one disobeyed.

With a flick of his manicured fingers, Dr. Mengele began his "selections": three-quarters of the group — the very old and the very young — to the "left" and death; the others, to the "right," to the living death of the Auschwitz concentration camp.

A young Hungarian gynecologist was among those sentenced to life. Soon after her arrival, Mengele instructed her to set up an infirmary in Camp C for ailing women prisoners. The idea of a clinic was another grisly Nazi joke. There were no medical supplies, no bandages, no beds or water. Nonetheless, Gisella Perl employed the pathetic facilities placed at her disposal and did everything in her power to save the lives of her fellow Jews.

An order was given for all pregnant women in Camp C to come forward to be transported to a different camp where the conditions were better, rations larger, and the work load lighter. [Most inmates suffered from the characteristic bloating of severe malnutrition. Numerous pregnancies, therefore, went undetected and only those women who voluntarily admitted their condition were transferred.] Group after group of pregnant women left Camp C. Even Gisella believed that it was to the women's advantage to volunteer to leave.

But to her immense horror, she soon discovered that pregnancy meant a gruesome — instant — death for the expectant mothers. They were to pay with their own lives, and with the lives of their unborn, for the crime of bearing a Jewish child.

There was no other special camp for pregnant women. Instead, the group from Camp C was surrounded by a gang of S.S. men and women who amused themselves by giving the prisoners a savage taste of hell before throwing them — alive — into the crematoria. The "less-fortunate" were spared for Dr. Mengele's sport, for his barbaric, hideous experiments which included kicking the mothers' stomachs to see how long they took to abort. In other cases, he personally performed vivisection on the mothers and their fetuses.

Gisella converted her horror into courage. From that moment, she vowed, there would be no more pregnancies in her section of the camp, no more candidates for the brutal sport of the S.S. officers or Dr. Mengele's vile experiments. After witnessing with her own eyes the torture meted out to her sisters, "Gisi," as the inmates called her, ran back to Camp C and went from block to block revealing to her fellow inmates what she had seen. And then, Dr. Gisella Perl, a devoutly religious woman, whose peacetime job and chief delight had been the care of expectant mothers and the safe delivery of their babies, became an abortionist. That irony of ironies could only have happened in the living hell called Auschwitz.

Every night, under the cover of darkness, in the rat-infested filth of the open-pit latrines, Gisi induced abortions in order to save the women from experimentation and certain death.With neither water for cleansing nor surgical instruments, she delivered the fetuses, and then swore the women to secrecy and sent them back to their barracks. Whenever possible, she had the mothers admitted into her "hospital" under the pretext of pneumonia — the only diagnosis which did not automatically mandate an immediate death sentence.

Always hurried, and in constant mortal fear that she would be caught and made to suffer the full intensity of the depraved Dr. Mengele's fury, she carried out her abominable act three, even four times a night. And each time she felt as though it were her own baby that she was killing. As she knelt down to perform the abortion amid the filth and excrement that covered the floor of the latrine, she prayed to God to help her save the life of the mother.

The Almighty showed his approval of her work, for every one of the women miraculously recovered — women in their fourth, fifth, sixth, seventh, eighth, and even ninth month of pregnancy. And they were able to continue working, a fact which saved their lives — for a short while, at least.

Of the women she aborted, some were from her hometown in Hungary, women who had been her patients before the war. Her very first delivery in Camp C was of a woman who — a millennium before, it seemed — had made her living embroidering beautiful baby clothing. Coming from an impoverished family, she had worked at her trade until late at night, dreaming about the baby she herself would one day bear.

Then she married. But month after month, year after year, the couple's most ardent wish had remained unfulfilled. Eventually, the woman had turned to Dr. Perl, and six months before the Nazis invaded Hungary, the treatment had borne results. "I will give you the most exquisite present," the overjoyed expectant mother had promised Dr. Perl.

At every appointment she had repeated her pledge, but in the end it was Dr. Perl who gave *her* a present — the gift of life. In the ninth month of the woman's long-awaited pregnancy, beside the cesspools of Auschwitz, Gisella Perl delivered the embroiderer's baby boy.

She held the warm, tiny infant, in her hands and sent the mother back to her barracks. Then she kissed his smooth face, caressed his soft hair, and placed the silent newborn among the latest group of corpses — those which had been laid out that night. Had the baby been discovered alive, the mother, Dr. Perl and all of the other pregnant women whom Gisella still hoped to save would have been doomed.

At 8:32 P.M., on Tuesday, March 28, 1948, in the gleaming white fluorescence of Mt. Sinai's sterile operating theater, Gisella repeated her private prayer. Moments later, utilizing the most advanced surgical instruments, she delivered the embroiderer's second child, as smooth and as soft as the first had been, and as perfectly formed. She placed the squalling infant in his mother's arms.

"Oh, Gisi! He's beautiful," the new mother whispered in awe. "A gift from God."

"He's much more than that, my dear," Gisella said. "He is God's revenge."

AUTHOR'S NOTE: Years later, Gisella Perl lived in Israel and was affiliated with Shaare Zedek Hospital in Jerusalem, where the pediatrics department bears her name. She personally delivered over three thousand Jewish babies. "They are my answer to Josef Mengele," Gisi asserted, "each one a life for a life."

Reading the Signs

וַיִּשְׁמַע יִתְרוֹ כֹהֵן מִדְיָן חֹתֵן מֹשֶׁה אֵת כָּל אֲשֶׁר עָשָׂה אֱלֹקִים לְמֹשֶׁה וּלְיִשְׂרָאֵל עַמּוֹ כִּי הוֹצִיא ה׳ אֶת יִשְׂרָאֵל מִמִּצְרָיִם.

And Yisro, priest of Midyan, Moshe's father-in-law, heard all that the Lord had done for Moshe and for Yisrael, His people, and that the Lord had brought Yisrael out of Egypt.

(Shemos 18:1)

When the Torah was given, the Midrash, relates the kings of the world began to tremble with trepidation. Apprehensively, they asked Bilam about the terrifying noise emanating from Mount Sinai.

Bilam explained that the Torah was being presented to the Jewish people. Duly calmed, the rulers all returned home as if nothing had happened.

Yisro was the only non-Jew in the world who was truly affected by what he had "heard." Yisro alone could not disregard this earth-shattering event.

Whenever God sends a signal, only the wise hearken; the common man remains oblivious, continuing his daily existence as though nothing out of the ordinary had happened.

Michigan National Trust had a lot of rich customers, but they all paled alongside Joe Goldsmith, whose assets were vast enough to keep three full-time employees at Michigan National busy full time. The irony was that twenty-five years earlier, Goldsmith had been a penniless young refugee who had washed up on the shores of Lake Erie. His second cousin drip-dried him at his merchandising display workshop, where he acquired a profession that would serve him well in the coming years.

During the Depression, Joe built theater sets for federally-funded arts programs, and after the war, he started constructing homes for GI's returning from "Over There." He then moved on to land developing in suburbia, only to graduate to large-scale condominiums, apartment buildings and luxury homes for the very, very wealthy — a fraternity to which he rightly belonged.

Joe's office was done up like a Beverly Hills movie set: every piece of furniture had bow-fronts and Sheraton legs, Chippendale backs, tufted seats and George II arms. There were hand-crafted Eames chairs in calfskin leather, School of Tiffany vases, glazed tiles in a narrow band just under the ceiling cornices, a round Regency table, Wilton-weave carpet, brilliant red Chinese silk wall covering framed by narrow gilded moldings, framed by a band of bronzed webbing, framed by more gilded moldings. It made one's eyelids flutter.

The office, of course, was but a shadow of the decor of Joe's mansion. Since Dorothy Goldsmith had been unable to decide between Early Colonial, French Renaissance, or Victorian, a separate wing was devoted to each. These days Joe left the decorating to his wife; he devoted his attention to transportation, or more specifically, to two (in case one got dirty) of the most expensive BMW roadsters ever made. Needless to say, the mansion was only for tax shelter purposes and summer vacations. There was also a winter home in Florida, a spring pied-à-terre in New York, and a fall retreat in the Poconos.

Over the years Joe Goldsmith not only built homes and buildings, he also built a reputation as one of the wealthiest members of Temple Beth Ezra. Temple Beth Ezra, or "TBE" as it was affectionately known, was a cross between a country club and a fraternal organization. The Temple was set on a twelve-acre property outside of Detroit. There, in the privacy and security afforded by high stone walls surrounding the site and 24-hour security guards, the families of TBE gathered for the myriad social events that the Goldsmiths and their cronies believed American Jewish life was all about.

The list was impressive. There was the Men's Club, the Bowling League, the Women's Club, the Israeli Folk-dance Club, the pre-school, the kindergarten, the afternoon school, the Midrasha, the youth clubs, and "activity rooms" where teenaged youth could hang out and do nothing. TBE had everything but religious services. ("Our members perform many other mitzvahs," Rabbi Sally Segal was wont to say. "And besides, prayer is such a private matter; we don't feel we have to formalize it through congregational gatherings.")

Of all of Joe's innumerable possessions the one he treasured the most was his daughter, Miriam. Miriam, better known as Muffy, was Joe and Dorothy's pride and joy. From her early youth, TBE had been a part of Muffy Goldsmith's life. She attended the Sunday school and the Midrasha. She participated in all the events, the functions and the parties. And she rejected them all.

"I don't want a Bat Mitzvah," she informed her parents, to their stark and utter dismay. "I just want to be left alone."

"That's impossible!" Joe said. "You have to be Bat Mitzvahed. You're Jewish, aren't you?"

"Of course she's Jewish, dear," Dorothy said, trying to calm her husband down. "Rabbi Sally said so."

"What does she know? She doesn't even speak Yiddish!"

"Please, don't start with that. She's a nice person. Didn't she come over when we were having problems with Tante Bella?"

"Well, yes," Joe admitted.

"Remember how she took her in when we went on vacation? She fed her, bathed her, even taught her how to beg for food. Tante Bella never knew how to do that before."

"Your Tante Bella never knew how to do a lot of things. Except lie around the house."

"Don't say that. Just because she wouldn't associate with you, that's no reason to hold a grudge against her. I loved my Tante Bella."

"If you loved her so much, why did you have her put to sleep?"

"What else would you suggest? She could hardly see any more. She kept bumping into the furniture. She was having all sorts of digestive problems. It was the most humane thing I could do."

"Maybe. But I still say you shouldn't have had the Rabbi say Kaddish. After all, Tante Bella wasn't a relative."

"Rabbi Sally says she was like a relative."

"Yes, but who ever heard of a Rabbi saying Kaddish for a dog? For $500 a month, no less!"

"Look, Joe, let's not get into it. I'm sure if Rabbi Sally will talk to Muffy, she'll change her mind about the Bat Mitzvah."

Just then, Muffy walked in. "I heard that. And I won't change my mind. I don't like the Temple. It's full of fakers. And that includes the Rabbis."

"That does it!" Joe yelled. "Every other guy has a daughter who respects her parents and obeys their wishes. I get a rebel! Listen to me. You're going to have a Bat Mitzvah and that's that. You're going to do what Rabbi Samantha says..."

"Sally," Dorothy interjected.

"Sammy?"

"Sally, Joe, Rabbi Sally. Rabbi Samantha was the rabbi before Rabbi Sally."

"You're going to do what Rabbi Whatever-Her-Name says and we're all going to have a nice party. I've already told the landscapers that I want a model of Israel constructed in our backyard. Then I've hired some actors to come dressed as Arabs and give the place a little local color. The caterer and her staff have already agreed to dress up as Israeli soldiers. I got a great deal on an orchestra. They play all the Jewish music — *"Havah Nagilah," "Chiri Bim," "Hatikvah"*... You're gonna love it."

"You mean *you're* gonna love it. Me? I'm gonna walk out."

Muffy Goldsmith had her Bizarre Mitzvah and it was a memorable affair, as ostentatious events go. The caterers dressed up as Israeli soldiers were double-timing all over the battlefield. The waiters ran around looking like pug-nosed Bedouins desperately in search of sand. A giant tent was pitched to house the shuk. Peddlers inside hawked their wares to imaginary customers and avoided the donkeys allowed to run about within the confines of the tent.

The Bat Mitzvah consultant, whose specialty was theme parties, overlooked nothing. She rented camels from the zoo to give the guests unforgettable rides, and the beasts were especially cooperative in providing the proper ambience and aroma for the affair.

Indeed, only *charedim* were missing as the Goldsmith grounds were turned into an Israel theme park. Rabbi Sally said it was one of the most moving events she'd ever attended. It was also one of the most expensive events she'd ever attended. In fact, for just a few bucks less, Joe could have flown all 450 guests from Detroit to Israel, instead of making Israel come to Detroit.

With such a gala assumption of the responsibilities of Jewish womanhood, perhaps it was no wonder that Muffy's Jewish education came to a halt at the tender age of twelve. It was probably all for the good, for how could the Five Books of Moses be expected to compete with videos, computer games and Hollywood high life?

Actually Muffy didn't succumb to these temptations as completely as her peers did, for she had a hobby and a blossoming career ahead of her. She was the most celebrated art student in Bloomfield Hills High School and was readily accepted to the Rhode Island School of Design.

Along the way her rebellious nature burgeoned as if she had been reincarnated from the Sixties.

"She's as stubborn as you are," Dorothy told her husband after one particularly noisy argument.

"She's worse. If I had ever raised my voice to my father the way she raises hers to me, I wouldn't be here to tell you about it! The next thing you know, she'll come and tell us that she wants to go to some far-off place."

And the next thing they knew, she did. In an act of Providence she left Rhode Island and announced tonelessly, "I'm tired of learning about art. I want to learn about life."

"Does that mean you're going to go out and find a job?" Joe asked hopefully.

"No. It means I've joined the Peace Corps. They're sending me to Samoa."

"Some more what, dear?" Dorothy asked politely.

"Samoa is a country in the South Pacific. I'm going there to teach English to the natives."

"You can do that in Detroit!" Joe fumed. "Were you ever downtown? They can't read or write there. That's probably why they overdose!"

"Whaaat?" Dorothy and Muffy asked in unison.

"Because they can't read, they don't know how much of the drugs to take..."

"Darling," Dorothy corrected, before her husband made a bigger fool out of himself in front his daughter, "there are no instructions printed on those drugs."

"Regardless, she doesn't have to go to some jungle somewhere, or whatever it's called. I'll buy the island and when it's civilized, she can go for visit."

"You can't buy a country," Dorothy protested.

"Why not?" Joe demanded. "They bought Manhattan and they purchased Louisiana. If they could buy such great real estate for trinkets, I'll get this far-off island for a song."

"Dad, you know American history," Muffy scoffed, "like I know the construction business."

"You know something about construction?" Joe asked, all hopes and optimism.

"No, I don't know, and I don't want to know. Nor do you know what you're talking about. I'm leaving. Goodbye!"

"You can't be serious!" Joe stammered, looking to his wife for support as the front door to the house banged shut.

But Muffy was serious, and so was the Peace Corps. After several months of training, she was sent to the South Sea Islands, 2,000 miles south of Hawaii and 3,000 miles east of Australia. Or, to put it another way, Samoa was about as far from the Bloomfield Hills suburb of Detroit as she could get.

Muffy was dispatched to American Samoa. Its capital, Pago Pago (population 4,000), was an island paradise nestling under blue skies and rife with lush tropical forests, majestic mountains and friendly islanders. One good-natured native caught her eye the very first day she met him. His name was Talolo.

He worked, along with 1,000 other employees, processing tuna brought in by the international fishing fleet that operated in the Pacific. As part of her duties, Muffy was assigned to teach the islanders how to read and write, and Talolo was one of her students.

The two were chummy from the outset and thus, when Talolo made a special request, Muffy was happy to oblige. He handed her an old, beat-up looking book and said, "This book has been in my village for many years. Can you help me read it?"

Muffy was surprised to discover the volume to be none other than the Bible. She smiled at the thought of teaching a native Samoan about the story of the Jews. "Are you sure?" she asked.

Talolo was positive. And so they began, "In the beginning..." Talolo proved to be a good student and an even better friend. The two enjoyed exchanging ideas and comparing backgrounds and cultures. Their Bible-reading class became the high point of their days.

Throughout the weeks and months they studied together, Talolo neglected to mention one thing — he was in line to be a *matai*, a chief of his clan. This was a source of embarrassment to him when he compared his Samoan ancestors with the Israelites. After all, the Hebrews knew there was just one Creator, while thousands of years later, many, if not most, of his Samoan brothers still weren't convinced.

Every few months, Muffy would send her parents a postcard from Pago Pago. She told them all about her job. She told them about her shack. She told them about the weather, the scenery, the politics. Finally, she told them about Talolo.

"We're going to be married," she wrote at the bottom of

a card depicting dark, muscular Asiatic men at a tribal fire dance.

"She's going to do whaaaaat?!" her father raged, beginning what his wife knew to be an apoplectic fit. His wild eyes bulged out of their sockets. His normally ruddy face flared with anger.

"Now dear, remember your heart. I'm sure he's really very nice," Dorothy said, trying to remain as calm as her friends and acquaintances were when their children intermarried. "I bet Rabbi Sally..."

"I'm sure he's very nice," Joe mimicked. "He's also probably very... uh... uh... Polynesian — you know what I mean? How in heaven's name could she decide to marry a native? The guy probably runs around all day in a sombrero."

"Dear, I think you mean a sarong."

"Sarong, sombrero, serape — it's all the same. How in heaven's name can she do this to us? Imagine what the guys will say when I bring some dark-skinned, voodoo-practicing native into the Temple. Fellas, I want you to meet my new son-in-law — Tallulah! It sounds like the finale in a concert, 'Ta la la la...'

"'Mr. Tallulah,' they'll say, 'nice to meet you. My, that's a beautiful ring you have in your nose. And that spear, is it hand-made? And tell us about those little shrunken heads you wear around your neck. How did you manage to get that ping pong racket under your lip and the chicken bones in your hair?'

"Can you imagine? She can't be serious. Dorothy, *tell* me she's not serious. Tell me I'm dreaming."

But Joe's dream proved to be a full-blown nightmare. Late that night, Joe and Dorothy succeeded in getting their daughter to the Peace Corps phone in Pago Pago. It was a short phone call but very much to the point. "You get on a plane and get back here now!" roared Muffy's father. Muffy's mother was a bit more diplomatic. "Couldn't you take up painting again, or dancing instead?" her mother offered. "Your father and I miss you so much, and we could set you up in your own little garret somewhere in New York or London. Then we could come visit you on weekends. It would be wonderful!"

"I'm sorry, Mom. Talolo and I love each other. We're going to be married in a few weeks by the Island's administrator. I'm sure when you meet Talolo you'll love him just as much as I do."

"Love him!" Joe huffed. "I bet he doesn't even know how to play golf or the first thing about the stock market. Love him, my eye! What would we talk about? Sacrifices?"

"You know what Rabbi Sally said about loving all of mankind," Dorothy tried to soothe.

"If you quote that dimwit one more time..." Joe railed. "She'll never have the problem of having a primitive Neanderthal for a son-in-law. And anyways, she was only referring to fellow Jews who maintain our identical beliefs and economic status."

Dorothy replaced the receiver and began to cry bitter tears. And although the conversation was over, the story wasn't, thanks to a momentous moment — the moment that Mrs. Goldsmith met, or perhaps better expressed, was overpowered by a thunderous intensity known as Rebbetzin Hecht. The Rebbetzin had heard about the Goldsmiths' predicament over the Jewish Internet (Dorothy whispered her secret to Ethel who divulged it to Sadie the hairdresser who relayed it to Roberta who told it to Fran — in the presence of her daughter-in-law, who knew Rebbetzin Hecht) and the Rebbetzin wasted no time in suggesting, in her uniquely diplomatic way, what to do.

"I heard your daughter's about to marry a *sheigetz*," she

said with her typical tact. "I'm sure *you* don't want it, your *husband* doesn't want it, and the *Almighty* doesn't want it. So that just leaves your daughter — what's her name?"

"Muffy," Dorothy Goldsmith replied rather meekly.

"Muffy? What kind of a Jewish name is that? In Europe, we didn't know from Muffys. Of course, we didn't know from Pogo Pogo either. Anyhow, you listen to me, not Muffy. You want that your daughter should drop this *sheigetz* like a hot potato?"

"Well, yes."

"Okay, then the first thing you got to do is start lighting Shabbos candles."

"You must be mistaken. It's my daughter *Muffy* who has to leave her boyfriend, not *me*. So why do *I* have to light Shabbos candles?"

"Because you're her mother, and the *Zohar* says that a parent can still affect a child, even when they're apart. You go home and start lighting Shabbos candles, and then we'll engage in some other sure-fire methods."

That Friday night, Dorothy Goldsmith lit two Shabbos candles, just as Rebbetzin Hecht had ordered. The candlesticks she used had been given to her by her grandmother when she was wed more than thirty years ago. Each solid brass candlestick was contrived of two golden lions supporting the candle-holders. In the warm glow of the candlelight, Dorothy whispered a silent prayer that her daughter come to her senses, preferably before too many people learned what she intended to do.

Weeks passed and Muffy and Talolo were married in Samoa. Dorothy didn't know exactly how to respond. So she sent her daughter a pair of antique brass candlesticks, identical to the ones she was lighting at home.

Muffy was amused. "She probably expects me to become a *balabusta*, right here in Pago Pago.

Talolo was amazed. His big brown eyes grew as round as saucers, as he stared at the brass objects before him. "I've never seen anything so beautiful!"

Muffy and Talolo set up their house in a small village about an hour from Pago Pago. On weekends, they would visit Talolo's family in the coastal town of Viata several kilometers away. In celebration of their first visit, Talolo's family made a feast to honor his new bride.

In an *umu*, a stone oven about four feet around, Talolo's mother made a fire out of coconut shells and sticks. When it began blazing, she added rocks to absorb the heat. Then she threw in several freshly killed chickens, a young pig, about a half-dozen fish, yams and other vegetables. The whole concoction was wrapped in banana leaves then covered with the hot rocks and another blanket of banana leaves. A few hours later Talolo's mother served her guests this feast on a long plank table, along with generous helpings of melons, mangoes, papayas and coconut milk. The entire community was invited. At the height of the festivities, Talolo's mother arose, walked over to the blushing bride and said a few words in Samoan.

"What did she say?" Muffy whispered to her husband.

"She said, 'You came on an airplane thousands of miles just so you could be Talolo's wife. As a sign of honor and acceptance, I have given you the name "Lupe Lele," which means flying dove.'"

Muffy was very touched. She had always hoped for some sign of acceptance, but this was so sudden and sincere that her eyes welled with tears of pride and joy. Yet before Muffy could get used to her name or her mother-in-law, one of Talolo's four brothers stepped up.

Like Talolo, he was about five-foot-seven, with a slim muscular build and close-cropped black hair. Unlike Talolo, he wasn't smiling.

Once more, words were spoken in Samoan. By the tone of his voice, however, Muffy knew something was wrong. She hoped she hadn't committed a faux pas in some way. If she had, she hoped Talolo would apologize for her. Once again, she turned to him for a translation.

"My brother Sosimo has accused me of betraying our heritage. According to him, I am no longer fit to be a *matai*. If I do not forsake you, he will claim his right to my position."

"So give it to him."

"I can't."

"Why not?"

"I have to be dead first."

Back in Motown, Dorothy was lighting her Shabbos candles every Friday night without fail. After four weeks, she visited Rebbetzin Hecht with an unencouraging progress report.

"I see we haven't done enough," the Rebbetzin concluded gravely. "Obviously we have to strengthen the dosage. So, in addition to lighting Shabbos candles you have to take on another mitzvah. I know — you'll keep kosher."

"Keep kosher?" Dorothy gasped.

"Sure, it's a cinch. Just throw away all your dishes and buy new ones. What could be simpler?"

"Well, I don't know. My husband is pretty stubborn about certain things and filet mignon is one of them."

"Fill a *minyan*? Tell him that there's plenty of *minyanim* in Oak Park and in Southfield."

"Are you positive keeping kosher will help get our Muffy back?"

"Of course I'm positive. And stop calling her Muffy. You named her Miriam. So that's her name."

That night Dorothy spoke to her husband. "You know, Joe, I'm tired of the china we have. It's so boring. I'd like to change it."

"Are you serious? That stuff cost $150 a place setting."

"So? I'll find a worthy charity to donate it to."

"You're going to donate fine china to charity? You've got to be kidding! I'll tell you what, why don't we just invite the poor and homeless to have dinner here. It would be messy in the short run but cheaper in the long run."

Dorothy ignored him. "And as long as I'm getting a new set of dishes, I might as well get a new set of pots and pans to go with them."

"Sure, why not. I'm positive the same charity that's going to be serving its guests on fine china would just love a complete set of Le Cruset cookware to go with it! Why, it would be downright shameful to cook and fry in anything else!"

Dorothy did change her dishes. But changing Joe proved to be somewhat harder. "Whaddaya mean I can't have veal parmesan?"

"Joe, I told you. I decided to keep kosher..."

"KOSHER!!" Joe boomed so loudly, waves began crashing on the Great Lakes. "The last time I heard kosher mentioned was when Rabbi Sally proclaimed from the pulpit that California lettuce picked by Mexican migrants was unkosher. She knows from kosher like she knows from Yiddish!"

"Forget Rabbi Sally..."

"A pleasure!"

"It was Rebbetzin Hecht's idea. She assured me it would help us take care of the situation with Mu— I mean, Miriam and Talolo."

"Who are these people Hecht, Miriam, Ti La La. Can't life just go on being normal? Listen here, just give this Rebbetzin a contribution and tell her it's undemocratic to mix religion with the state of affairs. I'm sure she'll appreciate a donation much more than our keeping this kosher stuff."

Joe and Dorothy battled it out till the wee hours of the morning. "How come," Dorothy challenged, "you let me eat macrobiotics and go on the Pritikin Program, and dozens of other exotic diets, and now all of a sudden you're so negative about kosher?"

"Because if you want to eat seaweed, that's your *meshugaas*; keeping kosher means we're *all* crazy!"

"Saving our daughter is not crazy! I admit I don't know the Rebbetzin very well. And you may be right. She may only be after a contribution. But right now, she's the only one who is even interested in doing something about the situation. So I want to do whatever she says. We can always change our minds."

"Okay, okay. Only tell her to start working on Muffy and stop making demands on us!"

The Rebbetzin pursued her spiritual activities with unparalleled fervor. When she peeled potatoes, she recited Psalms; when she went shopping, she recited Psalms. And every syllable was uttered with one intention in mind: that Miriam wish to be wed only to a Jewish husband.

Back in Pago Pago, Lupe Lele (née Miriam a.k.a. Muffy) and Talolo lived an idyllic, bucolic life. They truly loved each other, and even more important, they liked each other. The days spent together seemed like hours; hours seemed like minutes. Muffy felt happier than she had ever felt before.

The daily reading lessons in the Bible inexplicably provided a spiritual satisfaction which bolstered their relationship. Indeed, the only blot on their picture-perfect existence was Sosimo. Enraged at what he felt was his brother's betrayal, Sosimo pitched a private battle against his brother and his foreign bride.

The first salvo was a dead chicken delivered to their door. Next was a collection of pig bones. Muffy was afraid to ask what these symbols meant, although she really had no doubt as to their intent.

"Can't you do something?" she asked. "I mean, can't we call the police?"

Talolo laughed bitterly. "There's only one thing for me to do."

"What's that?"

"Meet my brother in a fight... to the death."

After several months, Joe was accustomed to eating kosher food. He even began to brag about his wife's newfound religious zeal. "Yep, she's a real fanatic. If I bring home something that doesn't have one of those funny little marks on it, she does two things. First, she throws it out of the house. Then she throws *me* out of the house!"

At the same time, Rebbetzin Hecht was storming the gates of Heaven and cajoling her cronies to join her. Since Muffy still hadn't turned around, Rebbetzin Hecht concluded that it was again time to increase the dosage. The Rebbetzin picked up her phone and after the preliminary social amenities, got down to business. "Mrs. Goldsmith, I think it's time we take on another mitzvah."

"But Rebbetzin Hecht, we really have been doing all we can. Any more mitzvahs and my husband and I will both be *tzaddiks*."

"That may take a little more than additional *mitzvos*," Rebbetzin Hecht commented drily, "but regardless, since we haven't heard good news, we've got more work to do. I want your husband should stop working on Shabbos."

"Mrs. Hecht, you're going too far. My husband's work is his life. If he quit working on Shabbos, he would be miserable. Even worse, *I* would be miserable. Please, you have to understand."

"Mrs. Goldsmith, our Sages say that keeping the Sabbath is like keeping the entire Torah. We need that merit to help your daughter. But we have to start one step at a time. Staying home from work on our holy day is that step."

"Could you be the one to tell my husband?"

"Sure — what's to tell?"

That night, Joseph Goldsmith fought with all his might. But even thirty years in construction wars which had fllled his soul with confidence, esprit de corps and self-righteousness hadn't prepared him for the power and strength of one Rebbetzin Chaya Liba Hecht. In plain *mama loshen*, she told him who's who and what's what. She warned him and she scorned him, she yelled and she *kvelled*, she lied ("I'm telling you, it's gonna be easy and you're gonna love it!") and she cried. By the end of the evening, he felt like a quivering mass of jello.

"Look, Rebbetzin, I'll do what you want." he conceded wearily. "But if this doesn't work, I'm going to sue you for anything and everything my lawyers can come up with."

"Don't worry. It will work. I'm willing to bet your fortune on it! And there's just one more thing: Chanukah is coming up, so don't forget to light Chanukah lights. I want Mrs. Goldsmith to send a *menorah* to your daughter — I'm sure it will help.

In the lovely, picturesque, quaintly beautiful island of Western Samoa, the happy, smiling natives were getting ready for a fight to the death.

Sosimo prepared himself for weeks. Fueled by the mystique of ancient rite and muscles that were flexed to perfection, he formally announced his challenge. It wasn't his fault that the victim would be his own flesh and blood. That's just the way it was meant to be.

Talolo was much more philosophical about the impending tragedy. It was as if he were resigned to his date with death. One night, he turned to his wife and asked, "What do the Jews say about dying? Is there a place where your spirit goes?"

Muffy didn't know. She strained to find an answer, any kind of answer, in the recesses of her memory. The Rabbis in Temple Beth Ezra never talked about it. Wait! She remembered that they explained that Orthodoxy believes in an afterlife; but obviously TBE's Sunday school didn't ascribe much worth to that doctrine.

"What about fate?" Talolo pressed on. "Tell me what the Jews think about fate."

Muffy demurred again. "Look, I honestly don't know. But if you promise to go back with me to the United States, or anywhere away from here, and forget about fighting your brother, we'll find out together."

Talolo remained expressionless, "Even though I could hide from Sosimo, I can't hide from myself. Sosimo and I will fight. And what will be, will be."

Talolo and Muffy's grass hut was set back from the main road that led into Pago Pago. Usually, they would sit outside and watch the moon chase the clouds across the sky. But that night they remained inside in complete silence, exchanging wordless glances.

Talolo was very nervous. "It's quiet out. Way too quiet." He stepped cautiously outside, and was abruptly brought to a halt. There was a whizzing sound as a spear landed at his feet. Jumping back inside their hut, Talolo warned Muffy, "They've come to get me."

A stifled cry caught in Muffy's throat. Her island paradise wasn't supposed to be like this. She longed to take Talolo and run with him back to her parents in Detroit. There, as nauseating as life was, at least she knew what to expect.

Talolo stepped outside and spoke to the darkness. A few seconds later, she discerned that their tiny hut was surrounded by Samoan tribesmen. Each man carried a spear to match the daggers in his eyes.

Talolo returned to his hut one final time. "What did you say to them?" Muffy cried.

"I said that I would leave you and go with them, as long as they promise not to hurt you."

"You can't go! What if they kill you?"

"I have no choice. If I stay, then both of us will die."

"Can't we do something?"

"Yes, I can go with them. And you can ask your God for help."

Talolo was escorted to Viata by half a dozen tribesmen. No one spoke. There was nothing to say. Talolo knew what to expect. He didn't know how to get out of it. Strangely calm, he made his way on what he was sure would be his final walk through thick walls of wilderness, triple canopied jungle, mountains unfolding into higher mountains, ravines and gorges and fast-moving rivers and waterfalls and exotic butterflies and steep cliffs and smoky little hamlets and great valleys of bamboo and elephant grass. During the breaks in the bush he glanced down at the six-inch fishing knife at his side that gleamed in the darkness. For years this appurtenance had been used exclusively to gut tuna. Now it would be aimed at his own flesh and blood.

At Viata, the men and Talolo walked another half-mile into the jungle, to his family's sacred burial ground. When they reached the site, Talolo found more men waiting.

"Where is my brother?" he asked.

"I am here," Sosimo replied.

Talolo could barely see him in the shadows. "Sosimo," Talolo said in a loud voice for everyone to hear, "I ask you not to fight me. You are too young to die. Even though our ancestors did not permit a *matai* to marry out of the tribe, those days are over. It is a new world now."

Sosimo's answer was brief. "You are wrong. You wish to destroy our heritage through your actions; therefore, you are the one who must die!"

Like a leopard Sosimo leaped out of the dark and caught his brother off-guard. Both men fell in the dust and Talolo spotted a long, thin blade in Sosimo's hand. It veered closer and closer to his neck and the sweat pouring into his eyes obstructed his vision. Talolo was surprised at how strong his younger brother had become, surprised and more than a little scared. Sosimo drove his shoulder into his brother's chest, and switched his tactics to try and get enough leverage to thrust the knife into the soft fleshy area between Talolo's ribs.

Muffy was frantic, her nerves were frazzled. She didn't

know whether to stay or to run. Talolo's last words were more of a command than a request, but she didn't know how to fulfill them. She had never been taught how to pray, but she couldn't sit idly by as her husband fought for his life.

In a fit of despair, Muffy looked around the hut helplessly and her eyes finally fell upon the worn Bible which had served as their reading workbook. She picked up the frayed pages in her hands. She opened the book and, with tears in her eyes, began reading: "And they said to Moses, Was it for want of graves in Egypt that you brought us away to die in the wilderness?"

Muffy put the book down and started to cry. Between tears, she called out, "God, how could this happen? Please help!" Over and over again, she repeated her request.

But the answer she willed did not come. The walls of the tiny hut seemed to converge with the impact of impending tragedy. In desperation, she picked up her Bible again and continued reading. "What have You done to us taking us out of Egypt? Is this not the very thing we told You in Egypt, saying, 'Let us alone that we may serve the Egyptians. For it is better for us to serve the Egyptians than to die in the wilderness'?"

Again Muffy's face was flooded with tears. "Please forgive me God, for finding You, for calling out to You, only in my hour of need. I'll make it up to You, I swear it. Please, I'll do anything. Just save my husband!"

After her pledge, the answer was practically immediate. The next verse read, "Moses said to the people: Have no fear! Stand by and see the salvation which the Lord will work for you today; for the Egyptians whom you see today, you will never see again. The Lord will fight for you, and you shall hold your peace."

Muffy repeated those words over and over again, uttering, muttering, wishing and praying, "Let it be, oh Lord, let it be!" Emotionally spent, she finally fell asleep.

Sosimo's knife was only inches from Talolo's heart. As it crept closer in their wrestling, Talolo realized that he could no longer remain on the defensive. He had to attack. Talolo worked his left arm opposite his brother's right and grabbed his wrist so that his brother's knife was, for the moment, blocked. Then he moved his head closer to his brother's and bit Sosimo's ear.

"Yeowww!" Sosimo screamed.

Talolo used this instant of surprise to flip Sosimo over. Now Talolo was on top. Still holding his brother's wrist tightly, he started slamming it against a rock. He rammed it incessantly, pulverizing Sosimo's knuckles on the jagged stone. Talolo could feel warm blood flowing down his hand, but he was not out of danger. Sosimo was using his free hand to poke at Talolo's eyes. Talolo averted him like a cobra dodging a mongoose.

Sosimo tried desperately to gain the advantage; Talolo was equally determined to prevent him. Eventually, Sosimo's grip gave way and the knife slipped from his battered fingers. Talolo flung it deep into the night. Sosimo renewed his attack with ferocity, trying to secure Talolo's knife. He clawed with both hands in an iron grip around Talolo's wrist and began forcing the silver blade towards Talolo's throat. Every second it seemed tc inch closer.

Talolo was tired, aching to be free of the tribal struggle that raged within him and without. But he knew that to rest was to die. With his free hand, he pushed against Sosimo's forehead, bending his brother's neck back. Talolo had the advantage now and Sosimo knew it.

In a swift movement, Talolo maneuvered the knife up to

Sosimo's neck. With one quick slice it would be over.

"Kill me!" his brother hissed. "It is your right."

Talolo looked into his brother's bulging eyes. "By your bravery, you deserve to be a *matai*. By my cowardice, I do not," and with that he threw his knife into the jungle.

Both men deliberately disentangled themselves from one another's grasp. Each was heaving violently. Each mistrusted the other.

"You know what this means," Sosimo said, gasping for breath.

"Yes," Talolo replied. "You are the new *matai*."

It took Talolo several hours to shuffle back to Pago Pago. At the outskirts of the city he realized that his strength was sapped and to trudge just one more step might be fatal. Thus he collapsed on the spot and awoke several hours later.

Talolo's loving wife was worried sick. When she saw him finally stagger up the steps, she wasn't sure if it was Talolo or his ghost. Perhaps Talolo also wasn't certain, but Muffy clarified matters by crying, "You're alive! Thank God, you're alive!"

The next eight days Talolo spent resting and recovering, but by the fifth day he felt up to resuming their Bible readings. By this time, however, they both felt that their book was no longer just an English primer. After rereading the verses which Muffy had recited they understood that they had been saved by a Force much higher than themselves.

One week later, Talolo announced, "Now that I am well we must prepare to leave Samoa for good."

"To where?"

"I simply don't know, but we must get ready."

As they prepared themselves for their departure they no longer looked at Pago Pago as Paradise, but as a rest stop on their way to... where, they did not know.

Muffy assumed that Talolo would find a job on a fishing vessel working out of Japan or perhaps Singapore. She was certain that they would either end up in the Far East or join the 20,000 other Samoans living on Hawaii. But she was off by a hemisphere.

One day, out of the blue (sea or sky, by which overseas mail is delivered), Muffy received a package from her mother.

"What is it?" Talolo asked, holding it upside down and inspecting it from all angles.

"It's a Chanukah *menorah*. Jews are supposed to light Chanukah candles to remember, I think, the victory over the Greeks."

Muffy explained the story of Chanukah to the best of her recollection, and Talolo was duly impressed. He saw personal analogy in the victory of light over might and felt that commemoration by lighting candles was especially fitting.

With no intention of waxing profound, Talolo declared, "This *menorah* is not just a gift from your parents; it is a sign from Above."

"A sign?" Muffy asked, not following her husband's drift.

"Yes, here is the sign I've been waiting for. Now we know where we're headed."

Muffy begged Talolo to explain himself.

"Do you remember the verses you came across the night of my battle?"

"I'll never forget them."

"Of how the Lord effected miracles to lead the Jews out of Egypt in order to bring them to their homeland?"

"Yes, yes," Muffy said, nodding her head, "but how did you see all of this in the *menorah*?"

"Just look: all the branches stem from the source. Now do you see? It's time to go home."

AUTHOR'S NOTE: They did, and they have children enrolled in yeshivah, a source of tremendous pride for their now fully observant grandparents — on their mother's side, that is.

Right or Dead Wrong

...וַיְהִי קֹלֹת וּבְרָקִים וְעָנָן כָּבֵד עַל הָהָר וְקֹל שֹׁפָר חָזָק מְאֹד וַיֶּחֱרַד כָּל הָעָם אֲשֶׁר בַּמַּחֲנֶה.

[The day the Torah was given,] "...there was thunder and lightning, a heavy cloud on the mountain, and an extremely loud blast of a ram's horn; all the people in the camp trembled."

(Shemos 19:16)

The Midrash comments:

> *When the Lord gave the Torah, no bird twittered, no fowl flew, no ox lowed. None of the ofanim stirred a wing, and the serafim did not say, "Holy, holy..."* (Yeshayahu *6:3). The sea did not roar, and creatures spoke not. The entire world was hushed into breathless silence, and God's voice went forth.*

At the very zenith of this drama, an entire nation heard God declare, "You shall not commit murder." Having reached such a lofty spiritual level, did the Jewish people really need to be reminded of something so basic? Was this command not a slight and an undeserved insult?

Rabbi **Isaac Sher** explains that the Torah embraces every facet of life. If one veers from the Torah path, there is no telling where he may end up. If the commandments are neglected and the Torah way of life abandoned, the person may, in the end, even come to commit murder!

Moshe Shechter stood on the cold, deserted subway platform, trembling like a man with a raging fever. An unprepossessing figure in black hat and dark suit, he would not normally have earned a second glance from any passersby, but the swollen, red-rimmed eyes behind his glasses and the anguished expression that contorted his mild features caused even the jaded Transit Authority policeman to wonder.

Moshe wasn't the average *avrech*. Even as early as elementary school he had shown a lot of promise. His rebbes had labeled him an *illui* and a *masmid*, designations which continued to be applied to the outstanding *talmid chacham* he had become. He gave a *shiur* in his *kollel* and his only desire in life was to study Torah and raise his children properly. Blessed with a wonderful wife, a beautiful family and an adequate livelihood, Moshe's world was complete. Until last week.

The patrolman continued to stare but Moshe was too preoccupied to notice. In his mind he sat at Channie's hospital bed looking down at his beautiful baby's angelic face, with its golden frame of tight curls, soft rosy cheeks, and shining blue eyes.

"They're wrong!" he told himself, but he was far too intelligent to indulge in self-deception. He had seen the x-rays himself and there was no mistake. Channie's wheezing and coughing, which had not responded to weeks of conventional treatment, had been finally diagnosed as an obstruction in her lung, a growth which was impairing her breathing and threatening her life.

The doctors at Mount Sinai had delivered the news gently, but even with all their years of experience, could not hide their concern. They too were enchanted by little Channie's cherubic beauty and wished they could sound more optimistic.

Moshe would gladly have changed places with his child, plucked the vile growth from her chest and implanted it in his own, anything to spare her suffering. The surgery was yet to be scheduled and in the meantime he spent long days and sleepless nights at his daughter's bedside, anxiously watching her tiny chest rise and fall with each labored breath; uttering *Tehillim* with a fervor he'd never known before; playing silly games to entertain her; and holding back the tears. In a few weeks' time, the cold steel of the surgeon's scalpel would slice through his baby's flesh — the very thought was like a physical blow. And only afterward would the pathology lab determine the nature of the growth.

"If only it will be benign," Moshe kept saying to himself between the silent prayers he sobbed by heart.

At midnight he was unexpectedly relieved by another family member, who had to physically drag him away from Channie's bed. He stepped outside the hospital, so absorbed in his problem that he found it hard to relate to a city that continued to function as if nothing had happened.

Moshe tried to stop a taxi to take him home to Brooklyn, but the cabs sped by like yellow bullets. After twenty minutes without success, he walked towards the subway station, too groggy to remember that few sane people ride the subways at that hour.

Having to wait for a train that refused to come was more than Moshe's frazzled nerves could handle. His uncontrollable trembling increased until he imagined the entire platform was shaking beneath his feet, but it was only the first rumblings of the subway train, arriving at last.

As the train emerged from the dark tunnel and began its screeching halt that rose steadily in pitch before reaching its ear-splitting crescendo, Moshe's mouth opened involuntarily and released a long-suppressed scream.

There were only three other passengers in the car at that hour: two Blacks engrossed in changing the cassette on their enormous "Ghetto Blaster" at one end, and a reeking derelict at the other. To walk through to the next car would have required an effort beyond Moshe's present ability, so he chose a seat near the drunkard, distancing himself as much as possible from the bone-jarring noise that passed for music.

Even when the Black youths finally got off, Moshe could not muster the will to move from his seat. His eyes roamed unseeing over the graffiti-adorned subway posters, the color-coded subway map, the vandalized fire extinguisher, and returned to his traveling companion.

The man was large-framed but his body was cadaverous, and he was obviously inebriated. In his hand was a brown paper bag that outlined a whiskey bottle. Razor lacerations crisscrossed his gray-tinged face and his deepset eyes, partially hidden below drooping lids, were moist and bloodshot. The stench that rose from his filthy clothes intensified as he raised the bottle to his lips and dribbled cheap rotgut down his shirt.

When the man's gaze fell upon him and remained there, Moshe became frightened. He felt faint; the tension of the past week, the fatigue coupled with fear made his stomach churn. He needed air. He turned to the grime-sealed windows, but he knew there was no hope of raising one without a crowbar. Suddenly the fetid smell grew stronger and closer.

Moshe looked around and discovered that the drunkard had arisen from his seat and was standing over him, staring intently into his face.

Moshe realized he had to escape, perhaps try to ring the alarm bell or pull the emergency brake. But the man was too close, much too close. Moshe's blood froze in his veins and his heart pounded in his chest. The derelict raised his arm threateningly and heaved his empty bottle to the far side of the car, where it smashed against a bench. Moshe drew back from the drunk's foul breath and rotting teeth and tried to avoid his glance.

"You've grown a little bit but you're still the same skinny midget. Don't you recognize me, Professor?"

Moshe recoiled as if struck by a live wire. "Impossible," he stammered, "it's impossible! Binyamin Greenbaum?! How can it be? What has happened to you?"

Before Binyamin could answer, the train conductor announced: "West Fourth Street."

"I, I have to change trains here," Moshe said, making his way towards the exit.

"Me, too," said Binyamin, not taking his eyes off Moshe. The doors snapped open and they disembarked.

Moshe crossed over to the "Downtown" track and sat down on a bench to wait for the Brooklyn-bound IRT. To his astonishment, Binyamin took the seat alongside him. Moshe found it difficult to speak — what could he say? He couldn't believe that this repulsive individual had once been his classmate.

"Binyamin, how did this happen? How could you have fallen so far from our days in yeshivah?"

"The name is *Benjy*, Professor, Benjy *Green*. And I'm not a young yeshivah *bochur* anymore, or hadn't you noticed? Look at me, Professor. Look at my hands." He lifted his trembling fingers to the light. "You see that? That's what 'junk' does to you."

"What? Drugs too?" Shechter exclaimed in a stricken voice.

"Yes, Professor. Soon I'll need another 'fix' and then I'll take your money just as fast as I'd swipe an old lady's handbag to get what I need."

"No! Benjy, you must let me help you!"

"It's too late. No one can help me now."

"Benjy, I beg of you. Go to a drug rehabilitation center. I'll come as soon as I can. As soon as..." he stopped abruptly, remembering why he couldn't come now. Tears welled up in his eyes and spilled down his cheeks. Benjy continued to stare at him blankly.

"Benjy," begged Moshe, "Binyamin, it is *I* who needs help — *your* help. I have faith in you. You must promise me that you will stop this, promise you will go to a rehabilitation center, please PROMISE! You must promise me, for perhaps in the merit of this my daughter will be spared..." He sobbed as he poured his heart out and told Binyamin about Channie's tumor and the operation she would need. But Benjy sank back into his drunken stupor and closed his ears to the sound.

A train was approaching. Moshe shook him and said, "Where can I get in touch with you?"

"Nowhere," he mumbled. "Well, I guess you could leave a message with my mother. I give her a call every couple of months. At our old house on Ninth Avenue." Moshe quickly scribbled his own phone number on a scrap of newspaper.

"Please, Binyamin, don't let me down. Call me — I beg of you!" Moshe hurried onto the train and looked through the windows at the huddled form of a ruined man.

The courtyard of the Beis Yosef Yeshivah in Boro Park was in a commotion. The students were conferring secretly in every corner of the school, for something terrible had happened: during recess one of the boys had sneaked into the teachers' room and had stolen Rabbi Yaggid's gradebook!

Yaggid knew that the culprit was from the eighth grade but he didn't know who; everyone had his suspicions. The principal was outraged and assembled the class, informing them in no uncertain terms that if they didn't tell him by the end of recess who had stolen the gradebook, they could forget about the class trip to Washington, D.C.

The students were torn: they subscribed to the unwritten code of mutual help which made snitching on a classmate a crime akin to manslaughter. But failure to report the felon meant jeopardizing the trip to Washington, the highlight of the school year. There was also the small matter of conscience, of telling the truth. What would they do?

Moshe Shechter was always considered the best pupil of the class. Short in stature and with an unathletic physique, he was a serious boy who devoted himself to learning. Intent on his studies, he never joined the other boys for recess in the schoolyard, and today was no different. The events of the morning, therefore, were slow in penetrating his thoughts.

"*Nu*, Professor, so what do you say?" came the taunting voice. Moshe lifted his head from his Gemara and saw the class low-lifes standing in front of his desk, led by the biggest bully of all — Binyamin Greenbaum. "*Nu*, Professor, say something already!" and they all burst out in raucous laughter.

Moshe turned red. He didn't know what they wanted from him. It wasn't the first time they had made fun of him, and for the life of him he couldn't figure out why they did. Greenbaum, their brawny leader, obviously had something against him.

Moshe thought about this a lot. What had he ever done

to Greenbaum that he should pick on him so? He was half Binyamin's size, so he certainly couldn't be a threat to him.

Yet Greenbaum was always throwing a ball or a yo-yo at him and then pretending it was an accident. He even ambushed Moshe several times on the way home from school, sometimes to torment him, sometimes to beat him up.

But Moshe held his peace. He found different routes to walk home, which wasn't easy since they lived on the same street.

Beis Yosef never had any *nachas* from Binyamin Greenbaum. He came from a broken home and barely was eligible for promotion from one grade to the next.

Everyone wanted to throw him out of the yeshivah, but the principal justified keeping him on by saying, "I cannot bear responsibility for this child's future if he is forced to leave grade school. Who knows what will become of him?"

The bell rang and recess was over. As usual Moshe didn't even bother answering Greenbaum, although he was now fairly certain who had stolen the gradebook.

The principal entered the classroom and fear gripped the pupils. "This is your last chance! I expect the person responsible to stand up like a man and confess." The room was charged with tension. Students turned to stare at Greenbaum who had his own gaze pointedly fixed on the ceiling. "They can all rot," he thought to himself, "I'm not telling..."

Five minutes passed and the principal bellowed: "Well?" The classroom was utterly silent. Suddenly, scrawny Moshe Shechter, the teacher's pet, rose and said in a quavering voice: "I am the one." Jaws dropped in amazement and disbelief. The principal muttered, "It's impossible, impossible!" "I did it," Moshe repeated, his voice clearer now. "The others need not suffer because of me and miss their trip. I am to blame."

That night Moshe walked home late. Only one streetlight was burning on the whole long block. Suddenly, he heard footsteps behind him — it was that awful bully Greenbaum. His heart thumped loudly. There was no one on the street to help him.

Moshe started to walk quickly but the footsteps behind him quickened too. They got closer and closer. Moshe started to run but Greenbaum was faster and stronger.

"Professor," Binyamin called as he grabbed him by the shoulder and spun him around. Moshe was in a panic, too frightened to look up from the ground. Greenbaum forced his chin upward until their eyes met.

"Professor, I just wanted to say thank you," and he vanished into the darkness.

At dawn Benjy Green awoke. His whole body ached, and at first he couldn't remember where he was or how he had gotten there. And then memory came flooding back in a rush. Benjy sat up on the bench. There were few people on the street and they all kept their distance. He knew why, but he couldn't care. He was used to it.

"So, the Professor thinks he can help me, huh?" then Moshe's strange words came back to him: "It is *I* who needs help... I have faith in you... my daughter will be spared." The shaking started again.

"Alright!" he said aloud, deciding at last. "Where is that scrap of paper with his number?" He rummaged through his clothes. Where was it?

He dug nervously into every pocket, searching as if his life depended upon it. Deep down he knew that this phone number was his last chance, his only remaining link with the real, normal world he had abandoned so long ago.

"Oy," he groaned in despair. "What have I come to since my days in Beis Yosef? I'm nothing. An addict, a drunken bum, a sub-human creature people cross the street to avoid." He sobbed and rocked back and forth on the bench, arms crossed tightly against his stomach to quell the sickening tremors.

Suddenly he felt the scrap of paper. It seemed to galvanize him. He dug in his pockets frantically and found a solitary coin and began to search the lonely street for a phone-booth. He dialed with quivering fingers, not even waiting to hear the voice at the other end. Moshe was just leaving for the hospital when the phone rang.

"Professor? This is Benjy. I..." His voice faltered.

"Yes, my friend?" Moshe urged.

"Friend," thought Benjy. When was the last time someone had called him "friend?"

"I'm taking your advice and going to a drug center. I tried once before, but it was murder, believe me, and I swore I'd never go back. This time I'm doing it for your little girl." Benjy hung up.

Moshe couldn't believe his ears. Binyamin Greenbaum had sunk to the lowest depths of depravity, yet he was willing to admit himself to the rehabilitation center for Channie's sake, a little girl he had never even met. But where was he? Why did he hang up? Moshe had no time to do anything about it — he had to get to the hospital.

After Channie fell asleep, Moshe slipped out of the room and began an exhaustive telephone search to locate Benjy. He spent fruitless hours talking to operators and thumbing through all the boroughs' directories. He was at his wits' end.

At last a clerk from the City Commission on Drug Rehabilitation remembered something: "Wait just a minute," she said, "there is one more place — the Waverly Center. They take only the most critical cases there — the 'goners.'" Moshe called and quickly verified that Benjy had been admitted that morning. He grabbed a taxi to the Center.

Moshe introduced himself as a friend of Green's and said that he was prepared to do anything he could to help. But the counselors were very cautious. "This is a most severe case. He's hopelessly addicted. Even if he can make it here, there's no guarantee he'll make it on the outside. There are serious complications, too. Try calling in about a week..."

When Moshe called again he asked if he could come by. "There's really no point in coming now," the attendant advised. "You can't imagine what he's going through and he still hasn't gotten over the worst of it. The man is in really bad shape. But he's aware of your involvement — and that's what's keeping him going. Don't come now, it's too early. He's got to do this on his own — no one else can do it for him."

A few days later, little Channie underwent surgery. The Shechters were on tenterhooks waiting for word from the doctor. They prayed, and cried, and waited. At last the surgeon emerged from the operating room with a smile on his face and the magic words on his lips: "It was benign. She's going to be all right."

Moshe phoned the Waverly Center and this time a doctor came on the line. "Are you next of kin?" he asked.

"No," Moshe replied, "just a friend."

"In that case, you must be the 'Professor.' Benjy says he owes his life to you. But I have to tell you, Benjy is a very sick man. There's extensive liver damage and his heart's not too strong either. Can't say how long he's got — even if he does kick his drug habit." Moshe was stunned.

"When can I visit him?" The doctor suggested he wait a little longer and assured Moshe he would convey his message to Green.

Five weeks after he was admitted to the Center, Benjy was able to leave for a few hours by himself. He remembered with a smile the telephone conversation he'd had the night before: the Professor had related that Channie was recuperating rapidly and thanked Benjy — profusely! — for the role he had played in her recovery. Benjy promised to visit after a stop at his mother's place. It would be his first real "social call" since — he couldn't remember when.

It was bitter cold outside and winds gusted all around him in a whir. Benjy took several deep breaths of fresh air before descending the staircase to the subway. As he passed a vending machine, he caught sight of his reflection in the streaked mirror. He almost didn't recognize himself. He not only felt like a new man, he looked like one.

The Center had given him fresh clothing, and he had shaved carefully and combed his newly-trimmed hair. His mother would be pleased, he thought, and then he started to shiver with apprehension at this first contact with humanity outside the Center. He needed a drink. He bought a candybar instead and boarded the waiting train.

At one of the stations, a woman got on and sat on the bench facing his. She opened her pocketbook, removed her wallet to check the contents, and replaced it. This commonplace act triggered a reflex in Benjy's brain that made him forget where he was coming from and where he was headed. "One quick snatch and it's mine," he thought.

The train moved on and the woman, along with many of the other passengers, dozed off. She released her grip on the purse in her lap; Benjy waited for the right moment.

Just then the lights went out and the darkened train came to a halt. "A blackout," one passenger sighed. "Who knows how long we'll be stuck here."

Benjy moved cautiously. Soon the purse would be his and no one would be the wiser. But the shaking in his hands began to act up again; they refused to cooperate. "It'll pass in a second," he told himself, and then he heard something strange that made his entire body quake.

"Hey! What's that noise? Who's crying?" But the crying he heard came from within his soul. "What's the matter with me?" He was drenched with sweat and the sound of weeping grew louder. "It's not me," he gasped, "it's *to* me! It's the Professor!"

"You promised me... In your merit Channie was saved... you promised me you wouldn't steal... you promised to change... you promised me..."

Benjy's head spun; he felt faint. He leaned back against the bench and tried to regain control of himself. "Get out of here, Professor!" he screamed in his heart. "Leave me alone. It's hard! It's so hard — I can't promise! The money's right here. I need it! No..."

The electricity in the train returned. The second it flickered on Benjy saw a pickpocket's nimble fingers dive into the lady's purse and remove her wallet. The blood rushed to his head. He hurled himself at the thief and shouted:

"Don't take it! I promised him, DO YOU HEAR ME? If *I* didn't steal it, neither will you! I promised. I kept my word!"

But the mugger wasn't impressed with the ravings of a madman. He threw a punch at Benjy's face, jabbed an elbow into his ribs, and Benjy dropped to the floor. His weakened heart in a wasted body couldn't withstand the injury.

Moshe waited and waited for Benjy. After three hours of tense anxiety, he called the Waverly and was told only that Benjy Green had left in the morning , saying he was headed for "the Professor."

By mid-afternoon Shechter could contain his fears no

longer. Could Benjy still be at his mother's? He hurried out and headed for the address on Ninth Avenue.

At the steps of the brownstone, a group of people had gathered; the scene made Moshe's heart skip a beat. "Did something happen?" he asked with trepidation. "That poor woman," responded a neighbor. "They just told her that her son was killed." Another man joined in: "And did you hear what the police say? He was trying to save some lady from a mugger!"

"What?!" Moshe exclaimed incredulously. "But he was so weak!" Everyone turned towards him, wondering how he was involved.

"That's exactly what they said," the neighbor continued. "As soon as the lights went back on in the train he jumped like a lunatic at the other guy and yelled: 'Don't steal! *I* didn't steal. I promised!' Maybe you know what he was talking about, huh, Mister?"

A few months after Channie's operation the Shechters had a son. Despite all their questioning, no one could pry out of Moshe his reason for giving the baby a name foreign to the family: Binyamin Chaim.

Moshe would only say: "I am paying back a debt, for a promise that was kept."

With All Your Being

...וְהִגִּישׁוֹ אֶל הַדֶּלֶת אוֹ אֶל הַמְּזוּזָה וְרָצַע אֲדֹנָיו אֶת אָזְנוֹ בַּמַּרְצֵעַ וַעֲבָדוֹ לְעֹלָם.

[If a Hebrew slave refuses emancipation, the Torah instructs,] ...[his master] shall stand him next to the door or doorpost; his master shall pierce [the slave's] ear with an awl, and he shall serve [his master] forever."

(Shemos 21:6)

The Midrash comments:

> *... [A] gentile slave who loses a tooth or an eye is freed. "For Cham...saw the nakedness of his father [and] told his two brothers..." (*Bereshis *9:22); consequently, he was cursed with slavery. A slave sustaining an injury similar to that which brought about Cham's downfall — i.e., to his eyes or his teeth — shall therefore be freed.*

From this, Rabbi **Chaim Shmuelevitz** deduces that the organs of the body are punished for the sins they commit. The Jewish servant's ear is pierced, for it ignores what it heard at Mount Sinai: that the children of Israel are to be God's slaves, no one else's.

If you ask most Americans when the Civil War took place, chances are they'll scratch their heads, jog their memories from elementary school, and reply, "around 1860." But another civil war occurred one hundred years later. This one was fought at home *and* thousands of miles away. It divided generations, families, and friends. It cost 50,000 American lives and millions upon millions of dollars. It was Viet Nam.

To anyone who lived through it, the Viet Nam era was an unforgettable clash of cultures: the traditional Buddhist mentality of Viet Nam vs. the capitalist interests of France and America. Hawks vs. doves. Old vs. young.

By 1967, more than 325,000 American soldiers were stationed in Viet Nam, participating in the world's first TV war. It was a bloody show. Every night, Americans sat in the comfort of their living rooms and watched their sons give their lives to save another nation's honor. Almost thirty boys a day were killed in the line of duty, with hundreds more wounded. In fact, the U.S. Army suffered more casualties each week than the South Vietnamese Army it was supposed to be helping! Nearly 400 U.S. planes had been downed by 1967. And America had six years of combat still ahead of her, in a conflict that was to last 18 months longer than World War II.

For boys over the age of 18, 1967 was a time of choices: they could dodge the draft by seeking refuge in Canada or Sweden; they could enlist in the Army, Navy, or Air Force and hope to get a safe assignment; they could sign up for the National Guard and stay stateside; they could declare themselves conscientious objectors and sit out the war behind bars; they could apply for a Divinity student deferment; or they could risk being drafted. Each carried implications that could change, and in some cases end, the chooser's life.

Jeffrey Gross was born in 1949. January 28th, to be exact. And when the great draft lottery was held eighteen years later, Jeff's number came up. Literally. It was 73. According to the Selective Service System, if your number was under 140, you could expect to be drafted. And so for Jeffrey Gross, the choice had to be made, and soon.

Complicating his decision was the fact that he had been accepted to medical school. If he was really serious about becoming a doctor, he couldn't fool around with his future by opting for either a C.O. deferment or a one-way trip to Canada.

So Jeff decided that the best way to beat the draft was to enlist under the Berry plan, which would keep him out of the Army's clutches until he finished med school. "At least this way I know who's going to be paying for my education," he told his parents, "my dear old Uncle Sam."

Jeffrey spent the next few years at Ohio State medical school. While he was only moderately religious, every day Jeff Gross faithfully whispered devout prayers for the war to end before he went on active duty.

But it didn't. The U.S. was becoming more and more embroiled, the action was hotter than ever, and the Viet Cong were spilling American blood like water. Medical personnel were especially vital to the war effort. After all, they were the ones who sewed, patched up, operated, and cured the wounded so they could go out and get shot up again. If you were unlucky enough to be sent into the field as a paramedic, statistic-based rumor had it that you would last three days.

Dr. Jeffrey Gross had not only heard the rumors, he had seen the facts. From his base at Fort Huachuca, Arizona, he examined hundreds of soldiers who had made it back alive — although not necessarily in one piece — before their discharge. For some it was the loss of an eye or an arm that destroyed their morale. For others, it was the loss of a friend.

Jeff knew what the future held in store. And he pulled every string, performed every favor, and paid off every officer he could to avoid it.

For the moment, luck was with him. When his overseas assignment came, he didn't go to Hue (it didn't exist anymore; as the officer in charge stated at the time, "We had to destroy Hue to save it."), Da Nang or My Lai. He didn't even go to Tan Son Nhut, the huge air base that served as the first stop for thousands of American troops. He was sent to Heidelberg, Germany.

In Heidelberg, Dr. Gross' practice revolved around NATO more than 'Nam. Contrary to popular belief, the U.S. still maintained a hefty military presence in Europe. Despite the fact that America was bogged down in war, her commitment to her NATO allies had to be kept. And Jeffrey Gross was only too happy to help.

Most of his days were spent taking care of the accidental cases of broken arms and incidental cases of viruses. "It's not bad," he wrote his parents, "as long as I forget it's Germany."

Throughout his fledgling medical career, Jeff tried to circumcise newborns whenever possible — even though they weren't Jewish — figuring that it was good practice for when the mitzvah of *milah* would present itself. As an obstetrics resident at Ohio State, he had had the opportunity to perform hundreds of circumcisions. "Do the circ, jerk," the third-year residents would command the lowly interns, but years after his internship, Jeff was still glad to be the "jerk."

Once when Jeff was stationed briefly at Fort Benning, outside Savannah, in "Joja," young Captain Mark Meyers had a special request. "Dr. Gross, would you be willing to circumcise my son according to Jewish law?"

This was the first time Jeff had ever been asked to do a traditional bris. "I don't know much about it," he replied honestly.

"Well, you've got eight days to learn," Captain Meyers grinned.

Jeff waded through the literature, but all he found was one article in a 1951 *New England Journal of Medicine* and another in a 1962 copy of *Clinical Pediatrics*. Both left a lot to be desired. So, in the finest military tradition, he decided to "be all that he could be" and find a *mohel*. Fortunately, he didn't have far to look.

For over twenty years, Reb Yosef Samuels had performed *brisim* for the Jewish community of Atlanta. Reb Yosef introduced the young doctor to the intricacies of *priyah* and *metzitzah, hatafas dam*, and much more.

Patiently and painstakingly, he went over the *halachos* of *bris milah*, explaining when the bris may be performed on Shabbos and when it must be postponed. But in his tutorials, Reb Yosef did more than just teach the laws; he also conveyed the significance of *milah* as an affirmation of Abraham's ancient covenant and a guarantee of the redemption of the Jewish People.

Exposure to the sagacious *mohel* and the time-honored, Biblical rite catalyzed Jeff's dormant religious upbringing, strengthening his commitment to Judaism and to the performance of *bris milah*. With Reb Yosef's coaching and his own estimable medical skills, he became a first-rate *mohel*, except for one flaw: he wasn't completely observant. Thus, Rabbi Samuels made him promise to use his instruments and acumen only on Jewish children, and only where no Orthodox *mohel* was available.

Jeffrey Gross pledged his agreement. He even arranged for Reb Yosef to join him at Fort Benning for the bris of Captain Meyers' son. In the next three years, he performed several *brisim*, mainly for the sons of officers stationed overseas.

But little did Jeff know that his pact with Reb Yosef would soon be tested. It all started with a phone call from Rabbi Steven Arnold, the Jewish chaplain assigned to Jeff's division.

"Dr. Gross, you are known as the best *mohel* in USAEUR, certainly at the 130th Station hospital. I know that since your arrival in Heidelberg you have been anxious to perform *brisim* on Jewish babies, so let me hand you the biggest 'assignment' of your career: Iron Mike's wife had a boy last Wednesday in Weisbaden."

"Iron Mike Smithson?"

"The one and only."

"I didn't know he was Jewish."

Some men are born to be soldiers. Iron Mike Smithson must have had a pre-natal head-start even on them. Everything about the man said "military" in capital letters.

Iron Mike had been first in his class at West Point. He served two tours of duty in Viet Nam, receiving so many medals and ribbons that he didn't have room for them all on his dress uniform, despite the dimensions of his colossal chest.

Jeff thought about it. "I suppose I can perform the bris, but I'll have to see if I can get leave from the hospital to travel to Weisbaden."

"Oh, that won't be a problem."

"Why are you so sure?"

"Because Colonel Smithson's father-in-law happens to be the CINC-AT."

"The Commander-in-Chief, Atlantic Forces?"

"That's right."

Between Iron Mike and the CINC-AT, Jeffrey Gross was momentarily stunned. So much so that he forgot to ask the most critical question regarding *milah*.

"I suggest you brush up your technique," the chaplain continued. "You're going to have some very important guests looking over your shoulder."

Jeffrey Gross wasn't the kind of person to get nervous. But he was very much aware of his "audience." One false move or inopportune remark could result in his being transferred from the cool corridors of the military hospital in Heidelberg to the hot, deadly jungles of Viet Nam.

The five days between Chaplain Arnold's call and Jeff's appointment passed all too quickly. That Monday, he was taken by MPs to the maternity ward in Weisbaden to examine the baby. Still recovering from her caesarean section, Mrs. Smithson wasn't available for the usual pre-bris consult.

On Wednesday, Jeff arose earlier than usual. He mentally went through the procedure, checked his medical bag, reviewed his uniform — which was noticeably lacking in decorations of any kind — and uttered a silent prayer to Heaven (and his mentor, Reb Yosef) that all should go well.

As Dr. Gross' jeep pulled up outside the medical center in Weisbaden, he saw row after row of staff cars from various divisions of the American Army and its NATO allies. He also noticed private cars, no doubt carrying American politicians and maybe even a reporter or two.

"This must be some party!" Jeff remarked to the MP who drove him. "I just hope the guest of honor doesn't make a scene."

Inside, the waiting room on the second floor had been cleared to make way for fifty guests. An array of delicacies stretched from one end of the room to the other. Jeff could see cakes, fish, *hors d'oeuvres* and liquor. At the far end, he could also see Iron Mike Smithson and his patriarchal-looking father-in-law pumping hands and bearhugging the brass.

Like radar, Chaplain Arnold zeroed in on the young doctor and quickly escorted him to where the colonel and CINC-AT were standing.

"Gentlemen," Rabbi Arnold addressed his two superior officers, "allow me to introduce you to the man of the hour,

Dr. Jeffrey Gross."

Jeff automatically began to salute, but shifted swiftly to accept Iron Mike's outstretched hand. In a second, the bone-crusher's set of pincers had bonded Jeff's five fingers into a single flipper. He hoped the damage would wear off before he had to operate.

"Doctor, I hope your hand is steadier than mine at this point. I think I would rather face a full division of Viet Cong than that knife of yours."

Jeff managed a weak smile, which was rather difficult since he was still reeling from the handshake. He desperately tried to think of something clever and witty to say, but he was too much in awe of the myth surrounding the man and too much in agony over the pain surrounding his knuckles. Finally he said, "I'm sure you won't feel a thing."

Both Colonel Smithson and his father-in-law laughed heartily. "How long have you been performing these circumcisions, son?" asked CINC-AT, an immaculately attired man in his early sixties with a shock of gray hair and a fatherly manner that put Jeff at ease.

"About four years, sir," Jeff replied, his eyes drifting down to the commander's nametag, which read: "DeMartino." DeMartino! Suddenly, bells and whistles, alarms and sirens, horns and Klaxons, and tocsins and flashing lights went off in his head. "Oh, my gosh!" he thought. "I forgot to find out whether or not the kid's Jewish!"

Jeff began to panic. His mind raced with the speed of an SST: "If the baby's not Jewish, I can't do the circumcision. If I don't do the circumcision, I'll embarrass both Iron Mike and his five-star father-in-law. If I embarrass them, I'll be handed my marching papers to Viet Nam — if I don't get court-martialled and sent to the brig for insubordination first."

Finally, he got hold of his rampaging thoughts. "Before you freak out, find out," his inner self admonished.

Casually, almost too casually, Jeffrey asked CINC-AT, "Sir, may I have your daughter's name for the circumcision prayer?"

"Her name? Why, it's Maria."

"I see. Maria. And she hasn't converted to Judaism by any chance, has she?"

"No-o, not that I'm aware of."

Fortunately, Iron Mike had been drawn into a half-dozen other conversations by a corps of well-wishers. Out of the corner of his eye, Jeff could see him excitedly talking to his army buddies.

Jeffrey Gross wanted to run and hide. In his mind's eye, the reporters were having a field day, writing headlines like BABY BAWLS, SOLDIERS BRAWL, DOC GOES AWOL and JEWISH SURGEON WOULD RATHER FIGHT THAN STITCH.

All too soon, Jeff could see Iron Mike tearing himself away from a corps of well-wishers and coming toward him to get the show on the road. "There must be a way out of this mess," Jeff muttered to himself. "Maybe I can diagnose the baby as ill. But too many doctors around here would disagree... Maybe I can tell them *I'm* ill. But that will only postpone the circumcision..."

From out of nowhere, an idea flashed in his mind. It was a risk, but he had no choice. Jeff took a deep breath and turned to his commander-in-chief.

"Excuse me, General."

"Yes, son?"

"May I ask the General for his advice on a personal matter?"

"Certainly, my boy."

"General, if you made a vow to someone and then you were put in a position where you had to break that vow or jeopardize your career, what would you do?"

The General smiled. "You sure know how to ask tough questions. To be honest with you, I don't know how I would respond in your particular instance. But I will tell you that 'Honor Above All' is a motto I believe in and try to live by."

Dr. Gross took another deep breath and came out with it: "Then General, I cannot ritually circumcise your grandchild."

"What?!"

"Several years ago," Jeff went on calmly but quickly, "I made a vow to an old man, and maybe even to God, that I would not perform the Jewish circumcision ceremony on a non-Jewish child. And Jewish law states unequivocally that the religion of the child is determined by the mother. For this reason, if I am to be faithful to any code of honor, I may not perform this ceremony..."

At that moment, Iron Mike came bustling back in. "Let's get moving. I told the nurses to bring in the baby..."

General DeMartino turned to his son-in-law. "Dr. Gross cannot circumcise the child."

"What do you mean, he can't circumcise my son?"

"Mike, the doctor says he can't do it," his father-in-law repeated.

"He must," Colonel Smithson shot back. "Everything has already been arranged."

"The child is not Jewish," the General explained.

"Not Jewish?" Colonel Smithson exploded. "He's as Jewish as I am!"

"I'm afraid you know more about military history than about your own heritage," CINC-AT chided his son-in-law. "According to Jewish law, the religion of the child follows the mother, not the father."

Iron Mike was livid. "Dr. Gross, I *order* you to perform the circumcision of my son," he said stiffly. "If you refuse, you will be transferred to a tactical unit, where you can practice your surgical skills on those who really need them."

Jeffrey could already feel Iron Mike's iron grip doing a repeat performance on his neck. He turned chalky and involuntarily gasped for air.

"Dr. Gross," the General interrupted. "You will not perform this circumcision. And that's *my* order!"

The crowd in the room fell silent as father and grandfather began raising their voices. It was obviously a stand-off, but as they say in the Military, R-H-I-P, "Rank Has Its Privileges" — and it was obvious to everyone who outranked whom.

"May I have your attention," General DeMartino called out. "Dr. Gross has informed us that for ideological reasons, he cannot circumcise the child at this time." Jeffrey Gross felt about two inches tall and shrinking as some one hundred and fifty eyes stared down at him.

"However," CINC-AT continued, "I know you all join with me in congratulating Colonel Smithson and my daughter Maria on the birth of their son, Lincoln."

From the crowd, Jeff could hear a lot of murmuring, followed by a few hearty "Congratulations!" and "Mazel Tovs!"

"I would now like to call upon the proud father," General DeMartino went on, "to say a few words..."

Jeffrey Gross never heard Mike Smithson's speech. He felt ill and fearing that he would be the subject of the address, he silently slithered his way out of the medical center, where an MP was waiting to return him to Heidelberg.

Back at the 130th Station hospital, Dr. Gross was bombarded with questions. "How did things go? Did you meet

CINC-AT? Are they going to put you up for a ribbon?"

Jeff couldn't even begin to tell his colleagues what had happened. Or why. He could only wait for the inevitable transfer orders. As far as he was concerned, it was just a matter of time before he would be sent to Viet Nam. Actually, "sentenced to Viet Nam" would be more accurate.

He was right about being transferred. But he was wrong about the destination. Within three days, he was sent home to the U.S. A handwritten note was stapled to his orders:

"You did what you had to do. Now it is my turn. On my orders, you are to report to the base nearest to your hometown, where you are to finish your tour of duty. Coercion has no place in my army. Honor Above All."

The note was signed: Anthony P. DeMartino.

Celestial Convoy

הִנֵּה אָנֹכִי שֹׁלֵחַ מַלְאָךְ לְפָנֶיךָ לִשְׁמָרְךָ בַּדָּרֶךְ וְלַהֲבִיאֲךָ אֶל הַמָּקוֹם אֲשֶׁר הֲכִנֹתִי.

Behold, I am sending an angel before you to guard you on the way and bring you to the place that I have prepared.

(Shemos 23:20)

Why must the angel guard "on the way"? Doesn't man need Divine protection everywhere, whether he is stationary or in transit?

In Yoma 52 we learn that God's presence shields the Jews if they learn Torah. Travel, however, decreases Torah study *(Bereishis Rabbah 34)* by diminishing one's ability to concentrate. Thus, Rabbi **Yehonason Eibeshitz** observes, travelers whose source of Divine protection is perforce weakened, require angelic safekeeping.

When Rabbi Shmuel Salant paid a condolence visit to the Shapiro home, he felt obliged to reveal exactly how great a loss Jewry had suffered with Reb Hirsh Michel's passing:

"When the holy Rav Nachum of Shadik came across the midrash that says that there is a special hidden place on earth where God bemoans His exiled Kingdom, he began to cry. 'If the Almighty has a specific place to weep over the *galus,*' he said, 'then certainly we too should designate a secret place to pray for the restoration of the Divine Kingdom.'

"Adjacent to the Spring of Shiloach, where Rabbi Yishmael the High Priest used to immerse himself, is a skeleton structure within two inner courtyards, hidden from the public eye. Rav Nachum designated this ruin to be the hiding place of *Yerushalayim Shel Ma'alah,* and had a locksmith prepare a lock that could only be opened by special copper keys. These keys were entrusted to an elite group of men who had sanctified their bodies and purified their sight from an early age. In all of *Yerushalayim Shel Ma'alah,* only thirteen *tzaddikim* were deemed worthy of possessing such keys, and Rav Yehoshua Zvi Hirsh Michel Shapiro, *zt"l,* was the most deserving of all!"

Just Do Your Best

וְעָשׂוּ לִי מִקְדָּשׁ וְשָׁכַנְתִּי בְּתוֹכָם.

And let them make Me a sanctuary, that I may dwell among them.

(Shemos 25:8)

According to the Midrash, Moshe was bewildered by this command. "The entire universe cannot contain the Infinite. How, then," he asked, "can an enclosed structure do so?"

The Almighty answered that the Sanctuary would be built not according to His dimensions but according to those of man, allowing the Divine Presence to dwell within a finite space.

From here, the **Chafetz Chaim** [quoted by Rabbi Avraham Twerski] concludes that God does not expect the impossible from man in fulfilling His will. It would have been impossible for man to construct anything that could actually contain the Divine Presence. Man need only do all he is capable of doing — but anything less is a dereliction of his mission.

In the early 1940s, the first modern *mikveh* in New York opened its doors to a grateful community. Constructed in a converted brownstone where East Broadway meets Grand Street on New York's famous Lower East Side, it replaced the dilapidated Ridge Street facility that was housed in a building adjacent to a livery stable. Cart horses and horse-drawn wagons were quartered at the stable, and visits to Ridge Street were accompanied by sights and sounds distinctly antithetical to the concepts of sanctity and purification which "*mikveh*" embodies. The new facility, therefore, was a welcome addition to the thriving neighborhood.

Since before the turn of the century, the Lower East Side had been a haven for Jews from Eastern Europe. As world wars and civil strife devastated countries across the globe, more and more refugees flooded America's shores and many settled in the area closest to their port of entry. Family and friends from the "Old Country" awaited their arrival there and the infrastructure of a Jewish existence — including basic needs such as shuls, yeshivos and kosher food stores — was already firmly established. Three-quarters of all Jewish immigrants lived — at least for a time — on the Lower East Side, crowded into decrepit tenements along with Italian, Irish, Polish, Chinese and Russian refugees who found themselves in similarly impoverished circumstances. The Lower East Side teemed with humanity and bustled with commerce.

"My son, the doctor" is a phrase born on the streets of New York. It was there that the destitute Jews found employment of every description — from sewing lace handkerchiefs in the "sweat shops" of Center Street, to peddling rags and used clothing from push-carts — working fourteen to eighteen hours a day in order to send their sons to college. Only through secular education, they thought, could their children hope to rise above the squalor. Thus, the offspring of the greatest European talmudic scholars and the scions of noted chasidic dynasties evolved into a class of American professionals and businessmen. While many did not abandon religious practice in the process, the yeshivah and Torah study were no longer the focus of their activity.

Before World War II, a number of philanthropists poured huge sums of money into the renewal of the decaying slum neighborhood, erecting housing developments, parks and community centers, and the slum, if not eradicated, was at least pushed back and contained. Since the most urgent need was for decent housing, none of the religious institutions benefited from the philanthropy, and certainly not the old *mikveh*. While it did not fall into disuse, the area in which it was located became more hazardous than ever. Anyone who ventured there after dark did so in peril for his life: the slum that had been pushed back ended on Ridge Street.

The construction of the new *mikveh* was financed by a long-term mortgage of $25,000, a veritable fortune at the time, and the mortgager was a businessman who operated the facility as a private enterprise for seventeen years. Its new location made it both central to the sizable new housing projects inhabited almost exclusively by Jews, and accessible to pedestrian and vehicular traffic.

Its presence served to rejuvenate the old neighborhood, body and soul. Young families who would have relocated uptown or to the suburbs, chose to remain on the Lower East Side. The pleasant atmosphere and decor of the new *mikveh* and its convenient location encouraged countless residents to avail themselves of the facility, including many who had disdained and avoided the Ridge Street building.

In 1957, events took an unforeseen turn. Pete's House, an adjunct of the Grand Street Settlement Foundation for underprivileged youth, set its sights on the *mikveh* building, the rear wall of which abutted its gymnasium. The directors of the Grand Street Settlement viewed the *mikveh* premises as ideally suited for the expansion of the Pete's House gym and approached the mortgage holder with an offer he could not refuse. Word of the impending sale spread throughout the community and reached Rabbi Moshe Feinstein, the Rosh Yeshivah of Mesivta Tiferes Yerushalayim (M.T.J.).

Having resided on the Lower East Side since his emigration from Russia in 1936, HaGaon Reb Moshe was a familiar figure on Grand Street, although few could put a name to that distinguished face. Short in stature and with a luxuriant white beard and lively, twinkling eyes, the Rosh Yeshivah could frequently be seen in the company of his learned sons and *talmidim*, striding majestically from his Grand Street apartment to his rabbinical school at the far end of East Broadway. Partly because of his great humility and partly because of the preeminence of Reb Aharon Kotler *zt"l*, Reb Moshe was not then a well-known personality outside of the tight Yeshivah circle. Nonetheless, he was a highly-respected Torah scholar and educator.

When Reb Moshe learned of the impending disaster, he realized that immediate action was called for. It did not require genius to predict what would happen to the level of observance in the neighborhood, and, ultimately, to the Jewish character of the community itself, if the *mikveh* were to fall.

His initial approach to the mortgager met with failure; repeated appeals to the man's religious convictions and conscience fell on deaf ears. As a source of revenue, the facility had not turned out to be the "gold mine" that the man had hoped it would, and the opportunity to unload it for a tidy sum was too tempting to pass up. There was no question of building another *mikveh*: property values in New York had skyrocketed and the cost would have been prohibitive. The only hope, then, was to raise the funds to meet the price that Pete's House had offered and for the local community itself to assume responsibility for the operation of the facility. This hope, however, was somewhat divorced from reality.

Thousands of Jews of every stripe called the Lower East Side their home, but scattered as they were among a dozen or so apartment complexes and hundreds of *shtiblach*, any thought of uniting them behind a cause (the significance of which eluded many of them) constituted little more than a pipe dream. Never before had they amalgamated for any purpose — certainly not a religious one — and it was unlikely that any attempt to bring them together would meet with success. Reb Moshe, however, was not dismayed. The cause was too vital to be dismissed — so vital, in fact, that it took precedence over many of his myriad obligations.

In addition to the enormous responsibilities he bore as Rosh Yeshivah of Mesivta Tiferes Yerushalayim, where he delivered a daily *daf shiur* and personally examined each of the *semichah* candidates, every available moment of his time was accounted for by his personal learning schedule. He began his day at four in the morning and from then until he retired very late at night, Reb Moshe was actively engaged in Torah study and in recording his *chiddushim* and *piskei halachah*. His telephone, always close at hand, rang incessantly with *Klal Yisrael* on the line, and the Rosh Yeshivah had difficulty finding the time for the *dinei Torah* and occasional *gittin* which he hosted in his house every afternoon. Despite all this, he allocated countless hours to this project and proved to be a tireless campaigner when it came to a cause of such importance as the *mikveh*.

Recognizing the need to conduct matters in a proper, businesslike fashion, he called a meeting of local merchants and prominent businessmen and asked them to join him in this effort. Few could deny his impassioned appeal for their cooperation, but for a neighborhood that was, at best, lower-middle class, the sum required was beyond their limited means. Wealthy people did not live on the Lower East Side.

A committee to save the *mikveh* was formed and like any wise board chairman or chief executive who surrounds himself with an advisory panel of experts, Reb Moshe selected some of the more successful business people as committee members. The Rosh Yeshivah himself sat at the helm. The task they had undertaken seemed overwhelming but Reb Moshe set an example that was impossible not to follow. At the end of their exhausting workdays, the committee members made time to attend frequent hours-long plenary meetings and campaign strategy sessions. The Rosh Yeshivah said, "Just as we are enjoined to set aside a tithe of our income for charity, so are we obliged to allocate a tithe of our time and energy for our community." The committee did that — and more.

At the meetings, not a moment of awkwardness or discomfort passed for the committee members, several of whom were overawed by the presence of the brilliant scholar. Reb Moshe always deferred to their greater commercial expertise and acumen, and treated them as equals, calling them "my esteemed friend" and "my honored colleague." No task — regardless of its triviality — was too demeaning, for the Rosh Yeshivah endowed the committee's endeavors with an aura of spirituality. Saving the *mikveh* became a holy mission.

Notices were distributed to all the yeshivos and *shtiblach* and posted in stores and shops, followed by a door-to-door fund-raising effort. Night after night, fair weather or foul, these dignified committee members personally knocked on every door in the neighborhood, begging donations. Had every Jew on the Lower East Side been willing to contribute five dollars, enough money could have been raised to buy the *mikveh and* Pete's House, and even put a down payment on the Grand Street Settlement, to boot. But this was not meant to be.

A pathetic pile of bills and coins was dumped each week on the Rosh Yeshivah's desk and the committee members were losing heart. Their disappointment in their fellow residents was keen. People who would have unhesitatingly purchased a box of *treifa* Girl Scout cookies — only to throw it in the trash upon the little uniformed salesgirl's departure — dropped nickels and dimes into the *mikveh*-solicitors' waiting hands, or closed the door in their faces. Clearly, more extreme tactics were required.

Armed only with the force of his charismatic personality, Reb Moshe *himself* went out door-knocking. But his activities bore little more fruit than those of his "esteemed colleagues." Men of means would root around in their pockets for loose change to hand to the illustrious "*meshulach,*" and the Rosh Yeshivah learned on his own flesh the indignities his co-workers had suffered. His efforts, however, were not in vain.

The very fact that the Rosh Yeshivah would so demean himself for this cause served to drive home its salience, galvanizing the community at last, and the fund-raising campaign was given a much-needed boost. The campaign chest began to swell as contributions poured in, some from the most surprising quarters.

Encouraged by this development and by Reb Moshe's unswerving faith of optimism, the committee took a bold step. Since there was no possibility of raising the entire sum in time to meet the mortgage holder's deadline, they borrowed the remainder from "*Gemach*" funds and from private parties — and *personally* signed for the loans. If their fund-raising efforts were to fail, the committee members themselves would be burdened with awesome debts.

Three years after this holy mission was undertaken, the *mikveh* mortgage was ceremoniously burned at a gala dinner and responsibility for operating the facility passed to the community at large. To this day, it stands in the heart of the Lower East Side, renovated, refurbished and ready to serve the flourishing neighborhood.

The moment Reb Moshe Feinstein shouldered the burden of saving the *mikveh*, he ceased to be "merely" a Rosh Yeshivah and became instead a *Rosh Kehillah*, and the *kehillah* came first to know, and then to love and honor, the diminutive giant who dwelled in their midst.

Equal Partners

וְעָשׂוּ אֲרוֹן עֲצֵי שִׁטִּים...

And make the ark out of shittim wood...

(Shemos 25:10)

Why this distinction? *Midrash Tanchuma* explains that this phraseology prevented one Jew from boasting to another, "I have contributed more for the *aron* than you; therefore, I shall learn more Torah [than you]. You did not provide for the ark as I did, so you shall have a smaller portion in the Torah."

The **Chafetz Chaim** added that, just as the Torah belongs equally to all Jews, so does the privilege of supporting its study. Just as God commanded the entire nation to construct the repository of the Torah, everyone is equally obliged to foster Torah learning. The student and his supporter receive the same reward, provided that both sincerely contribute whatever their gifts.

Philanthropist Joseph Tanenbaum was careful to maintain a low profile if charity stood to gain thereby. A case in point was a *Chinuch Atzmai* fundraising dinner that Joe attended years ago. Joe instructed the chairman not to mention his magnanimous donation until the very end of the evening. He was concerned that if his contribution were to be announced first, it would discourage others from giving: prospective donors might erroneously conclude, "My $10,000 will look like nothing compared to Tanenbaum's fabulous donation," and decide not to give at all.

Selfless Service

וְאַתָּה תְּצַוֶּה אֶת בְּנֵי יִשְׂרָאֵל וְיִקְחוּ אֵלֶיךָ שֶׁמֶן זַיִת זָךְ כָּתִית לַמָּאוֹר לְהַעֲלֹת נֵר תָּמִיד.

And you shall command the Children of Israel that they bring you pure olive oil beaten for the light, to cause the lamp to burn always.

(Shemos 27:20)

Although the Almighty obviously does not need our light, the Midrash provides a reason for this symbolic act and offers an analogy to this paradox:

> *A man who could see led a blind man along a journey. When they reached their destination the sighted man asked his companion to light a lamp. "I make this request," he explained, "so that you will not feel beholden to me. Thus each of us will have done something for the other from which he personally has no benefit.*

Rabbi **Zelig Pliskin** cites Rabbi **Yeruchem Levovitz** who taught that this Midrash illustrates the perspective one must always maintain when doing a favor for someone else. One should desire to help others or raise their spirits even if one does not gain thereby.

In the Shaarei Chesed area of Jerusalem there lived an elderly widow who earned her meager livelihood by selling wines. Probably unable to distinguish between a Dry and a Semi-dry, and certainly not between a Chardonnay and a Cabernet, she had not chosen this profession, but rather had inherited the modest enterprise from her late husband.

Every *erev* Pesach, after *bedikas chametz,* Reb Shlomo Zalman Auerbach would trek to this woman's "store" — that is, to her house — to buy wine for Pesach. He was particular to make the purchases himself, and never sent an emissary wine-shopping on his behalf. In truth he had no need for the wine, for there were always enough bottles in his house from the many packages of *mishlo'ach manos* he would receive on Purim, enough to last for an entire year, and most of that wine was kosher for Pesach.

As time went by, and this widow became advanced in years, she was no longer able to maintain her business, and eventually she closed her "store." However, on *erev* Pesach she instructed one of her grandchildren to buy the particular brand of wine that Reb Shlomo Zalman would always purchase, along with a few other bottles, so that the former wine department of her home would still have the ambiance of a liquor store. She had always welcomed the Gaon's annual visits, as well as his patronage, and didn't want him to stop coming when he found the business had closed.

Reb Shlomo Zalman was wise to her little deception, but he never let on. He continued to make his modest purchases, thanking the woman profusely each time for enabling him to prepare for the Seder.

The Virtue of Audacity

וְהָיָה עַל מֵצַח אַהֲרֹן וְנָשָׂא אַהֲרֹן אֶת עֲוֹן הַקֳּדָשִׁים
אֲשֶׁר יַקְדִּישׁוּ בְּנֵי יִשְׂרָאֵל לְכָל מַתְּנֹת קָדְשֵׁיהֶם וְהָיָה עַל
מִצְחוֹ תָּמִיד לְרָצוֹן לָהֶם לִפְנֵי ה׳.

And [the forehead plate] shall be on Aharon's brow, that Aharon shall bear the iniquity of the holy things that the Children of Israel consecrate as all their sacred gifts; it shall be on his brow at all times, that they may be accepted before the Lord.

(Shemos 28:38)

The Midrash *(VaYikra Rabbah 10:6)* asserts that the forehead plate atones for brazenness. Why should the symbol of brazenness rest upon the brow of the *Kohen Gadol* at all times?

The **Baal Shem Tov** teaches that vices can and should be used constructively. Anger, arrogance, slovenliness, and audacity as well — all can be redirected.

The characteristic of brazenness can actually be an asset when, for example, immorality beckons. In a world where anti-Semitism is still rampant, boldness can enable a Jew to resist assimilating and contend with the taunts of his detractors.

After 450 years of Czarist dictatorship, the Russian people were beginning to long for freedom. The suffering of World War I led to the February Revolution in 1917, otherwise known as the Liberal Revolt which began as a simple strike and a demand by the people of St. Petersburg for bread. Government troops sent to put down the Revolution joined the protesters and forced the collapse of the government. A temporary government was then formed but it proved too weak to withstand the powerful and influential Bolsheviks (Communists), who pressed for revolution. Their aim, ostensibly, was to provide the people with "Peace, Land, and Bread," along with fulfillment of their motto "All the power to the Soviets."

The Bolsheviks formed the "Red Army" to carry out their objectives and eliminate perceived threats and opposition. They took power in the October Revolution, otherwise known as the Bolshevik Revolt, following which the whole of Russia was plunged into a bloody civil war that lasted until the beginning of 1921.

The Jews of the Ukraine, whose villages were the scenes of many of the major battles, were directly affected by the war. As soldiers passed through the towns and settlements, they frequently abused, looted, assaulted and murdered the Jews of the area. It was not uncommon for a battalion to enter a village just to pillage and massacre its local Jewish population. Officially, however, the Red Army adopted a position of not tolerating anti-Semitism among its troops and, on occasion, actually punished soldiers guilty of attacking Jews.

In the course of time, a good number of Jews began to look upon the Soviet Regime and its Red Army as their protectors. It was an ironic situation in which, as terrible and murderous as the Red Army was, its opposition — the "White Army," or the counter-revolutionaries — was composed of Cossacks who were even more anti-Semitic. One of the slogans of the Cossacks was "Strike at the Jews and save Russia!" — and practically everywhere they went, they left a stream of Jewish blood in their wake.

Jewish boys were routinely drafted into the Red Army. Indeed, the Steipler Gaon's two brothers, boys whom he personally regarded as far brighter and more knowledgeable than himself, were forced into the army and were never heard from again. Similar tragedies befell countless families among our Jewish brethren.

Despite the takeover of the Russian government by the Bolshevik dictatorship, Reb Yoizel Horowitz and his Novardhok disciples remained firm in their determination to oppose Communism and its atheistic tenets. But even a man as determined as *der Alter* soon realized that open resistance was the wrong strategy. The Communists had a straightforward method of dealing with even the slightest hint of opposition: execution by a firing squad.

In addition to eliminating their political opponents, the Bolsheviks also took steps to abolish the practice of Judaism. To this end, they established the *Yevsektsia* (Jewish Section), a branch of the Russian Communist Party, whose purpose was to "impose the proletarian dictatorship among the Jewish masses." It was headed by assimilationists, self-hating Jews who vigorously and enthusiastically joined the Bolshevik effort to eradicate their own religion.

The *Yevsektsia* unhesitatingly applied the Bolsheviks' ruthless ways to strike at the religious and national organizations of Russian Jewry. In a swift reign of terror, Jewish communities were dissolved and their properties expropriated — including shuls, yeshivos, *chadarim*, and *Talmud Torahs*. Libraries were confiscated, and their holy books burned.

The *Yevsektsia* was willing to support a Jewish community and Yiddish-language press that would expound Communism among the Jews of Russia. But what they would not allow was the continuation of Torah observance — and they would stop at nothing to prevent it.

They banned religious education. The shuls, yeshivos, and *chadarim* which they had seized were converted into clubs, workshops and warehouses. Stiff taxes were levied against rabbis and other religious leaders to force them to leave their positions. The demands of religious Jewry for the freedom of observance promised by the Revolution was met with mockery and punishment.

Many Novardhokers, including Reb Yoizel's own son-in-law and heir to the Novardhok leadership, Rabbi Avraham Yaffen, were imprisoned and sentenced to long terms of hard labor. Through various clandestine means, students of the Novardhok yeshivah managed to smuggle *gemaros* and *mussar* books to their jailed comrades, so that their learning continued even under the cruel thumb of the Communists.

Since the postal service during that era was unreliable, Reb Yoizel had to direct his disciples, dispersed all over Russia, by means of short, cryptic telegrams, worded in the jargon of rabbinic expressions which would not be understood the authorities. The Novardhokers' lives were imperiled daily because of their learning Torah, and the question of *mesirus nefesh* — sacrificing one's life in order to uphold the Law, and thereby sanctify God's Name — was faced again and again.

One story from that period tells of a group of Red Army soldiers that stormed into a Novardhok yeshivah. The commanding officer drew his gun and demanded that the Rosh Yeshivah close the academy immediately or he would face the firing squad.

Moments before this incident, a telegram from *der Alter* had been smuggled past Red Army lines by other Novardhok disciples and brought to this yeshivah. The telegram read simply, "Our Merciful Father." The words were the very same as the first two Hebrew words of the prayer for the souls of Jews who sacrificed their lives rather than convert. To the students, the message was clear.

The Rosh Yeshivah rose from his chair and unbuttoned his coat. He strode purposefully toward the officer, opened his coat wide and said calmly, "Shoot!" Immediately, the students of the yeshivah followed his lead. One by one they rose from their seats, unbuttoned their coats, and lined up behind the Rosh Yeshivah. "Shoot!" they each repeated.

The soldiers were stunned. Never had they encountered such audacity, such bravery. They were accustomed to seeing their victims' eyes bulge with terror, to hearing anguished cries, pleading and begging for mercy — all of which was generally followed by the soldiers' vicious kicks and deadly gunfire. Either out of total confusion, or respect and admiration for an act of such raw courage, the soldiers withdrew without firing a shot and the Novardhokers returned to their Torah study.

Fiery Faith

זֶה יִתְּנוּ כָּל הָעֹבֵר עַל הַפְּקֻדִים מַחֲצִית הַשֶּׁקֶל בְּשֶׁקֶל
הַקֹּדֶשׁ עֶשְׂרִים גֵּרָה הַשֶּׁקֶל מַחֲצִית הַשֶּׁקֶל תְּרוּמָה לַה'.

This they shall give, everyone who passes among those who are numbered: half a shekel after the shekel of the sanctuary (a shekel is twenty gera); a half shekel shall be the offering unto the Lord.

(Shemos 30:13)

The Midrash elaborates on this verse: God showed Moshe a fiery coin and instructed him, "Let them give a coin like this."

Moshe was surprised when he heard that a simple coin could atone. Therefore, explains the **Kotzker Rebbe**, God demonstrated that expiation requires far more than a mere monetary donation. Burning enthusiasm and fiery devotion are necessary as well. An elevated spiritual level with celestial sincerity has the power to atone.

It was Sunday morning, but the sky was black with angry thunderheads. The wind howled and rain poured down in icy sheets that stung like a thousand needles of steel. Waves as high as mountains crested, then crashed down upon the rolling deck. The sea, a seething witches' brew, foamed and churned with the great ship and all on board trapped in its hellish turbulence.

The vessel heaved and pitched violently, hurling crates and crockery about like chaff in a winnow. Zevulun ben Yissachar wrapped himself in oilskins and struggled up the slippery gangway to the upper deck. He watched in helpless terror as the storm tore relentlessly at the mainsail until it hung from the central mast in tatters.

The ocean slammed against the oaken hull. Lashed to the helm, the shipmaster fought a brave but futile battle to hold the schooner on course. It seemed that it could not be any worse than this — and then it was.

Fiery forks of lightning rent the heavens and struck the foremast a mighty blow. Despite its beer-barrel girth, the mast was felled like a sapling beneath the blade of a woodsman's axe. It smashed a hole in the deck the size of a cannonball and the cruel sea gushed in through the breach.

The captain cried "Abandon ship!" and all who dared, did, grabbing planks of wood and empty kegs as they leapt over the side. But Zevulun patted his pockets for the *tefillin* which he always kept on his person and then grabbed a coil of thick rope and swiftly tied himself to the rail. He was a poor swimmer and his fear of the ocean depths was keen. He prayed for a merciful death.

Zevulun ben Yissachar was a merchant seaman by trade. Six months of every year he plied the waters from the Iberian coast to the Phoenician Gulf, buying and selling silks and spices, a profitable business which enabled him to spend the remainder of the year engaged in the study of the holy Torah. Would he even touch those precious sacred tomes again? he wondered. Would he ever again see his beloved wife and children?

The bodies of his shipmates, swallowed whole and gone without a trace, failed to appease the ocean's fury. For two more days and nights the implacable tempest battered his ship, driving it at last onto the rocks. As the schooner broke up on the craggy coast of an uncharted island, Zevulun, still bound to the rail, was brutally thrown from the deck on impact. He floundered in the shallows, clutching flotsam from the wreck, until, sapped of strength, he washed up on the beach with the tide.

The storm subsided early Wednesday morning. Zevulun lay unconscious in the sand while the bright sun dried the shreds of clothing that clung to his limbs and torso. A freshening breeze ruffled his salt-caked hair. Zevulun stirred.

He dragged his pain-wracked body to the shelter of a tree where he rested, gathering energy, and offered a prayer of thanksgiving to his Creator. His eyelids and lips were blistered, his tongue was swollen from thirst, and crusts of dried blood covered his bare arms and feet. He doubted he could last long without sustenance. Grasping the bole of the tree for support, he hauled himself erect and began to forage for food.

On still shaky legs, with every bruised muscle screaming from the exertion, he headed inland. Dense foliage impeded his progress at every turn, indicating the presence of sweet water and the hope of fruit. But despite its abundance, the vegetation did not appear to be edible. The broad, thorny leaves were like no leaves he had ever seen before and no fruit or nuts dangled from the lofty branches. Lush verdant bushes in every shade of green flourished among the trees, bare of berries; still he searched for the fresh water spring that fed them.

The leaf-littered earth gave way abruptly to a neat, well-tended path. Zevulun followed the winding, narrow lane through the forest to a large clearing, in the heart of which stood dozens of small, wooden houses. He gazed upon the village in wonderment. Until that moment, he had been certain that the island was uninhabited. It was so odd an assumption to have made that he paused to analyze the thoughts which had led him to that conclusion.

The silence, he realized at once, yes, the absolute, utter silence of the place. Not a bird chirped in the trees, no sound of small, scurrying creatures reached his ears; neither the buzz of conversation nor the hum of industry, neither the tinkle of laughter nor the cry of a child penetrated the barrier of silence which enveloped him.

Yet the wooden structures appeared to be anything but abandoned. Like the path, they were well-cared for, with small patches of garden in front and crisp curtains at the windows. "Hello!" he called, but no human voice responded. His eyes searched the village. There was no sign of life.

Zevulun was struck by his total isolation, the agony of his loneliness, the hopelessness of his situation. How he longed to see a face, to hear a voice besides his own! His need for human fellowship was as desperate as his hunger and thirst. Tears of sorrow coursed down his ravaged cheeks and he prayed to the Almighty for comfort and salvation.

He weakly made his way to the door of the first house and was just raising his hand to knock when he encountered a sight that filled him with awe. He rubbed his eyes with his fists, certain it had only been an hallucination. But when he looked again, it was still there. He touched it with trembling fingers to convince himself that it was not a figment of his imagination.

"It is truly a miracle," he said aloud, and indeed it was. For there on the doorpost of this modest hut in the midst of a clearing, in the depths of a forest on a deserted land, was a *mezuzah*.

With unbridled joy, he rapped his fist against the door, the pain and exhaustion gone from his body, the memory of his ordeal forgotten. He could barely contain his excitement.

He pounded at the door with all his might, but no one answered. He hurried to the next house and there, too, he found a *mezuzah*, but again no one answered his knock.

On every doorpost in the entire village a *mezuzah* was affixed, and Zevulun went from one house to the next knocking and calling out and knocking again, until he practically collapsed from fatigue and frustration.

In despair, he grasped the nearest doorhandle, intending to break in if necessary, but to his astonishment the door yielded easily and swung open on silent hinges.

Clearly, the owners were absent, although signs of recent habitation were everywhere. Barely a speck of dust powdered the sparse furniture; a ruffled apron hung from a peg, its long ties still curved with the memory of a bow; an iron pot on the stove bore the still-discernible aroma of a pungent stew. And on the table stood a large bowl filled to overflowing with dried fruits and nuts.

Wordlessly, Zevulun thanked the absent homeowner and begged the man's forgiveness for his intrusion and presumptuousness. To partake of another's food without permission was a deplorable act, and had it not been a matter of survival, the idea would never have occurred to Zevulun. He praised God for His compassion and dined on the fruit as though it were the most sumptuous repast.

Sated at last, he lay down to await the owner's return, determined to recompense his unknown host in whatever way possible. In moments, Zevulun was asleep and when he awoke, a new day was dawning. It was Thursday, he reckoned, and thoughts of how he would celebrate — indeed observe — the coming Shabbos began to torment him. The absent homeowner had not returned.

The little house, as well as the rest of the tiny village, remained silent. He went out to explore his surroundings, although his hopes of finding anyone had long since dimmed.

With the remainder of the dried fruits and several handfuls of nuts tied in a scrap of cloth, Zevulun set out on the path leading through the forest.

By evening, however, his worst fears had been confirmed. After a long trek, he discovered that he was indeed on an island, and even from the top of the highest tree he was unable to sight any nearby land mass. The only cultivated area was that of the abandoned village; all the rest of the small island was a virtually impenetrable forest. Dejected and disheartened, Zevulun followed the path "home."

As he neared the village, a strange sound caught his attention. He quickly turned towards the noise and discovered that the path branched off to the right. He had not noticed the fork earlier; now he followed it past an unusual rock formation and down a shallow incline, the strange sound growing increasingly louder as he went.

At the end of the path lay a large pool of clear water, rivulets trickling down to it from countless crevices in the surrounding rocks. Zevulun knelt at the edge of the pool, scooped water into his hand and tasted it. It was icy cold and sweeter than any wine he'd ever known. He sluiced his sunburned face in its coolness and slaked his terrible thirst.

On the far side of the pool stood a lone wooden structure similar in design to those in the village, but substantially larger. Thinking that perhaps the villagers were gathered in this building, Zevulun approached the imposing front door with a glimmer of hope. Here, too, a *mezuzah* was affixed to the doorpost.

Inside, Zevulun discovered a simple, but beautiful, shul. The last rays of the setting sun poured in through the windows as if the forest had parted to make way for the sunbeams. The *aron kodesh* was bathed in a Heavenly glow and Zevulun recited his evening prayers with great devotion.

An oil lamp, half-filled and still burning, illuminated the interior even after sundown. Zevulun opened a worn, leather-bound volume and immersed himself in learning. He studied far into the night, dozing now and then on the hard bench.

At dawn he washed in the pool, then recited the morning service. He knew he must soon begin preparations for the Sabbath, but he could not think of how to go about it. Only a few small nuts remained in his cloth pouch and these he devoured slowly. His explorations of the island had uncovered no edible growth, and he was painfully aware that this might be his very last meal. If the villagers failed to return soon, he feared he would be compelled to raid yet another home, and even then, there was no assurance of finding anything.

He returned to his study of the sacred tome, hoping to delay the inevitable as long as he could. Hours passed. Suddenly, Zevulun looked up from the text, sensing a subtle change in the atmosphere. He ran to the window, but the tangled forest blocked his view of all but the limpid pool. The sound of trickling water had an extra intensity now, altered in some indefinable way.

His heart nearly burst with the joyful realization that the sound he heard was the sound of humanity. He raced down the path to the village. The sight that greeted him there was dazzling.

The tiny abandoned village was now completely transformed. Everywhere people were hurrying about their business: women scrubbed laundry in huge sudsy vats; men carried baskets and parcels with a purposeful stride; children swept doorsteps and scampered and sang merrily; and the air was full with the heady aromas of cooking and baking —

the unmistakable fragrance of Shabbos.

"Come," said a man as he passed Zevulun, handing him a cumbersome package. Zevulun, dumbstruck, followed obediently. A moment later, they entered the very house where Zevulun had discovered the bowl of dried fruit and nuts, but before he could speak, the mistress of the house greeted him warmly.

"How wonderful! A guest for Shabbos!" She showed him to an alcove and laid out a clean suit of clothes upon a freshly-made bed. "Quickly," she said, "there isn't much time."

Zevulun began to stammer his thanks, but the man swiftly drew the alcove curtain. He shucked his rags and donned the splendid attire his hosts had so graciously provided and reflected that had the mysterious villagers not returned, he would have had no way of celebrating the Sabbath properly.

The children of the household arrived. Through the curtain he heard the sounds of furniture being moved about, of tableware rattling, pots and pans banging, the bustle and hubbub of Shabbos preparations overlaid with the happy humming of Sabbath songs.

Although he had not lingered over his dressing, by the time he emerged from the alcove, the immaculate home was ready for the Sabbath. The woman, a snowy apron over her long, dark dress and a lacy kerchief wrapped around her head, blessed the Sabbath oil lights and her husband and sons called "Good Shabbos" as they hurried out the door. The man gestured impatiently for Zevulun to join them, which he did.

The village square was as crowded as a marketplace with men and boys heading for the shul in the forest. Zevulun was struck by the warm glow that radiated from all the smiling faces of the villagers, the hearty "Good Shabbos" with which they hailed one another, and the orderly, ceremonial way they filed down the path past the pool.

"Ah, a guest!" each one called when he saw Zevulun. "Next Shabbos you'll stay with me." Zevulun smiled with pleasure at their hospitality and generosity towards a total stranger, wondering at the same time if indeed he was destined to remain on the island for so many weeks.

There was no doubt that the island and its inhabitants were most extraordinary. The possibility that it was all an illusion crossed Zevulun's mind, but he quickly rejected the thought. It was too real, too tangible to be a fantasy. His curiosity was overwhelming but he dared not disturb the serenity of the Sabbath by asking questions. What would he do if his inquisitiveness were to offend his benefactors or break the miraculous spell? He decided he must delay his interrogations until after Shabbos.

But why, he wondered, had no one thought to ask him whence he had come? Was it merely politeness, or a singular absence of curiosity? Was the sudden appearance of a complete stranger in their midst a commonplace occurrence? The beauty of the *tefillah* banished all care from his mind.

Never before had Zevulun heard the Friday night service sung so gloriously. The strains of *Lecha Dodi* filled the shul with joyful music, uniquely melodious and spiritual, the notes ascending straight to the Heavens. "Surely this is how the angels sing," Zevulun thought to himself, for he could imagine nothing earthly to be so magnificent and inspirational. He could not fathom the Almighty's reasons for bringing him to this mysterious island, but for Zevulun, to have been permitted to experience this uplifting *tefillah*, made the entire ordeal worth enduring.

Dinner Friday night at his host's table was no less sublime. The children, their cherubic faces gleaming in the glow of the Sabbath lights, politely questioned their father concerning the intricacies of the Torah and the ways of *mussar*. The *zemiros* they sang were as captivating as birdsong and the meal — truly a celestial feast — was indeed food for the *neshamah yeseirah.*

Shabbos morning was equally exhilarating. Throughout the *tefillah* the voices of the islanders blended together harmoniously in a virtual symphony of the soul. They heeded the Torah-reading avidly, appearing to absorb not only the words but the timeless lessons as well. The Sabbath meal was a celebration that nourished the spirit, with food fit for kings and ethereal, intoxicating songs.

Not a single profane or mundane matter intruded on the Shabbos tranquility. The afternoon was devoted to Torah study, followed by *minchah* services and a *seudah shlishis* that were the essence of sanctity and holiness. And as the Sabbath drew to a close, Zevulun was gripped with melancholy and a terrible sense of loss. The terror of the storm that had wrecked his ship, destroying his livelihood and casting him away on this remote island, the tragedy of his separation from his home and loved ones, all paled to insignificance alongside this incomparable Shabbos experience. He wished it would never end.

Zevulun prepared himself to offer up a *motza'ei Shabbos tefillah* that would convey his profound gratitude for the Almighty's benevolence. He prayed with greater devotion and fervor than ever before, concentrating his entire being on each word. So engrossed was he in his devotions that he did not notice when the other worshippers completed theirs. While he was yet immersed in the *Shemoneh Esrei,* the others recited the *Havdalah* service, lifting the candle high to light the way for the departing Sabbath Queen. Still Zevulun lingered over his prayer, and when he was done, he found the shul deserted.

The path through the forest was eerily silent; starlight

twinkled among the gnarled tree limbs and rustling leaves, illuminating his way. He hurried to the home of his generous host, anxious to express his appreciation for all the kindness and hospitality and to ask the questions which had seemed so unimportant throughout Shabbos but which now pressed with great urgency.

With an uneasy feeling, Zevulun rapped on the door. The village, which had been so recently a veritable hive of activity, was still. No one answered his knock. He ran to the next house, and the next, and the next — but all were as empty as they had been when he had first arrived. In desperation he opened door after door, calling out, begging the villagers not to hide from him, but his mournful cries were met with silence.

He raced down the path to the beach, praying for a glimpse of the boats upon which the islanders had surely sailed, but there was only the glassy sea and the rising moon on the horizon. He fell to his knees and cried in anguish, "Please, I beseech you, do not abandon me! I cannot bear to be alone again!" But the only sound was the monotonous lapping of waves upon the sandy shore.

Despondent, he groped his way back to the shul to seek solace in the sacred texts. He opened a massive volume and quickly became engrossed in the complexities of the subject matter before him. Soon the pall of sorrow lifted. He studied through the night, napping briefly just before sunrise. When he awoke, he felt refreshed and not at all hungry. It was as though the Sabbath past continued to sustain and nurture him.

But his nerves found no respite. What was this enigma he was experiencing? he wondered. He searched the island again and again day after day, desperate to determine the whereabouts of its inhabitants. But he found not a single clue. It was hopeless. Only when his mind was completely occupied with exploring the ancient tomes in the little shul was he at peace.

Occasionally, when he paused in his studies to drink at the pool and breathe the clean, fresh forest fragrances, he again considered the possibility that all that had transpired had been no more than an illusion, a dream which yet held him firmly in its grip. But such thoughts led nowhere and he hastily drove them from his mind and returned to his investigation of the Holy Scripture.

One thought, however, refused to be driven away. It pried relentlessly at the edges of his consciousness, demanding attention. It was the awareness of the approaching Sabbath and his hopeless inadequacy to celebrate it.

With neither wine nor challah on hand, how could he sanctify the holy day? How would his pathetic semblance of Shabbos compare with the villagers' undefiled, reverential Sabbath in the eyes of the Lord? The vision of a barren Shabbos table, a repast of plain water and stale nuts, devoid of moving *zemiros* and inspiring *divrei Torah*, tormented him.

On Friday afternoon, however, the welcome sounds of feverish activity drifted through the windows of the shul. With heart pounding, Zevulun sped to the village, overjoyed to find that the people had returned and that they were once again preparing to greet the Sabbath.

"Happy to see you again!" a householder called cheerfully across his porch railing. "Don't forget, you promised to be our guest this week!" Zevulun was delighted to have been remembered.

Everything was as before: the prayers were as inspiring, the meals as delectable, the *divrei Torah* as edifying and the *zemiros* as dulcet as those of the previous week. Zevulun felt he had been blessed with a glimpse of Paradise — not once, but twice! Comfortably seated at his host's table surrounded by angelic children and enveloped in an aura of enchantment, Zevulun cast aside his curiosity. The very mention of the villagers' unexplained disappearance seemed a profanity. Such queries were best relegated to after Shabbos.

The Sabbath passed all too swiftly. As the time for *maariv* drew nearer, Zevulun rehearsed the questions he intended to pose, taking extreme care to phrase them as inoffensively as he could. But once again, his need to acknowledge his gratitude to the Almighty took precedence, and while the villagers chanted the *Havdalah* benedictions, Zevulun remained intent in prayer.

Zevulun praised his Creator for delivering him from the clutches of the cruel sea, for providing sustenance, for enabling him to experience celestial Sabbaths, and for allowing him to partake of the fruits of the World to Come. And when he emerged at last from his devotions, the villagers were gone.

Although he knew it was futile, he searched for them no less intensively than he had the previous week. He lit a torch from the flame of the shul's still-burning oil lamp and ran through the forest, this time in the direction away from the village. Perhaps a secret cave sheltered the people all week long, he wondered, or maybe they had repaired to another village, hidden among the trees?

"Stop," his inner voice rebuked him, "you know that you search in vain! What use is your pursuit of specters and wraiths?" He did stop then, for he was certain his inner voice spoke the truth. The pious villagers could only be Heaven-born and Heaven-sent, Divine messengers dispatched to earth to demonstrate the spirituality of Shabbos.

The lesson was not lost on Zevulun. As he walked slowly back to the shul, his mind whirled with thoughts and plans. He knew now that he had been completely wrong about his inadequacy to celebrate the Sabbath in a way that would find favor in the eyes of the Lord. For more than the enjoyment of good fellowship, more than the splendor of sumptuous feasts, more than all the material pleasures, Shabbos was a celebration of the spirit.

Even if he were to have nothing but the water from the pool for *Kiddush*, it would be the water that God in His mercy provided, the cool, sweet draft which had refreshed his tortured body after the harrowing shipwreck and which continued to sustain him throughout the week. Even if his meals were to consist of no more than a handful of stale nuts, still he could sing joyous songs of praise to his Creator, still he could speak the words of Torah, though none would hear but the Almighty Himself.

Zevulun's delight at this discovery was marred only by the knowledge that he was destined to live out his days on this far-flung isle, bereft of his cherished family and severed from society. But it was not for him to question the ways of the Lord. He turned instead to the task before him.

All week long Zevulun prepared himself for the coming Shabbos. Each passage he studied in the ancient volumes took on new meaning, for now he considered the words not merely in the context of the explicit subject to which they related, but in the context of the whole of God's Creation.

When he drank at the pool, the glittering stars reflected therein heightened his awareness of the universe, the vastness and limitlessness of the Lord's domain, and his own minuteness and insignificance within it.

When *erev Shabbos* arrived, it was not Zevulun who sought out the villagers, but the villagers who, entranced by the melodies emanating from the shul in the forest, sought out their erstwhile guest. They joined him in the stirring Friday night service, made even more exquisite by Zevulun's empassioned devotions. Throughout the Sabbath, he regaled them with brilliant *divrei Torah* and paeans of praise to the

Almighty which he had composed.

After *minchah,* the villagers set up long tables in the shul arrayed with every imaginable delicacy and together with Zevulun they feasted upon an otherworldly *seudah shlishis.* Then the eldest among them arose and addressed Zevulun in a sonorous voice:

"Honored visitor," he began, "we are aware that it was your respect for the sanctity of the Sabbath that prevented you from questioning us about our unusual existence. Now that you have demonstrated your ability to celebrate Shabbos as the Almighty intended, I am authorized to explain all that you have witnessed on our island.

"Many, many years ago, our ancestors were banished from the Holy Land by the wicked King Nebuchadnezzar, and they escaped to this remote isle. Here they established a community steeped in Torah and devoteed to service of the Holy One, blessed be He. They were only humble peasants with little money or material possessions, but here wealth had no significance. Their lives were dedicated to the study of the Divine Law.

"They cultivated the fields and raised small crops in order to satisfy their simple needs, and dreamed fervently of one day returning to Eretz Yisrael. As the decades passed and word of the rebuilding of the Temple reached them, their longing to rest their eyes once more upon its golden splendor became almost unendurable. It became the core of their existence.

"The enormous expense such a journey entailed, however, was far beyond their limited means. After much deliberation, it was decided that they would each contribute whatever they could to finance the journey of a handful of representatives, chosen by lot.

"And thus the tradition was born, a tradition carried on by generation after generation of our people, for hundreds of years, even until our own time. Each year money was pooled, lots were drawn and a delegation dispatched to the Holy Land. In some years, when the harvests were good, perhaps four or five islanders were able to embark on the voyage; in other years, only one or two could go.

"As was the custom, the Chosen Ones departed amid much fanfare and celebration and set sail in good time to reach the Holy Land before Sukkos. We would gather on the beach to bid them farewell and make them vow to relate to us every detail of *Yerushalayim*'s glory.

"They would bring sacrifices on behalf of our people in the Temple and sojourn for several weeks in the Holy City, in order to absorb its blessed beauty and wondrous sights. And we would anxiously await their return, posting scouts in the treetops to announce their ship's approach.

"Upon their return, the Chosen Ones were greeted with jubilation such as you have never seen. For three days and three nights they would tell of their experiences in the glorious Land of our dreams, about how the *Leviim* had sung and the *Kohanim* had performed the *avodah*. They would describe the drawing of waters at the *Simchas Beis HaShoevah*, the hosts of worshippers at the Temple, and the joy that suffused every day of the feast.

"One year, three Chosen Ones embarked on the annual pilgrimage, but within weeks the sails of their returning ship were sighted on the horizon. This was an unheard of occurrence as the delegation was not meant to return until much later. We hurriedly assembled on the beach to welcome our brethren in our customarily festive fashion, waving and singing our usual songs of welcome.

"Before long, the ship itself came into view, but the Chosen Ones were nowhere to be seen. We dared not think what dire fate had befallen our brothers. The ship anchored far out at sea and a rowboat was lowered. Three men dressed in sackcloth climbed aboard the boat and were rowed towards the shore. Surely these could not be our Chosen Ones, we thought, for the delegation was always clothed in finery, as befitted the occasion. But as the boat drew nearer, we recognized them.

"We continued to wave as hard as we could, even though our comrades did not respond. With stoic expressions they sat motionless in their rowboat and finally climbed down. With none of the usual rush and excitement, they waded to the beach and we could see the desolate pallor of their faces, the ashes upon their heads and the immeasurable sorrow in their eyes. They would not speak; they could not. We begged and beseeched them to explain why they were so sad. At last, they tearfully reported the devastating destruction of our beloved Temple; how they had seen it aflame and the Jews driven into exile. The Chosen Ones described in horrid detail the Holy City laid waste.

"A great wailing rose up from our people, a moaning and keening that fairly rent the heavens. So overwhelming was our anguish that, one by one, we fell to the ground — every man, woman and child among us — without the breath of life.

"When our souls arrived at the Gates of Heaven, our appearance seemed to create a problem. Our lives had terminated, yet our deaths were premature, brought about by our everlasting love for Eretz Yisrael and deep devotion to the *Beis HaMikdash*.

"And so, the Heavenly Court decided that, in the merit of our reverence for the Holy Land and for the Divine Torah, we would be permitted to live out our years one Shabbos at a time — Shabbos being akin to the World to Come — until the number of Sabbaths equalled the number of days we were each allotted. Thus, every *erev Shabbos*, our souls return to earth to celebrate the sacred Day of Rest in the manner of the Heavenly Beings.

"Now, you, Zevulun ben Yissachar, have been privileged

to witness a Celestial Sabbath. Go back to your home and emulate all that you have seen."

"Wait!" Zevulun cried. "How...," but the elderly villager interrupted him. "It is almost time for us to depart," he said, "and we must *daven maariv* and recite the *Havdalah* service before we go." Immediately, the *maariv* service commenced and Zevulun was prevented from asking the most vital question of all.

As the *Havdalah* candle sizzled out in a puddle of sweet wine, the elder pressed a scrap of parchment into Zevulun's hand. "When you are ready to leave our island," he whispered, "go down to the beach and think of your loved ones. Read that which is written here and then cast this parchment into the sea." And with those words the elder and all of the islanders disappeared like the smoke of the candle.

Zevulun did not hurry down to the beach — not that night. He sat on the bench in the little shul in the forest and sang to the departing Sabbath Queen. He recited *divrei Torah* aloud, to console his spirit for the loss it suffered when Shabbos ended.

After the *Melaveh Malkah*, he walked through the forest inhaling the spicy fragrance of the foliage and drank again the sweet waters of the pool. All through the night and all the next day he studied the sacred texts and relived in his mind the weeks he had spent on the island, an island sanctified by the lives of those who truly yearned for Eretz Yisrael — by those who knew how to observe the Day of Rest.

Finally, his heart filled with the joys of Sabbath Island, Zevulun strolled slowly down to the shore, retracing the path where his Heavenly adventure had begun.

He gazed out upon the calm sea, so vast and yet a mere

droplet in God's mighty Hand, to lie tranquil or rise up in mountainous waves at His command. Zevulun thought of his home and loved ones, of telling them and everyone he knew about the way the angels celebrate Shabbos. Then he read the Ineffable Name inscribed on the parchment. A tear rolled down his cheek and fell upon the inscription, and the parchment began to dissolve. Quickly, he cast it into the seafoam, and Zevulun ben Yissachar left Sabbath Island — where Shabbos, Eretz Yisrael and the World to Come were one — forever.

Rebels Without a Cause

וַיַּרְא אַהֲרֹן וַיִּבֶן מִזְבֵּחַ לְפָנָיו וַיִּקְרָא אַהֲרֹן וַיֹּאמַר חַג לַה' מָחָר.

Aharon saw [the golden calf,] and he built an altar before it; Aharon called and said, "Tomorrow is a feast for the Lord."

(Shemos 32:5)

It might appear that the Jewish People were not to blame for the atmosphere of panic that resulted in the construction of the golden calf. After all, the Nation's trusted leader, Moshe, had disappeared forty days earlier, stranding millions of men, women and children in the desert. They knew not what lay in store. Perhaps the miraculous manna, which had been provided to them in Moshe's merit *(Taanis 9a)*, would cease to fall; perhaps the well would cease to provide sweet water; perhaps the Clouds of Glory would shield them no longer.

Furthermore, a fearful, anxious, and confused Nation reasoned, "If Moshe has encountered strict Divine Justice, what will befall us?!"

Yet thousands were slain for worshipping the golden calf *(Shemos 32:28)*, receiving no dispensation for acting under duress.

Rabbi **Avigdor Nebanzahl** explains that a claim of duress cannot be substantiated here: Before ascending Mount Sinai, Moshe instructed, "Wait here for us, until we return to you; and behold, Aharon and Chur are with you — whoever has [difficult] matters should approach them" *(Shemos 24:14)*. Moshe appointed very competent replacements to address any issue that might have arisen in his absence.

Yet the Nation hardly took advantage of them. They murdered Chur for attempting to prevent the creation of the golden calf. And Aharon was instructed, not consulted. As the Midrash relates, "Do not read, 'he built *[vayiven]* an altar *[mizbe'ach]*.' Rather, 'he understood *[hevin]* from him who was slaughtered *[min hazavuach]*.' "

Upon learning of Chur's murder, Aharon despaired of dissuading the People. Indeed, the Midrash reveals that he was threatened, "As we have done to him, we shall do to you." True, the Nation was under duress, but that only justifies their sense of panic; their abominable behavior and speech were those of a people rebelling against Torah authority.

After enduring the hardships of transatlantic passage in steerage and the humiliations of Ellis Island, thousands of Jews poured into New York monthly until, by the turn of the century, they accounted for over a quarter of the city's population. These Jewish immigrants were the classic greenhorns.

Three distinct types characterized the teeming masses. Perhaps the most prominent group were the *shvitzers*, the hustlers driven by the desire to discover gold in the streets of America. Having jettisoned their cargo of Jewish observance long before they docked, they felt no commitment to tradition, only to getting ahead. And get ahead they did, advancing from sweatshop workers to managers, from subcontractors to contractors, from jobbers to manufacturers, from peddlers to shopkeepers, from retailers to wholesalers. Entrepreneurs, their sole interest was in making money, and within a generation they emerged as the *alrightniks*, satisfied with their accomplishments and acquisitions.

Then came the radical free thinkers, who wished to transplant their political ideology to America. Socialists, anarchists, and various combinations thereof, they came with ideas and ambitions shaped by the tyranny of absolutism and pogroms, and viewed America through the distorted looking glass of eastern European politics. Obsessed with theoretical questions that were thoroughly irrelevant to the "new world," they could arrive at no consensus regarding the nature of the revolution to come. So they rallied around their shared disdain for the so-called "clericalism" of traditionalist Jews, ridiculing mitzvah observance and instituting Yom Kippur balls and other public mockeries of Judaism.

The last group of greenhorns were the observant Jews themselves, who endeavored to transplant their time-honored practices and professions into their new milieu. Shunning the sweatshops, which operated on Shabbos, these immigrants preferred peddling from pushcarts. By 1888, they had established over 130 different congregations in New York.

These pious Jews looked around and saw themselves surrounded by exactly what their *landsleit* had predicted: *a treifa medinah. Chilul Shabbos* was rampant and Jewish education was at a nadir, with *kashrus* — its level of supervision pathetic — all but unobserved and assimilation already in high gear. Something had to be done.

Against the advice of those who understood the New Country better than they, the religious leaders naïvely decided to introduce in America the system of the chief rabbinate which had proved so effective in Europe. This form of organization could ensure a unified body to promote and direct religious observance and monitor the community's functionaries.

The proponents of the plan expected to finance the learned chief rabbi they would import from Europe by imposing a nominal tax on kosher meat. The very idea that a chief rabbi could operate authoritatively in the chaos of New York's uncontrolled freedom revealed how green these activists were.

Such an institution, subsidized by an unpopular tax, had indeed been the practice in eastern Europe, where it had worked mainly because the *kehillah* had functioned under governmental authority. In the "old world," the kosher meat industry had not been rife with corruption and scandal, or difficult to regulate or supervise.

Nonetheless, supporters of the plan gamely hammered out a constitution governing the rabbinate, which gave the chief rabbi absolute control over all religious matters. Specific guidelines were drafted concerning the issuance of *hechsherim*, one of the thorniest problems to be tackled.

Selecting a chief rabbi to enforce these by-laws was by no means a facile endeavor, but at least there was unanimity of purpose and resolve. There was but one search committee and a united consensus of every congregation in New York supporting its work.

While history bears dramatic testimony regarding the Providential emergence of our Nation's leaders, one cannot help but wonder: what compels gifted individuals to assume these positions?

Certainly not ambition, for any leader of a Torah community is by definition a paragon of modesty and most scrupulously avoids the limelight. Only one steeped in Torah values and imbued with a genuine love for his People can ever be the rabbi of a community, especially a community like New York.

No one fit this description better than Rabbi Yaakov Joseph. A brilliant disciple of the Volozhiner yeshivah, Rabbi Joseph possessed a saintly personality and powerful oratorical gifts.

His reputation obviously preceded him, for the day Reb Yaakov Joseph arrived in America — July 7, 1888 — bore all the trappings of a holiday. An enormous crowd, clothed in their festive attire, traveled to the port in Hoboken, New Jersey, to greet the chief rabbi. After this royal welcome, the assemblage escorted him all the way to his tastefully appointed new home at 263 Henry Street on New York's Lower East Side. The pomp and circumstance, however, were disarmingly ephemeral.

One might imagine that New York Jewry would have hailed the arrival of such a distinguished and beloved figure from the old country. Yet instead of showering him with garlands, groups without and within the traditional community began to assail and vilify a man they had never spoken to or even seen. No sooner had Rabbi Joseph unpacked his bags than the Anglo-Jewish press, controlled entirely by irreligious and even anti-religious elements, began spewing forth a torrent of furious condemnations.

Undaunted by his detractors, Reb Yaakov Joseph immediately set about achieving the objectives for which he'd been hired. His first goal was to improve the abysmal *kashrus* supervision in the slaughterhouses. Needless to say, ritual slaughterers and butchers alike resented Rabbi Joseph's interference. So did the residents of the Lower East Side, who were asked to pay a nominal tax to subsidize new *kashrus* supervisors. Joining in the protest were the rabbis who had lost their income when Rabbi Joseph and his *beis din* had pronounced their *hashgachos* unreliable.

As though the actual *kashrus* of the meat were irrelevant, the opposition contended that America was the "land of opportunity," and that this fanatical foreigner had no right to deny its citizens their prerogatives and privileges. In due time, the penny surcharge on certified-kosher chicken was dubbed "*karobka,*" the Czarist government's tax on kosher meat. Once this emotionally charged accusation had been leveled — conjuring up all the evils and persecutions the immigrant community had escaped from — reasonable discussion was impossible and the rabidly anti-religious press jumped into the fray feet first. Reb Yaakov Joseph was denounced as a scoundrel who delighted in bleeding poor widows and orphans with a tax levied only for his own gain and that of his wealthy patrons.

An *ad hominem* smear campaign (there isn't a more delicate term) was initiated, spearheaded by an association of butchers actively supported by the rabbis whose *hashgachos* had been rescinded by the rabbinate. Since the goals of the association had been clearly enunciated, its members had no reason to employ subtle tactics; their verbal assaults were explicit and direct and no holds were barred.

As this special-interest group was firing away, other factions began to plot and scheme. Jews of primarily Galician and Hungarian origin, for instance, claimed that the chief rabbinate was unfairly controlled entirely by *Litvaks,* as Reb Yaakov Joseph and all his *dayanim* were from Lithuania. The chief rabbi himself was willing to compromise on this point, but his overtures were rejected out of hand. Instead, without regard for the grave consequences of its actions, the Galician/Hungarian constituency hastily appointed their own chief rabbi. In a disastrous domino effect, the chasidim followed suit, squelching all hope of city-wide Jewish unity.

By now there was no longer even a modicum of meaning or dignity left to the office of the chief rabbinate. Notwithstanding, even after the rug had been yanked out from under his feet, Reb Yaakov Joseph continued to weather the storm, remaining a paragon of self-restraint and self-respect.

No matter what perfidious new charge was hurled at Rabbi Joseph — and the assaults were virtually limitless — he refused to stoop to the same shameless mudslinging that typified his opponents' tactics. Both in public and in private, he would not speak out against his detractors, and he even forbade his supporters to brand as *treif* any meat not slaughtered under his supervision (although its *kashrus* was dubious at best).

But as much as Rabbi Joseph tried to rationalize and excuse his critics' unpardonable behavior, his generosity was never reciprocated.

When the rabbinate attempted to levy a modest tax to offset the expense of supervising the production of matzah meal, Rabbi Joseph's enemies considered this the last straw. At less than a quarter of a cent per pound of matzah, this tax was minuscule, but it was rich fodder for the press and the mobs eager to do away with the chief rabbi once and for all. Whatever dwindling support Rabbi Joseph had retained now withered entirely and the rabbinate's sponsors found that they could no longer afford to pay him.

In a bitterly ironic twist of fate, Reb Yaakov Joseph was reduced to working as a simple *mashgiach* for the butchers of New York. Bereft of his title and an object of scorn, he eked out a living until 1895, when the butchers discontinued his salary. Thus Reb Yaakov Joseph, the pious scholar, kosher-consumer advocate, and tireless activist for Torah education and observance in America, was left penniless and without any source of income.

Remarkably, the avalanche of degradations failed to break the rabbi's proud spirit, but it did take a heavy toll on his health. Soon after he was robbed of his livelihood — and decades before the advent of Medicare or medical insurance — the former chief rabbi suffered a stroke that rendered him bedridden for virtually the remainder of his relatively short life.

What felled the office of the chief rabbinate and chipped away at Reb Yaakov Joseph in the process? One can point to several factors, but chief among them lies the inalienable American right to self-assertion, which was at loggerheads with *k'vod haTorah*. As the country that provides so many downtrodden peoples with the hope of an egalitarian life, the U.S. was hardly the place for a monolithic institution devoted to upholding the Torah's absolute standards. On the altar of personal freedom, *k'vod haTorah* was sacrificed, and with it this princely champion of Torah ideals as well as untold millions of Jewish souls that would never know or identify with their heritage.

How apt, then, that America's foremost symbol and prime victim of *bizayon haTorah* would yet provide a most inspiring affirmation of *chashivus haTorah*.

After years of confinement, isolation, and virtual abandonment by New York Jewry, Reb Yaakov Joseph regained the faculty of speech claimed by his stroke. This was truly cause for celebration, and Reb Yaakov Joseph could think of no more appropriate a way to articulate his gratitude than by delivering a *derashah* on *Shabbos Shuvah*.

Word spread that Reb Yaakov Joseph would be giving his first public lecture since New Yorkers could remember and attendance promised to be extremely high. After all, even the butchers could not deny (although the press certainly tried) that Rabbi Joseph was the finest orator in America.

Beis HaMedrash HaGadol on Norfolk Street, the largest shul on the Lower East Side, was packed to capacity a solid hour before the lecture was to begin. Hundreds were denied entrance but remained outside nonetheless to catch a glimpse of the ailing rabbi. As the mobs swelled, police were even called in to maintain order.

Approximately an hour later, slowly and feebly, Rabbi Joseph hobbled up to the very podium from which he had addressed a crowd of similar size upon his arrival fourteen years earlier. Now as then, a hush fell upon the assemblage, with everyone straining to hear every word.

But it was not the same Rabbi Joseph who had addressed them years before. The man who had stood before them then had sacrificed everything to travel to the new world and establish a new order in America. Now the speaker was the victim of those who had opposed that order.

"*Shteit in Rambam,*" America's greatest scholar began. Then he fell silent. Everyone craned his neck to catch the rabbi's next word, but it was not forthcoming. After a little while, the venerable rabbi's soft eyes filled with tears and his body heaved as he wept uncontrollably. When he finally regained his composure, he uttered his very last words ever to be delivered from the pulpit.

"Do you know what it is for me," he whimpered between sobs, "to forget a Rambam?" Unable to remember the quotation upon which he wished to base his address, the great *gaon* — luminary of Volozhin, *maggid* of Vilna, and apple of Reb Yisrael Salanter's eye — stepped down from the podium and sadly made his way home.

A more important address has yet to be delivered on the North American continent.

What was it that destroyed Reb Yaakov Joseph? Not the constant abuse and the daily insults; not the spurious accounts of his policies in the press; not even the ruthless butchers and their partners in sin. No. The inability to remember the words of the Rambam was the ultimate disgrace for the *tzaddik* who had countered abuse with respect and ignorance with scholarship. This was the monumental lesson in *chashivus haTorah* that Reb Yaakov Joseph managed to impart before his holy soul was summoned to the Heavenly Assembly.

We shall never know which Rambam Reb Yaakov Joseph had wished to quote at his *shiur*. But if the choice were ours, a meaningful citation would be the Rambam's inclusion of the laws of *k'vod haTorah* in his section entitled *Talmud Torah*, for quite simply, respect and honor for the Torah and its proponents are part and parcel of Torah learning and observance.

But if America's Jews were unable to bestow *k'vod haTorah*, they certainly knew how to bury it. On 24 Tammuz 5662 (July 28, 1902), Reb Yaakov Joseph died in his home on Henry Street. No doubt with a keen sense of guilt and remorse, the rabbinic leaders who survived him ruled that, in order to ensure proper respect for the deceased, the funeral should be delayed until July 30th to enable Jews from afar to attend. In the interim, New York's various congregations shamefully vied with each other for the honor of interring the rabbi in their shul's graveyard. His presence, they figured, would increase the value of the neighboring plots.

Mourners thronged to New York's Lower East Side from all over Jewish America. Travelers from as far away as the Midwest as well as trains from up and down the eastern seaboard were crammed with people wishing to finally award Reb Yaakov Joseph the respect that he deserved. The United Orthodox Rabbis of America estimated the size of the crowd at over 100,000 people, making it the largest funeral that New York had ever witnessed.

Despite this grand scale, everything progressed in an

orderly fashion — until the procession passed the large printing press factory of R. Hoe and Co., on the north side of Grand Street.

Near the corner of Sheriff and Grand streets is a triangular park formed by the acute-angled intersection of Grand and East Broadway. As the funeral cortege neared the park, the procession consolidated into four solid blocks following the hearse and its accompanying carriages.

The assembled advanced very slowly, not only due to the solemnity of the occasion but because they were inhibited in their progress by the multitudes of awestruck bystanders who sought to touch the hearse as an act of veneration. When the procession reached the park, it came to a virtual — and fateful — standstill.

The employees of R. Hoe and Co. were mostly Ukrainian immigrants noted for their vitriolic and frequently vented anti-Semitism. Consequently, when they looked out their windows, they were seized by an overwhelmingly insatiable craving for Jewish blood.

It did not take long for their devious minds to concoct a diabolical scheme to turn the funeral into an even more mournful occasion. The workers swiftly amassed every lethal-looking piece of debris on the premises and took up their positions. Then, in an unprecedented action taken on the shores "inhabited in order to establish justice, insure domestic tranquillity, provide for the common defense, and secure the blessings of liberty for ourselves and our posterity," a hail of fist-sized, iron nuts and bolts and a torrent of water from a fire hose rained down upon the defenseless masses.

The bedlam and confusion caused below generated great revelry and glee above. As scores of maimed and freshly wounded Jews lay soaked and bleeding on the street, some of their fellow mourners sought immediate retribution.

Umbrellas were thrust through the windows of R. Hoe's

ground floor while others availed themselves of heaps of stones and broken bricks from a nearby construction site. But the moment the mourners commenced their counterattack, the police on hand descended upon them, inflicting terrible beatings and arresting scores of innocent individuals.

As the police continued to bash heads and shout insults, the assault from above continued unabated, with the "missiles" becoming more and more deadly. In the chaos, the coffin was dropped as thousands sought refuge or vainly attempted to fight back. Eventually, the water that had drenched everyone below was shut off and, as a parting shot, the fire hose itself was tossed out the window and into the battered crowd.

Miraculously, the peaceful character of the cortege was eventually restored as the mourners regrouped to continue escorting Rabbi Joseph on his final journey. Along the way, however, police reserves who had been summoned from adjacent precincts arrived and deemed it only appropriate to make their presence known. Unexpectedly, and without any provocation, the policemen charged at the crowd, wielding clubs and hurling epithets as if they were in collusion with the employees of R. Hoe and Co.

The survivors, now about 25,000 strong, finally made it to the cemetery, where they laid Reb Yaakov Joseph — and the idea of a chief rabbinate in America — to rest.

Although Rabbi Yaakov Joseph only received the respect he deserved on the day he set foot on American soil and the day his body was interred in it, his passing inspired two important expressions of *k'vod haTorah.*

First, on the night after Reb Yaakov Joseph's funeral, America's greatest rabbis — who had traveled to New York expressly for this occasion from New Haven, Rochester, Boston, Pittsburgh, Cleveland, St. Louis, and elsewhere — swelled the ranks of those convening to discuss the plight of Torah education and mitzvah observance in America. The result was the inception of *Agudas HaRabbonim.*

Second, New York City enacted an ordinance mandating that a policeman be present at every funeral in New York City to maintain law and order.

The abominable behavior of the police at Rabbi Joseph's funeral was censured in an investigation commissioned by the honorable Mayor Seth Low. But to this day the presence of a police officer at every funeral is not, as most people imagine, to direct traffic; it is a tribute to the great *tzaddik* who sacrificed his life for *k'vod haTorah.*

Structural Instability

וַיַּעַשׂ בְּצַלְאֵל אֶת הָאָרֹן עֲצֵי שִׁטִּים אַמָּתַיִם וָחֵצִי אָרְכּוֹ וְאַמָּה וָחֵצִי רָחְבּוֹ וְאַמָּה וָחֵצִי קֹמָתוֹ.

And Betzalel made the ark of shittim wood; two-and-a-half cubits was its length, a cubit-and-a-half its breadth, and a cubit-and-a-half its height.
(Shemos 37:1)

According to the Midrash, when God commanded Moshe to build the *Mishkan*, Betzalel inquired, "Where will the Torah be placed?"

"First we'll erect the Tabernacle," Moshe replied, "then the *aron kodesh*, which will house the Torah."

"Moshe *Rabbeinu,*" Betzalel demurred, "that's no way to treat the Torah. First we should build the ark, and only afterward the *Mishkan*."

Because of Betzalel's concern for the Torah's honor, he merited that the construction of the *aron* be attributed to him by name. As it is written, "And Betzalel made the ark...."

The Jewish People began its spiritual life even before establishing its material well-being. We accepted the Torah at Sinai, a desolate region rife with snakes and scorpions, against which we were defenseless. And yet we embraced God's Law and cherished it with all our heart.

We were, in a sense, like an *aron kodesh* that welcomes the holy Torah scrolls and protects them from harm.

Ever since, we have been expected to observe and study the Torah in any situation — even under adverse conditions or when we are bereft of resources, for certainly our situation in the wilderness was no better.

Betzalel's argument fortifies this lesson. The honor of the Torah demands the construction of an ark to house it prior to the construction of the Tabernacle. First and foremost, the Torah must be secure; only then are walls erected around it.

Torah learning can thrive in the absence of a proper physical infrastructure. If financial viability and adequate enrollment were prerequisites for yeshivah construction, no house of study would ever be built.

Rabbi Dovid Dryan viewed his ritual slaughtering in the nascent Jewish community of Gateshead in the 1920s as a side line; he was chiefly engaged in fulfilling a mission. "A Jewish community must have a yeshivah," he maintained — an idea which sounded preposterous to the local residents. "Where will you find students and financing?" they questioned scornfully. But Reb Dovid was undaunted. Oblivious to their ridicule, he set out to recruit students.

After he succeeded in pursuading one boy and his parents to join his enterprise, he felt he could begin. The yeshivah was housed in the community's "tin hut" shul, which was more than adequate for the initial student body. On the opening day of the "yeshivah" Reb Dovid entered Gateshead's solitary store which carried kosher items, and said, "Please put this bread and butter on the 'yeshivah's account...'"

This first recruit served as a nucleus for the earliest students of "Yeshivahs Bais Yosef," Gateshead. A yeshivah must have a Rosh Yeshivah and so Reb Dovid turned to the Chofetz Chaim to select the appropriate scholar. Rabbi Nachman Landynsky, a graduate of the Novardhoker Yeshivah was the sage's choice. Only one schooled in the "outreach doctrine" of Novardhok would be willing to subject himself to such an exile.

Under the leadership of Rabbi Landynsky, the yeshivah began to grow until its enrollment numbered thirty students. In the late 1930s, however, a trickle of European emigrants began to escape to northern England, among them several *bachurim* who wished to continue their studies. Consequently, the Yeshivah began to expand and Rabbi Landynsky's insistence that a *menahel* was called for was vindicated. Several years earlier he had offered the job to his co-Novardhoker, Reb Eleazer Kahan — who had accepted the position.

The material responsibilities of the yeshivah remained in the hands of Reb Dovid Dryan. He found that the tangible existence of the yeshivah didn't make fundraising any easier. Wherever he went, people refused to accept the new reality and greeted him with ridicule. But the yeshivah's poverty was no laughing matter.

Another factor which impeded the yeshivah's development was the local climatic conditions and population. The weather in Gateshead is almost perpetually cold and rainy and the air is laden with soot from extensive coal mining in the region. The clouds, like the *shtenders* of the yeshivah, are carbon-coated and the odor of coal dust permeates the town.

The residents of the town were uneducated, ignorant coal miners who lived in drab, dismal surroundings. The town's major asset, from the perspective of the yeshivah, was that its total absence of distractions made it conducive to learning.

With the conclusion of World War II, Gateshead — originally a haven for a select few — became a refuge for hundreds of devout Jews. The yeshivah grew to a student body of 120 in a matter of weeks. But Reb Dovid still wasn't satisfied. A yeshivah of this size, he contended, must have a *kollel* (a project which actually got underway in 1940). And a *kollel* must have a *Rosh Kollel*.

Rabbi Eliahu Dessler, a noted scholar whose profundity of thought and oratorical abilities had made a tremendous impact in London, was selected for the job.

And the rest, as they say, is history.

From Lowly to Lofty

וַיַּעַשׂ אֵת הַכִּיּוֹר נְחֹשֶׁת וְאֵת כַּנּוֹ נְחֹשֶׁת בְּמַרְאֹת הַצֹּבְאֹת אֲשֶׁר צָבְאוּ פֶּתַח אֹהֶל מוֹעֵד.

And [Betzalel] made the washbasin of copper, and its pedestal of copper, out of the mirrors of the assembled women, who assembled at the entrance of the Tent of Meeting.

(Shemos 38:8)

Midrash Tanchuma relates that Moshe initially refused the mirrors which the women sought to donate to the Tabernacle, for he associated these furnishings with lust and vanity. Yet God declared, "Accept these gifts, for they are dearer to Me than others.... Through these mirrors, the women beautified themselves and produced multitudes of My people even in captivity." [Though Pharaoh had forbidden Jewish families to expand, the women defied him. The Midrash recollects, "As they fed their husbands, the women placed mirrors in view and teased, 'I am more attractive than you.' This tactic aroused desire, resulting in procreation."]

Why did God treasure the mirrors more than any other gift? That which is intrinsically holy, such as the priestly garments or the parchment of a Torah scroll, is static. However something profane or mundane which is used to achieve a sacred goal has the power to attain even greater heights of spirituality. The use of these copper mirrors in the *Mishkan* enhanced their already sanctified status.

Danny Horowitz never looked for trouble; he didn't have to. It sought him out with the accuracy of a heat-sensor missile homing in on a flame-throwing target — and with equally explosive results. From everything I've heard, "bedlam" was Danny's middle name, and that qualifies his story for inscription in the annals of yeshivah lore.

That Danny Horowitz eventually found his way to a safe and productive profession, and one that so serendipitously revolved around his penchant for science, was, perhaps, the most astounding event of his entire life. But in order to understand that, you'd have to know a great deal more about Danny Horowitz.

Now, the truth will usually endure a little embellishing, especially for a worthy cause, but in this particular case, there was no need to embellish. I have merely recorded the words of Danny's lifelong friend and admirer, who pledged up and down to their veracity, although in the end, I'll admit that doesn't amount to much of a guarantee.

You see, the source, Leibel Finkelstein, has a reputation for exaggeration and overstatement, a compulsion to rev up the facts. Most associates of Finkelstein consider it S.O.P. to discount 60 or 70 percent of anything he has to say. If Leibel were to tell you, for example, that he had been married four times, you could figure it was about a marriage and a half. It isn't a question of deceit. Just the opposite: he wants to spice up the truth a little, to make it so sharp that you can taste it exactly as he did.

For Leibel Finkelstein, a party to some of the events recounted herein, the facts, I think, were formed by sensation, instead of the other way around. When I listened to his tales of Danny Horowitz, I found myself performing rapid calculations in my head, subtracting superlatives, figuring the square root of an "absolutely," and then multiplying by "maybe."

Still, I have to hand it to Leibel: no matter how skeptical my gaze or quizzical my eyebrow, he never once backed down. He claimed either to have witnessed every detail of these events with his own eyes or to have heard about them first hand. When I challenged him about the bakery incident, from the fender to the shirt, he protested vehemently, insisting, "I was *there*! I was *there*!"

What he was referring to was the day Danny Horowitz decided to join his classmates who were *kashering* a local bakery. Under the watchful eye of their yeshivah's principal, Rabbi Nosson Greenfield, fifteen boys rubbed and scrubbed the place until it was surgically clean.

They went over every inch of counter space. Washed down all the bakery racks. Sterilized shelf after shelf, front and back. Sanded down the bench where the bread was made. And scoured the mixers.

The place was almost ready to receive Rabbi Greenfield's stamp of approval, when the two bakers who worked the early morning shift arrived. Shorty O'Brien and Vinny DiVito were products of two different cultures, from two different neighborhoods, with two different perspectives on life, but they kneaded well together.

"Not bad," they noted, bobbing their chins in unison. Indeed they were so impressed by the goings-on that they offered to pitch in and help the aching, perspiring boys. The air soon became redolent with the pungent fragrance of sweat and the bakery took on that unique aroma of a basketball locker room after double overtime. With these distinctive fumes wafting about him, Vinny removed his white silk Othello-of-Milan shirt.

"I don't wanna get dis baby dirty. It put me out eighty bucks," he said as he folded it up gingerly.

"Dat's all?" Shorty asked, admiring the high-style designer garment.

"Yeah, I bought it hot," Vinny explained, solving the mystery.

Danny, as usual, walked in late. And as usual, he didn't come emptyhanded. Sometimes he would have a live rabbit tucked under his arm, at other times an unfathomable science textbook, and frequently an unrecognizable object which his companions knew better than to inquire about. A question demanded an answer, and in Danny's case this meant either a protracted excursus, or a demonstration which always ended up with a *bang*!

On this particular occasion he was carrying a rather badly mangled car fender.

"Dis ain't no spare auto parts warehouse," Shorty O'Brien shouted to the latecomer above the cleaning din.

"Oh, I know that," Danny replied, placing the filthy fender down on the immaculate counter top. "Just a little accident." He smiled sheepishly. "You see, the only way I could avoid the dumpster behind the bakery was by taking a sharp turn into the parking lot. Miraculously there was a parking space right ahead of me, but it wasn't really meant for a vehicle of my car's dimensions. Come to think of it, I wonder if a bicycle would have fit into it. Anyway, I managed to squeeze in somehow, but I noticed that the cars on both sides of mine were sort of moving with me, know what

I mean? When I drove forward, so did they, and when I reversed, they did too. Aha! I deduced, our fenders must be engaged."

"*Mazel tov*!" fifteen voices wished as one, but Leibel claimed that the sardonic note was lost on Horowitz.

Undeterred, he continued describing his driving prowess. "I realized that any one of the cars could only leave the parking lot as part of a threesome, and that's probably more than their owners bargained for, not to mention the fact that the street isn't suited to triple parking even if you count the sidewalks. Furthermore, how would I ever find *my* car again, if it were driven off by a different driver in tandem with two others. The drawbacks were endless, so I did some incredible maneuvering to extricate my fender. And there you have it," he concluded, giving his fender a fond pat. "Quite literally, I might add.

"Well, now that I'm here, how can I help?"

"Grab a clean rag and start seasonin' d' pans," Vinny instructed. Stacks of brand-new bread pans and cake tins were piled against the wall. Before they could be used, they had to be well greased and the grease baked in.

Danny walked over to the corner, picked up a sturdy *shmatte* and immersed it in a five-gallon drum of cooking oil. He then carried the dripping cloth across the room, tracking up the floor as he went, and began to work the golden fluid into the iron-gray baking pans that had been collecting dust for weeks.

When this rag had served its purpose and gaping holes appeared in the material, Danny reached for a fresh *shmatte* and accorded it the same honor. In minutes, the formidable remnant bore not a trace of its former pristine whiteness; in fact, it was jet black. By this time Horowitz had really gotten into the swing of it and was applying all of his ample muscle to the chore. He attacked the next pan with vigor.

At this point, Vinny DiVito decided that he had finished his tour of duty and began to look for his shirt.

"Hey! Where is it?"

Shorty perked up. "Where's what?"

"My shirt. My good shirt."

"I dunno. Look around. Nobody baked it."

"I put it in dis corner. So it wun't get rooned."

A couple of the yeshivah students, eager to reclothe the gamy Vinny, joined in the search. DiVito's deportment, coupled with the manly aromas he was exuding, imbued them with a sense of urgency. One student thought he was onto something when he spotted the pile of rags in the corner. He sorted through the oil-drenched *shmattes*, examining the effect of grease on dirt until Horowitz brought him to an abrupt halt.

"There's nothing there," Danny called out. "Just filthy rags like this one here," and he held up the specimen he was working with.

For a moment that alabaster, niveous chalkiness, that canescent lactescence, that glistening snowy whiteness of the regal Othello-of-Milan pure silk eighty-smacker shirt reproduced itself in the color of DiVito's astonished face. But only for a moment. In milliseconds it was transformed into deeper and deeper shades of red, going from livid to violent in the blink of an eye. "DAT'S MY SHIRT!!!!!" he screamed, clutching a truncheon-sized rolling pin.

Vinny started sprinting across the bakery, dashing like a deer in hunting season, until he hit the trail of oil Danny had dripped on the floor. Impelled by a five-yard start, accelerated by a lust for vengeance, and fueled by Gold's Cooking Oil, DiVito crashed clangorously into an industrial mixer, the rolling pin clutched tightly in his hand, striking a stunning blow to his somewhat hollow cranium.

Horowitz was quivering with fear. In an involuntary gesture of throwing in the towel, he tossed DiVito's erstwhile shirt at the wounded baker accordioned into the mixer.

Vinny raised himself, removed the rolling pin from the furrow in his skull, and inspected the torn, streaked, greasy silk in his tremulous hands. In a voice one would normally attribute to Attila the Hun, he boomed out stereophonically, "YOU ROONED IT! MURDER-ER-ER!!!"

DiVito reached for the car fender and a quaking Danny Horowitz began to dictate his Last Will and Testament to the yeshivah guys who were standing around like hairy black-and-white trees in a petrified forest. "My set of magic tricks goes to Marty, my sci-fi books go to that freshman who keeps bugging me..."

In the midst of Danny's recitation and Vinny's wind-up before moving in for the kill, all eyes shifted to Shorty O'Brien, who had started laughing maniacally. "De kid killed ye shirt. You should have him arrested! You should have him collared! Get it? HAHAHAHAHAHA. Hey, I got a better idea! Put de cuffs on him! HAHAHAHAHA. *Buttonhole* him, Vinny! HAHAHA."

The boys nervously laughed along, hoping this diversion might effect a reprieve or earn a stay of execution. Vinny obviously wasn't amused, but Shorty couldn't stop laughing. In fact, DiVito was getting madder by the minute. The only reason he didn't go after someone was that he didn't know whom to hit first — the kid, or his partner.

At that critical moment seconds away from a bakery brawl, Rabbi Greenfield interceded. "Don't worry, sir," he said in a conciliatory tone while at the same time keeping well out of range. "The yeshivah, our school, that is, will shoulder the responsibility of reimbursing you for your shirt. As a matter of fact, I'll pay you back right now..."

"Back?" Shorty O'Brien repeated, laughing so hard he

was in tears. "Yeah, de Rabbi's gonna give you de shirt off his back! And he'll trow in de *shoulders* for nuttin. Just don't go near no oil spills! HAHAHAHAHAHA!"

Vinny lunged at his partner, who by this time was hysterical. "You tryin t' figure my neck size?" Shorty gasped as two meaty hands gripped his throat. "Wait! Get a new shirt! I'll pay for it. I'll pay for it! I saw more hot stuff dis mornin by dat street vendor dan dey got in de mall."

Vinny released his grip and Shorty whipped two crisp fifty-dollar bills out of his wallet.

"It was wort it, believe me," Shorty explained to the Rabbi. "Fer years we been workin side by side. Every day we plays jokes on each odder, but nuttin, *nuttin* ever even came close to dis!"

"Kid," Vinny said to Danny, "you're just lucky I'm a nice guy." DiVito slipped his car keys from his pocket and stalked out the door. As all of the boys resumed breathing, Danny ran out after the baker. Something about those car keys and the car make insignia on the chain made him fear that his own vehicle might be parked close, embracingly close, to DiVito's...

Talk about trouble, and Danny Horowitz's name always came up. If "bedlam" was his middle name, then "trouble" was his *nom de guerre*. Every science classmate of his can attest to that. On one less fortunate occasion than others, he carried out a science experiment that nearly ended up destroying the classroom, or so claims Leibel Finkelstein, unofficial Horowitz's High-Jinks Historiographer.

This particular incident started out innocently enough. Danny had exhumed the remains of an old Motorola television set from its curbside grave and lugged it laboriously some six blocks to the yeshivah. After denuding it of its cabinet and chassis, Horowitz attached a solar cell to the exposed picture tube for experimental purposes.

Simplicity was never Danny's aim. His presentation was intended to be both dramatic and captivating, not to mention innovative. Nothing pleased him more than to have his classmates sit enraptured before him as he played pedant and engaged in lengthy discourses. And nothing pleased *them* more than to kill a frequently boring hour of Mr. Sharf's science lesson with one of Danny's diversions.

The class found Horowitz's latest prop irresistible, and the teacher agreeably turned over his mantle to the would-be scientist. At first Danny passed his hand over the solar cell and the screen turned dark; then he removed it, and the screen turned light.

"Magic!" the class chimed in unison.

Since the first experiment had been such a huge success, Danny decided that the time was ripe to teach his classmates the rudiments of circuitry. He plugged in the television and began to explain how electric current travels. At one especially salient juncture, Danny raised his screwdriver, for want of a wooden pointer, for emphasis. Somewhere between describing the reaction to ambient conditions and the dispatch of an analog signal, Danny connected with current events and got the shock of his life.

What happened next would have been disqualified from *Ripley's Believe It or Not* as outrageously unbelievable. Hundreds of volts of electricity surged through Danny's arm, sending him three feet into the air. The screwdriver was released on the upswing and scored a direct hit to the wall clock, which came tumbling down.

This clock was not to have an uneventful journey in its conformance to the law of gravity. It landed (first) on a tall bookcase, dislodging several oversized textbooks. The tomes, in collusion with the clock (or what was left of it), tipped over the gerbil cage, emancipating the rodents in a rather spectacular way.

Leibel Finkelstein took a deep breath before he described what happened next. Mere words, perhaps, cannot do justice to Leibel's superb graphic rendition of a screwdriver in flight, a clock freefalling through a vertical textbook labyrinth, and gerbils excitedly celebrating their manumission. Trust me; it was awe-inspiring.

Books that were still tumbling from the shelf struck by the clock sent the gerbils into a panic. They scurried hither, thither and yon, colliding like furry bumper cars and emitting heart-rending squeaks and squeals from their inarticulate little throats. The science teacher, who was preparing to celebrate his wedding anniversary that evening, hadn't bargained on the day's turn of events and had unfortunately placed upon his desk a vase of flowers which he had intended to bring home to his wife.

The vase and its contents were in the direct path of the terror-driven rodents who unwittingly were about to receive their first swimming lesson. Not only did two pints of water and four daisies, two tulips, three carnations, ten roses, five chrysanthemums, seven tiger lilies, six gladioli, eight gardenias, and a wisp of wisteria give the gerbils the most aromatic wash of their lives, it also wreaked havoc on the students' science term papers innocently awaiting their grades. They began to hemorrhage blue and black ink down the front of the desk and all over the floor.

In the meantime, the original culprit (the screwdriver — not Danny Horowitz) shorted the television set, which began to convulse in protest. At first the faces of those seated in front of the TV were lit up in tones of first-degree-burn pink and cobalt-therapy blue. Their technicolor complexions then turned black as smoke belched from the TV and sparks flew through the air, triggering the schoolroom sprinkler system.

The overcast skies seemed to derive smug satisfaction from the showers deluging the formerly (although briefly) cheerful students in Danny's class. But in fact the action was only just beginning. The sprinkler system not only soaked everything and everyone; it also automatically activated the yeshivah's fire alarm and alerted the municipal fire department.

With alarm bells clanging, fire engine klaxons sounding, police car sirens wailing, students yelling, gerbils fleeing, water soaking, flowers floating, books sinking, and the TV stinking, Danny and his classmates made their way out of the science classroom and into the pages of history.

Leibel Finkelstein got very animated when he told this part of the story and his cadence quickened. Then he paused to mention that this was all a preamble to one of Danny's more monumental encounters with science.

Leibel explained that Danny really loved science, especially chemistry. Once in a lab, he was truly in his element — only it was one never to be found on the periodic tables. Surrounded by test tubes, beakers and burettes, awash in a sea of chemicals, he could concoct and titrate for hours. Even the TV-sprinkler fiasco could not dampen Danny's craving to experiment.

Compounding this love was an affection for science fiction, although his mother could have rightfully argued it was more of an affliction. Danny read every author he could get his hands on, from Asimov to Heinlein to Pohl and back again. If a new book came out, Danny was sure to have it. Marty Schmidt, Danny's roommate, was just as devoted to his stereo, the headphones of which seeming to be a natural outgrowth of his skull. So it wasn't long before the two boys became known as Hi-Fi and Sci-Fi.

If ever there was an unusual pair of roommates in this yeshivah, where in fact everyone was unusual and no one, absolutely *no one*, at least upon entering those hallowed halls, was stereotypically *yeshivish*, Horowitz and Schmidt were they. The two had an insatiable hunger for their hobbies, Horowitz — science, and Schmidt — electronics, much to the dismay of Rabbi Greenfield.

One day, as Danny sat voraciously reading the latest science fiction blockbuster, he emitted a long, low whistle, the kind that Marty knew meant trouble.

"Uh, oh. What's up?" he asked.

"I'm reading an explosive book."

"You mean it's really exciting?"

"No, I mean it explains how to make explosives. It's sort of like an anarchist's cookbook. I can hardly wait to try some of the recipes. They seem a cinch."

"Cinch? What about safe?"

"Don't worry. I'm real good at this stuff. When did I ever mess up an experiment?"

Schmidt eyed his roommate, looking for latent signs of dementia. He then began to reenact the recent TV episode, his hands simulating scurrying gerbils and sprinkling water. After this he folded his arms across his chest and set his features in an expression that seemed to shout, "Well, what do you have to say about *that*?"

Danny suddenly remembered the solar cell fiasco. "All right, so I do get carried away once in a while," he conceded, "but you have to admit it was a whole lot better than a pop quiz from Mr. Scharf."

Weeks passed and although Marty had forgotten all

about Danny's machinations, wood was burning in Horowitz's head as he contemplated his next science project. The result was a refined mix of gun powder and other combustibles sure to provide plenty of bang for the buck. (Un)fortunately, Purim was approaching, and this fact suggested an idea to Danny for how to inaugurate his latest product.

Horowitz's tinkering went virtually unnoticed by his class- and dorm-mates since each was so preoccupied with his own Purim *shtick* and costumes. These matters were of little concern to Danny, but Marty pressed him as to his choice of Purim persona. "You gotta decide, Danny. You need time to get your getup together."

"It's already decided."

"Oh, yeah? Well, what are you going as?"

"A MAD SCIENTIST!" the mad scientist announced triumphantly.

"For that you have to dress up?!"

"Wait until you see my props!" he replied, and Marty knew enough not to inquire further.

Purim night, which also happened to be the night of the yeshivah's big Purim *shpiel* — a major event in this yeshivah perhaps better known for its *shpiel* than for its level of learning — there were no absentees. The costumes were as varied as the personalities of their wearers. There were Biblical characters (one student dressed up as all twelve tribes), political characters ("You won't have me to kick around anymore!"), cartoon characters ("T-T-T-That's all folks!"), and plain old characters, some resembling neither animal, vegetable or mineral. Then there were the weirdos, like the guy dressed as a CD player ("Guess what I am!" [no one did]), to mention some of the less original getups.

Danny was clad in a lab coat, the pockets of which were bulging with oversized test tubes filled with an unidentified gray powder, that was Danny's own brew. This moonshine contained: 1) saltpeter, KNO_3 (potassium nitrate), 75%; 2) powdered charcoal, C (carbon), 14%; 3) powdered sulfur, S, 10%; 4) several drops of water, H_2O, 1%. Protruding from each tube was an extremely long wick which, by Leibel's account, had done previous duty as a gym sneaker shoelace.

After the *shpiel* was over, spirits were high and the boys began to dance and drink with great abandon. Soon they felt it was too stuffy in the school building so they went outside for some sobering fresh air. Shimie Nussbaum, looking as much like Humphrey Bogart as a yeshivah student could, was fooling around with a cigarette lighter. He wore a dirty tan trench coat, a wide-brimmed hat placed rakishly on his crown, and had a cigarette dangling from the corner of his mouth.

According to Leibel, Shimie Nussbaum could not be blamed for what happened next. He was already in his cups and the temptation was overwhelming. Thus, without giving it too much thought, or certainly not more than could be expected from him in his condition, Nussbaum took the cigarette lighter and lit one of the long wicks sticking out of Horowitz's lab coat. Had he only considered for a moment the kind of ingredients Horowitz was likely to have packed into a test tube, the landscaping around the yeshivah might have retained its original appearance, but that was not to be.

When Danny caught on to what was transpiring, nanoseconds before it was too late, a seizure of fear overcame him. The powder keg about to detonate in his pocket made Vinny DiVito's grip on Shorty O'Brien's throat seem like hush puppies.

"Shema Yisrael!" he shouted, covering his eyes with one hand and tossing the tube as far as he could with the other.

Leibel claims that the test tube exploded just before it hit the ground, but he conceded that there were other witnesses present, admittedly not in full possession of their faculties, who contest this moot point. In any event, an ear-shattering KABOOOOM!!!!! was heard, resulting in a scene that would have done Hollywood proud.

The dancing suddenly came to a dead halt and the boys began to flee in two directions: some ran to the sight of the explosion for a better view, and some ran for cover.

"Who did it?"

"What happened?"

"Did you see the flame?"

"Wow! Look at that crater!"

"Where's the meteor?"

Indeed a mighty hole was gouged out of the earth and two nearby trees now collapsed into each other's leafy embrace. "We kinda thought it looked pretty special," Leibel said later, but apparently Rabbi Greenfleld didn't share their opinion. As a matter of fact, he seemed considerably irritated, but that was before he'd surveyed the damage from close up. Once he'd gotten a better look, his face went Othello-of-Milan white.

He thumped his palm against his head several times and then sought out the one who was sure to be the culprit.

"Mr. Horowitz?"

"Reporting, sir."

Rabbi Greenfield stood silent for a moment, at a temporary loss for words. The product of a far more conventional yeshivah, he was accustomed to boys being admonished for raiding the *cholent* pot Friday night, for not showing up for *minyan*, and other semi-excusable misdemeanors. These kinds of infractions would have been practically a blessing in this yeshivah.

Nevertheless, nothing that he had seen since taking over the helm of the academy was even in the same stratosphere as what Horowitz had just perpetrated. Danny remained stationary and the other boys crowded around, pleading with their eyes for Rabbi Greenfield not to spoil their Purim fun. For long seconds the two stood there until Rabbi Greenfleld finally allowed a twinkle to enter his eyes. "Will you kindly cease and desist from any further attempts to alter the yeshivah's architecture or grounds." It was more a prayer than a request.

"I'll try."

And Danny Horowitz did try, until one hot, muggy night in early June. The day Danny was put to the test, and failed, is in part a funny story. Yet to hear Leibel Finkelstein tell it, you'd think it was intended as a straight tragedy. Leibel never once smiled, even as he described Danny's crazy antics. There was a dark, far-off look in his eyes, a kind of existential sadness, as if he were troubled by something hidden beneath the story's surface.

Whenever an audience laughed at Leibel's rendering, he would sigh and wait it out, displaying a modicum of tolerance. The one thing that he couldn't stand, though, was disbelief. He'd always get edgy if someone questioned one of the details.

Leibel would peer down at his hands, silent and thoughtful. After a moment his voice would flatten out. Then he'd tell the audience to listen up.

"You don't believe it?" he would challenge. "Fine with me. But you just don't know how science was a part of Danny Horowitz and how unusual a group of boys it was that made up that yeshivah.

"The humidity must have been 98%," Leibel said, scanning the sky with his eyes as if the weather report were written there. It was so hot that even the least studious boys were drawn into the *beis midrash* where there was air conditioning. Since the yeshivah was located on the perimeter of the inner city, it had to contend, all too often, with hostilities from the natives. The frequency of incidents seemed to have a direct correlation to the weather: "hot summer in the city" was often a catalyst for trouble.

On this memorable night, Leibel said, they came en masse, maybe twenty of them, brandishing ice picks, chains, and a cool, blank, doped-up look which was anything but friendly.

They began with the obscenities. The shouts, taunts, curses and foul-mouthed insults were almost unintelligible due to the local dialect, but the general idea was adequately conveyed. Obviously they were looking for a response, a counter-provocation, as it were, indeed any excuse to strike, but the yeshivah boys knew better than to get involved.

The failure to react infuriated the hooligans. Their fearless leader, a man whose head bore a striking resemblance to a bowling ball and had about as much sense, took charge. Rufus "Sly" Brown (everyone knew his nickname, Leibel inserted), menacingly hefted a rock.

"Watch dis!" he boasted and hurled the iron and manganese missile at one of the farthest windows. It crashed through the glass, accompanied by a shower of slivers.

Shimie Nussbaum, who had been watching the developments, concluded that the time had come to react. He tore into the *beis midrash* looking for Hi-Fi and Sci-Fi. "We're under attack!" he yelled. "And it's not a bunch of kids, it's a whole army this time! Marty, do you still have your PA system rigged up?"

"Shh!" Marty silenced him, afraid someone would hear. A few months earlier Marty had assembled a primitive public address system throughout the dormitory, for use in the event of a surprise inspection.

"Good," Shimie said, not bothering to lower his voice. "Get on the horn and tell everyone to man their stations." He turned to Horowitz. "Danny, do you have any more of your bombs?"

"Well, uh, er, kinda. I mean, maybe, but you know what Rabbi Greenfield said to me."

"Are you kidding?" Shimie asked, incredulous. "That was then, and this is now! This is a national disaster, a local calamity, our honor is at stake, the ozone layer is in peril, peace and brotherhood for all is on the line!"

According to Leibel, Shimie Nussbaum started waxing profound, spewing nonsense fast and thick. Although he clearly had no idea what he was talking about, he must have known what he was doing, because whatever it was that he said had the desired effect. In seconds Hi-Fi and Sci-Fi were dashing to the dormitory under a hail of rocks and obscenities hurled by Sly and his comrades in arms.

While Nussbaum was coordinating the counterattack, Rabbi Greenfield was resorting to more conventional means, like calling the police. The city's constabulary, however, had more important things on their mind that hot summer night, like finding some cold lemonade and similar matters of vital civic necessity. He might as well have called the Canadian Mounties and waited for them to arrive from the Yukon.

By the time Marty had alerted the boys and told them what to do and where to go, the natives had broadened their attack to encompass breaking car windows and snapping off radio antennas.

Shimie outfitted a battalion of freshmen with baseball bats and wooden screw-on legs from their dorm beds, but they were afraid to go out onto the battlefield. "Time to reconnoiter," he said and climbed up to the roof to get a better perspective on the situation. From that vantage point, he could see that things were deteriorating rapidly. He ordered Danny to let the first barrage fly. Horowitz, however, was still tinkering with the ingredients and wasn't quite ready.

Meanwhile, back at ground zero, Sly was accessing his rich criminal record for ideas as to how to expand the adventure. It didn't take him long. "Hey, man," he addressed his First Lieutenant. "Whaddaya say we trash de buildin'?"

"Dat's cool," Meathead agreed. "Les go!"

The twenty-man-strong phalanx started sauntering their way over. The lawn between the parking lot and the dormitory began to look like a giant caterpillar as the twenty gentlemen proceeded bopping up and down with a pumping gait, towards their objective.

Time was running out and Danny was still messing with his concoction. Shimie, always one to turn a disadvantageous situation into an advantageous one, or at least to make it appear like one, ordered, "Don't shoot 'til you see the whites of their eyes!" The irony of the directive was lost on the terrified students huddled together on the roof.

"Danny," Schmidt pleaded, "it's now or never. Let 'em have it!"

"Bombs away," Danny called, tossing the first test tube over the ledge. The teeth-rattling BOOM! that resulted heartened and emboldened his classmates and the second test tube was accompanied by a salvo of soda bottles, baseballs and select garbage.

The natives didn't know what hit them. Probably no one else in the world did either, except for Danny Horowitz and some science fiction writer. Meathead suffered a direct hit, and although he was dazed, there was no other noticeable effect.

"Hey, man!" Sly called out to his troops. "Dey got grenades! Les get outa here!" And ten times as fast as they had bopped in, they bopped out. Bombs bursting in air and a barrage of garbage causing a glare, gave proof through the night that the natives could beat a hasty retreat.

"Hurray! We got 'em!" the heroes manning the ramparts rejoiced. "The Guardian of Israel neither sleeps nor slumbers!"

"How could He," asked Hi-Fi, "with Danny Horowitz and his firecrackers?"

The boys were exuberant over their victory and immediately began planning a celebration when suddenly the wail of a police siren split the night. "Uh, oh," Danny whispered, knowing whom they would finger as the prime suspect.

"Flush the rest of the stuff down the toilet," Hi-Fi ordered. "You guys didn't see, hear or do a thing. Got it?"

Officers Sullivan and Munisteri arrived at the yeshivah with Rabbi Greenfield on their heels. The two officers just couldn't believe what they were seeing. Fresh craters pockmarked the lawn, making it look as though the moon had come to planet Earth. The acrid and unmistakable odor of gunpowder made tongue and eyes smart.

"Whatcha guys got here," Sergeant Sullivan asked, "a Howitzer?"

"No," an anonymous voice came from the rear of the crowd, "a Horowitzer."

The comment was lost on the cops, but as soon as Rabbi Greenfield heard Danny's name, he directed the minions of the law away from the dormitory and into his office. Rabbi Greenfield preferred that the police focus their investigation on the culprits who had started the incident, not on the mad scientist who had finished it.

Later that night, Sly was arrested again, on the grounds of attempting to cause bodily harm and property damage, but was eventually released because no one could positively identify him. "Too bad he wasn't arrested on the grounds of the yeshivah," Leibel commented.

Three months later Hi-Fi and Sci-Fi graduated from high school, and Rabbi Greenfield breathed a deep sigh of relief. In fact, Leibel added, Danny wished to stay on in yeshivah, but Rabbi Greenfield gently refused. He recommended that Horowitz spend the coming year at a yeshivah in Israel, in the hope that the boy would benefit from the Rabbinic dictum, "Change your spot, change your lot."

Not long after Danny arrived in Israel, he entered a bookstore to purchase some *sefarim*. This would be his attempt number who-knows-what at making it in yeshivah. According to Leibel, Danny's spirits were so depressed that he was not only praying for a solution, he was willing it. And there it was, in the bookstore.

It wasn't a glamorous kind of salvation, like a Heavenly Voice calling his name, a miracle unfolding before his eyes, a twinkling star, or Mr. Fortune fortuitously bumping into him. It was just a little sign which hung behind the counter.

DUE TO THE INCREASE IN THE COST
OF MATERIALS FOR INK, CAUSED BY THE ARAB
EMBARGO, ALL ITEMS WRITTEN ON PARCHMENT
HAVE INCREASED IN PRICE BY 30%.

"What do the Arabs have to do with the ingredients of ink?" Danny asked the man behind the counter. The salesman replied that ink was made from gall nuts and gum arabic which is produced in Arab countries like Syria, and the Arabs were carefully monitoring the export of their chemical products to ensure that they did not end up in Israel. "We get them, of course," the proprietor continued, "but it means paying extra duties because they have to go through several hands and come from more distant places."

Alarms and klaxons began ringing with urgency in Danny's head. For once they weren't the familiar wail of police sirens but the long-lost sound of his Divine calling. The opportunity to Make A Contribution.

Danny discovered that the ink used for all *parshiyos*, e.g., *tefillin, mezuzos* and *sifrei Torah*, contains tannic or garlic acid as the active ingredient. This is mixed with ferrous sulfate, FSO_4, which makes the compound black; separately, the two ingredients are clear.

The conventional method of manufacturing ink requires boiling all of the ingredients with gum arabic and then decanting for two weeks. As Danny began tackling the problem of economical substitutes for these ingredients, he discovered a far more significant problem with the conventional recipe. Since the ink is produced from ferrous or iron sulfate, after a while the ink oxidizes and begins to rust, creating a significant halachic problem. If the ink is no longer black, it is no longer kosher.

Danny put his scientific head to the problem and came up with a viable solution by adding inert ingredients to the formula which would prevent the oxidation process from taking place.

For once the Danny Horowitz Law which ensures a bang didn't work, but appropriately, it did cause an explosion — an explosion in Jewish observance. From a greasy shirt, to gun powder, to science demos, Danny ultimately found his place by developing a product that Jews are using and benefiting from worldwide.

"And," Leibel added with finality, "that's the truth!"

False Accusation

אֵלֶּה פְקוּדֵי הַמִּשְׁכָּן מִשְׁכַּן הָעֵדֻת אֲשֶׁר פֻּקַּד עַל פִּי מֹשֶׁה...

These are the accounts of the Tabernacle, the Tabernacle of the Testimony, as they were counted according to the commandment of Moshe...

(Shemos 38:21)

Why was it necessary to present a detailed accounting? The Midrash explains that Moshe specified all the costs of the Sanctuary primarily to silence those who suspected him of diverting certain contributions for personal use. To demonstrate how every donation was used properly, and how Moshe *Rabbeinu* was unfairly misjudged, the Torah inventories the entire Tabernacle.

He called himself Pincus, but he was better known as "the Professor." And just as he had no name, he had no home. Instead, he wandered from place to place, and from town to town, staying where he could for as long as he could. If you asked him where he was last, he would sigh and tell you that due to man's inhumanity to man, he had been forced to sleep in a variety of locales over the past several weeks, ranging from a bus station in New York to a park bench in Philadelphia.

Pincus ate sporadically and sparingly, his fare usually consisting of whatever his co-religionists could provide. Although he never asked for anything special, he did have a penchant for eggs, which was advantageous because he had been served thousands of them during the days and weeks and months and years that he had been on the road.

Actually, no one really knew how long he had been wandering. It seemed that he had been doing it forever, almost like the hidden mystics of old who would spend their time in a self-imposed exile, doing *mitzvos* and helping others. And maybe, just maybe, he was one of them: a man who spent his life giving others the opportunity to fulfill the mitzvah of *hachnasas orchim*.

Admittedly, not everyone subscribed to this theory. The local rabbi and the caretaker of the Hebrew Sheltering Society of Scranton, Pennsylvania, certainly did not. To them the Professor was just another drifting soul who came often and stayed longer than most at their facility.

Over the years, Rabbi Daniel Gellman had seen and served hundreds of Jews, Jews who for one reason or another ended up on the steps of the Hebrew Sheltering Society. There was the young Israeli who had met a nice American girl in Haifa and followed her halfway around the world, only to find out that she couldn't even remember his name. And the father of a seven-year-old girl from Montreal, who came collecting money for his daughter's operation and ran back when she called to tell him she missed him.

There were, of course, the cons and the crazies — people who, *nebach*, just couldn't fit in anywhere. Like the self-proclaimed presidential candidate whose family kept him on the campaign trail for years. And the retiree who tried to turn a two-night stay into a twelve-month vacation. Rabbi Gellman smiled when he thought of how he had convinced that one to leave. After a week of excuses, it was obvious that the man just didn't want to go. So Rabbi Gellman told him that, starting tomorrow, he would be charged five dollars a day rent. By 7:00 the next morning the pensioner was out the door.

Finally, there were those whom the Hebrew Sheltering Society really ended up helping, like the man with six kids whose car broke down on the way to Pittsburgh. Trying to put six lively little ones to bed without disturbing the other "guests" was quite a challenge. Then there was the wealthy doctor, who could have comfortably checked into the best hotel in the city, but who stayed at the Sheltering Society, where the food and the environment were both kosher.

Yes, there were a lot of different people who lodged at the Hebrew Sheltering Society, but the Professor was certainly one of the most colorful, for two reasons: first was the way he talked. Pincus boasted a florid vocabulary in English and fluency in Greek and Latin. Rumor had it that he was a former Classics professor who had suffered a nervous breakdown. But no one had ever bothered to find out for sure.

The second unique aspect of the Professor's personality was his self-esteem. He would become deeply insulted if it was even hinted that he was indigent, or limited in any way. The fact is that he always seemed to have enough cash to come and go as he pleased — a privilege acquired, according to hearsay, by selective borrowing from available *pushkas*. This hypothesis had as much corroboration as the one about his former occupation. But because of the Professor's lofty self-image, helping him out had certain restrictions: anyone could provide him with a meal, or some sort of clothing, like a "new" used hat, but woe to the individual who as much as insinuated that Pincus was in some way incapable of taking care of himself or his affairs.

Regardless of the rumors, Pincus was upright, and God-fearing, didn't bother anyone, and didn't want anyone to bother him. And that is exactly what made the episode with the lawyer so strange and puzzling.

It all started on a Tuesday night, when the Rabbi received a call from Max, a retired tailor who served as the caretaker of the Society's house on Chestnut Street. Part of the Rabbi's responsibilities as the local spiritual leader was to administer the shelter's admissions policy.

"Rabbi, we got a new customer. His name is Jake Birnbaum. He says he's a lawyer who needs a place to stay for a while. Can you stop by when you get a chance?"

"Yes, of course," Rabbi Gellman answered. "I'll be there within the hour."

In a matter of minutes Rabbi Gellman was at the Society's headquarters to meet Jake Birnbaum. Interviews of this nature were usually very brief. Papers had to be filled out and the rules of the house explained so that there would be no misunderstandings.

But one look at Birnbaum and Rabbi Gellman knew he could forgo the standard explanations.

The prospective shelteree was about six feet tall, with sparse brown hair and tortoiseshell glasses. In manner, in appearance and in expression, Birnbaum looked every bit the dignified corporate lawyer. His cashmere overcoat had the unmistakable cut of quality that only comes from expensive clothing purchased at the "right" shops. His gray pinstripe suit was obviously tailor-made. It was all wrinkled, however. Its rumpled condition indicated to the Rabbi that the wearer had recently spent a lot of time on a train or bus.

"If you don't mind my asking," Rabbi Gellman interjected into an otherwise *pro forma* procedure, "what brings you to Scranton?"

The attorney smiled wearily, his face etched with lines formed by both physical and mental exhaustion. "I attended law school around here twenty years ago. After I passed the bar I got married, moved to Florida, and set up a practice.

"We've been married for close to eighteen years, but now

my wife wants out. Just last week she filed for divorce. To tell you the truth, I was tempted to fight it to the very end. But now I feel that I shouldn't be motivated by spite. I realized that the fastest and least painful way to finish things was simply to walk away. And so, Rabbi, I left everything with her."

"I'm sorry to hear that. Our Sages tell us that the Divine Presence sheds tears whenever a Jewish marriage comes to an end. Needless to say, if I can be of assistance, please don't hesitate to ask. Max is responsible for the day-to-day operation of the house. Nadja, the Russian lady you may have seen, cooks and cleans for us. In the meantime, welcome, and please make yourself comfortable."

The Professor happened to be strolling down the hall and had come into the room to make sure he didn't miss anything interesting. "I overheard your tale of pain and woe, my esteemed friend, and I commiserate with you in your circumstances. I, like yourself, have been a victim of maltreatment by both individuals and institutions and have always attempted to handle my affairs in the most pragmatic manner possible. My lifetime experience is at your disposal."

"Thank you, sir," Jake smiled. "And mine is at yours."

Everything went smoothly the following week. Birnbaum spent his time interviewing with different firms in the area, and Pincus spent his time "researching the stacks" at the city library.

Late one afternoon, Max was walking by Jake's room when he heard a noise inside. Max knew that Jake was gone for the day; whoever was inside obviously knew it too.

One of the Hebrew Sheltering Society's rules was that no locks were allowed on the guests' rooms. However, it was understood that everyone's privacy was to be respected. Needless to say, someone was not respecting it right now.

Quietly and slowly, Max opened the door a crack and

peered in. The room was dim, but it only took a moment for his eyes to adjust. From the daylight that rimmed the closed window shades, Max could make out a bent form in a long trenchcoat searching through Jake's room. It was the Professor!

"PINCUS!" Max shouted as he pushed the door wide open. The Professor jumped, a startled look of guilt and shame coloring his face.

"What are you doing in here?" Max demanded.

"I... I... I was..." Pincus seemed to be frantically searching for an excuse. "I... I was looking for the attorney's newspaper," he blurted out. "It had an article on Third World economic policy and its impact on lending institutions in the U.S."

Max smiled in spite of himself and his anger. "Third World, my foot! You're looking for something else! Now beat it! And don't even think of coming back into Jake's or anybody else's room without permission!"

"I was not thinking anything of the sort! However, I see my innocence and unimpeachable integrity are being questioned!" Pincus ad-libbed in an effort to salvage his pride. But he still looked (and felt) like a little boy who got caught with his hand in the cookie jar.

As upset as Max was, and despite his innate, long-standing aversion to Pincus, he still had compassion for the pitiful sight of the Professor. His greasy trenchcoat hung like a mantle of disgrace on his bent shoulders. "Oh, God," Max invoked, "please help this man find himself."

That night, Max reported the episode to Rabbi Gellman. "Since I caught the Professor trying to steal, don't you think we should make him leave?" Max urged.

Rabbi Gellman thought silently for a moment. "I don't believe he wanted to take anything. I think he was simply curious."

"Curious?"

"It could be he that wanted to learn more about a man who would give up everything he had just to make peace between himself and his discontented wife."

"I'm not so sure. You know, he could take something out of Birnbaum's suitcase and sell it before anyone would be the wiser. Maybe the Professor has overstayed his welcome."

Rabbi Gellman looked at him and said finally, "Let's give him another chance. In *Pirkei Avos,* we find that Hillel taught, 'Do not judge your fellow man until you have stood in his place.' I've always found that to be sound advice."

Here the matter rested, and once again things settled into a routine. According to the rules, guests were allowed to stay a maximum of two weeks at the Sheltering Society. If space was available, they could rent a room for five dollars a day after that. For Pincus, the two weeks were almost up and he couldn't afford more than a few days' rent before heading out. It was late November and the raw winds of winter were just starting to be felt. This time of year Pincus would usually try making his way as far down south as possible. That way, if he ended up sleeping on a park bench, he wouldn't freeze.

On the last morning Pincus would be able to stay at the Sheltering Society without paying, Jake came down to the kitchen as Max was sipping a cup of coffee and Nadja was washing the dishes. As she worked, she hummed a Russian folk tune. The Professor was assiduously stuffing food into his mouth and into the pockets of his trenchcoat. His duffel bag was lying on the floor, bulging at the seams with all his tight-worldly possessions. Jake whispered unobtrusively to Max, "I have to talk to you privately."

The two men casually left the kitchen and went into the living room. Jake looked overwrought. "My cashmere overcoat is missing!" he said. "I've looked all over for it and it's gone. I'm sure I left it here."

Max's eyes rolled back in their sockets. "I knew it! I just knew there'd be trouble!"

"What do you mean?" Jake asked.

"I caught Pincus in your room the other day. He was obviously searching for something. You don't think these bagmen carry only refuse and broken umbrellas in their shopping bags, do you?"

"Well, what do we do? Confront him?"

"First, I'll call Rabbi Gellman. And then..." he added gravely, "I'm calling the police."

Back in the kitchen, Pincus sensed that Jake and Max were talking about him. If something was wrong he didn't want to be in the middle of it. The clock ticked away the minutes, but still Max and Jake did not return to the breakfast table. Pincus quickly finished his meal and shoved whatever edibles he could walk away with into his duffel bag. It was way too heavy to carry, so he started dragging it across the floor.

"Hold it right there, Pincus!" Max said sharply, striding into the kitchen. "Rabbi Gellman is on his way here to speak with you."

"What for? I have committed no crime!" the Professor said defensively.

"We'll let the Rabbi decide that!" And almost as if on cue, Rabbi Gellman walked briskly into the kitchen.

"Pincus, please come with me into the living room," he requested softly. Pincus left his bulging duffel bag lying on the kitchen floor and followed the Rabbi.

"I assure you," he declared self-righteously, "my conduct has been above reproach."

"I'm certain it has," Rabbi Gellman replied. "It's just that..."

At that moment, the sound of sirens shattered the neighborhood, wailing as though some unseen force was taking revenge upon the quiet city streets. Children from nearby houses ran to see the police car. Bicyclists pedaled out of the way, and joggers in the road hit the sidewalks mid-stride. The blue cruiser screeched to a halt just outside the shelter.

Scranton's police force is famous for taking crime seriously and, on occasion, overreacting. Two police detectives burst out of the car, ran up the front steps and pounded on the door. Max let them in and they marched into the living room with the tough, confident air that let everyone know they were capable of handling anything that might conceivably take place.

"My name is Sergeant Petersen. This is my partner, Sergeant O'Reilly. Someone reported a theft?"

"I did, Your Honor!" said Max, obviously mistaking the cop for a judge. "We have reason to believe that this man," he pointed an accusing finger at Pincus, "stole his," now pointing to Jake, "expensive overcoat!"

"That's preposterous!" the Professor protested. "I have never engaged in larceny, grand or petty, in my life. Mr. Birnbaum, I wish to retain you to represent me in this case, as well as in the libel suit I intend to file against this individual," he said. "And while you're at it, prepare a notice of claim against the municipality for employing such manifestly incompetent officers of the law."

"What? Let me get this straight." Jake couldn't believe his ears. "You want me," he queried, pointing to himself, "to defend you against the charge of stealing my coat?"

"Of course," the Professor replied. "*You* believe that I am not only *prima facie* innocent but also *res ipsa loquitur*. Therefore either *corpus delicti* or," he turned to the police, "*habeas corpus*."

"I don't know what to believe," a frustrated Birnbaum

said, shaking his head in confusion.

"Please, please, everyone calm down," Rabbi Gellman pleaded. By now, loud accusations were being hurled to and fro between Max and Pincus.

Rabbi Gellman was eventually able to stop the shouting. He then turned to the two policemen, who were taking this all in with a mixture of annoyance, amusement and boredom. "Officers, I'm not sure we really need your services..."

"First let's see if we can find out what's going on here," said one of Scranton's finest.

Suddenly, Pincus made a break for the kitchen. He had never liked cops and he feared that if it came down to their choosing between an employee of the Sheltering Society and him, he would end up behind bars for sure.

"And just where do you think *you're* going?" bellowed Sgt. Petersen. Pincus felt a strong hand clutching his arm. He managed to escape, leaving a greasy trenchcoat sleeve in Petersen's hand.

Pincus tried his hardest to shuffe away with his duffel bag, but it weighed him down like an anchor. In seconds, both patrolmen had him spreadeagled against the wall. The two officers methodically frisked him, searching for anything that might be used as a weapon.

"He's clean," said Petersen.

"What about the bag?" O'Reilly asked.

"Open it!" Petersen ordered.

"Where's your search warrant?" Pincus demanded heatedly. "I am fully cognizant of my rights as protected under the Fourth, Fifth and Sixth Amendments. And my attorney," he continued, pointing to Jake, "is sworn to protect them. Counselor Birnbaum, would you care to recite my rights for the benefit of these perpetrators of brutality who intend to further infringe upon my constitutionally protected privileges?"

Jake tried to hide a smile. "As your attorney, and as the owner of the missing coat, I think you should do as they say — or you might find yourself in custody, charged with resisting arrest, obstruction of justice, loitering, vagrancy and a half-dozen other serious crimes and misdemeanors I could think of."

Pincus looked at the men surrounding him. Slowly, he upended his overstuffed duffel and watched as his world poured out in a rush. In seconds, a jumbled pile two-and-a-half feet tall spewed onto the kitchen floor.

The assembled watched in speechless awe as the officers began excavating the contents of the duffel bag: the remains of a stale tuna-fish sandwich; five maps of various cities: Passaic, Hollywood, Casablanca, Bakersfield and Sheboygan; a Michelin Guide; three empty potato sacks; half a dozen assorted keys; the libretto from *Cyrano de Bergerac*; four cats-eye marbles ("A little girl gave them to me for good luck"); a wad of chewing tobacco; a small pocket *Tehillim*, sans cover; an assortment of vital literature including: *The Edsel Owner Repair Manual, Do-it-Yourself Dry Cleaning, The Wonders of Afro Sheen*, and *Creative Bonsai Gardening*; a slimy banana peel; a wallet containing a complimentary pass to "The Ed Sullivan Show," a snapshot of Elvis, a crumpled sheet of S&H Green Stamps, and a ticket stub from *101 Dalmatians*; several pieces of string, of varying lengths, and two rubber bands, of varying elasticity; a bundle of cloth which turned out to be a long, dirty brown scarf; a dogeared *Roget's Thesaurus*; a couple of soiled shirts; a pair of suspenders; two slogan-emblazoned sweatshirts (expletives deleted), size petite; three left sneakers, a copy of *Grey's Anatomy*; a rock collection culled from suburban America; a "Rock" collection culled from decadent America (LPs); two dozen (hopefully) hard-boiled eggs; and an article clipped from the *Times* entitled, "Third World Debt Threatens U.S.Banks."

"Quite a spread!" Sgt. O'Reilly said wryly. "But no coat."

"Coat? Coat? What about coat?" It was Nadja.

"Mr. Birnbaum's cashmere overcoat is missing. Have you seen it anywhere?" Rabbi Gellman asked.

"Yes. It be on couch. I put in closet two days."

"I have been vindicated!" shouted Pincus. "Yet I bear no malice towards those who have cast aspersions upon my character."

"You still were caught in his room!" Max said accusingly.

"I told Pincus he could read my *Times* when I was done with it," Jake explained.

"Excuse me, fellas," Sgt. Petersen broke in, "but is this case solved? 'Cause if it is, we gotta go."

"Yes, Officers," replied Rabbi Gellman. "Thank you for coming. We're sorry to have bothered you."

"No sweat," O'Reilly answered over his shoulder as the two patrolmen walked out shaking their heads.

Max was deeply ashamed for having blamed Pincus. He thought about what Rabbi Gellman had said about judging people favorably. "I suppose I shouldn't have jumped to conclusions, Pincus. Please accept my apologies. Is there anything I can do to make up for it?"

"You're a tailor, aren't you?" interjected Rabbi Gellman.

"Yes, I was one, but how does that help repair the damage I've caused?"

"You can mend Reb Pincus' coat, for a start."

"With pleasure!" Max agreed heartily, taking the old trenchcoat in one hand and the torn-off sleeve in the other.

"And then," Pincus added, "you and the good Rabbi could help me mend Jake's marital problems, by enabling him to see that a marriage of eighteen years' standing is worth saving."

Rabbi Gellman nodded his head as Pincus threw a solicitous arm around Jake's shoulder.

Max, gazing in dismay at the pitiful mess on the floor, turned to the Rabbi and asked, "Do you think we can relax our two-week rule in this case?"

Credit where Credit Is Due

וַיָּקֶם מֹשֶׁה אֶת הַמִּשְׁכָּן...וַיִּתֵּן אֶת בְּרִיחָיו וַיָּקֶם אֶת עַמּוּדָיו.

And Moshe erected the Tabernacle and fastened its sockets; he positioned its planks, inserted its bars, and erected its pillars.

(Shemos 40:18)

Midrash Tanchuma elaborates:

> *God said to Moshe, "Since you are anguished that you did not [personally] craft the Tabernacle, the artisans who did will not be able to erect it without you. This way, all Israel will know that it stands only through you. Therefore, I shall attribute its erection to you. As it says, 'And Moshe erected the Tabernacle....'*
>
> *Moshe responded, "But I don't know how to erect it!"*
>
> *"Just try, and I shall assist..., and I shall record that you have erected the Tabernacle."*

Asks Rabbi **Chaim Shmuelevitz**: Why should Moshe receive credit for something he did not actually accomplish?

Moshe did not shy away from this task, though it was beyond his ability. Since he struggled to do the impossible, with the loftiest intent, the Almighty intervened to assist him and ascribed the act to him.

God can enable us to achieve the impossible, so we must not shirk any responsibility, however awesome. If we make an earnest attempt we will succeed — and be credited for our effort.

When someone brought to Reb Shlomo Zalman's attention the plight of a particular widow, the Rav took immediate action. She desperately needed financial assistance for an urgent medical procedure. Time was of the essence, but to have the operation performed right away with a top-flight surgical team would require a lot of money, and Reb Shlomo Zalman's charitable resources were all but depleted.

He summoned Rabbi Dovid Goldwicht, one of his key assistants in philanthropic matters, to help him launch a door-to-door fundraising campaign. "You will start on this side of the street," the Gaon said, "and I will start on the other side, and please God by the time we meet, we will have raised the necessary sum."

The two did actually meet somewhere midway in the neighborhood, but "midway" was clearly the operative word: although they had visited every household in the community, they had raised only half the amount of money that was required.

Reb Shlomo Zalman was undeterred. The health of the poor widow was at stake and there was no time left for an additional, wider-ranging appeal. Something had to be done now, and there was only one person who could do it: Reb

Shlomo Zalman Auerbach himself.

The Gaon traveled to Hadassah Hospital to meet with the surgeon in person and have a heart-to-heart talk. The physician, a professor at the Medical School, was the foremost in the country in his field, and had the arrogant bearing of a man who knew it. By all accounts, his skill in the operating theater was matchless, and thus he could demand and receive an exorbitant, non-negotiable fee for his services.

Since their patients are usually sedated or unconscious, surgeons do not always cultivate a warm bedside manner, and this surgeon was one of the chillier members of that profession. Not (yet) religious himself, he was especially apathetic toward Orthodox patients and their problems, and even more so to the overtly religious old man who had abruptly barged into his office unannounced.

The intervention of a medical secretary had earned Reb Shlomo Zalman a few moments of the doctor's precious time, long enough for the Gaon to get the measure of the man. As sometimes is the case with medical practitioners, the surgeon was brilliant with a scalpel but had long since forgotten Who guided his hand. During the brief audience Reb Shlomo Zalman had been granted, the doctor glanced repeatedly at his watch, but the Rav was unimpressed.

With complete candor, Reb Shlomo Zalman told the professor the truth, that he and his colleague had worked feverishly to raise the funds necessary for the widow's operation, yet despite their arduous efforts had succeeded in raising only half the fee. "I wish, therefore, to make you a proposition," the Rav ventured. "Let's split this mitzvah evenly between us."

The silence in the well-appointed office was palpable as the doctor blinked and gaped over the audacious proposal. Then he thrust out his hand and the deal was struck. Several hours later, the widow underwent life-saving surgery.

Biographical Sketches

RABBI NISON ALPERT (d. 1986) — Primary disciple of HaRav Moshe Feinstein. Rosh Yeshivah of Yeshivas Rabbeinu Yitzchok Elchanan and rabbi of Agudas Yisrael of Long Island. Authored *Limudei Nison.*

RABBI YEHUDAH ARYEH LEIB ALTER [Sefas Emes] (1847-1903) — Raised by his grandfather the *Chiddushei HaRim,* he took over the Gerer dynasty as a young man and molded it into the largest Chassidic sect in Poland. Posthumously, his lectures on the Talmud, Bible and Festivals were published as *Sefas Emes.*

RABBI YITZCHAK MEIR ALTER [Chiddushei HaRim] (1789-1866) — The first Gerer Rebbe, who affected Chassidus throughout Poland. Authored *Chiddushei HaRim,* novellae on the Talmud and *Shulchan Aruch.*

BAAL SHEM TOV (1700-1760) — Established a *beis midrash* in Meziboz from which the Chassidic movement sprang forth, and his frequent travels helped it take root.

RABBI YAAKOV CULI (1690-1732) — Began *Me'Am Loez,* a popular homiletical Bible commentary written in Ladino and completed during the 18th century.

RABBI ELIYAHU DESSLER (1891-1954) — Established a *kollel* in Gateshead Yeshivah and later became *mashgiach* of the Ponevezh Yeshivah. Authored *Michtav Me'Eliyahu.*

RABBI MORDECHAI DRUK — *Rosh Kollel* of Bais Zevul and popular orator in Yerushalayim.

RABBI YEHONASAN EIBESHITZ (1690-1796) — Rosh Yeshivah in Prague as well as rav of the "Three Communities" — Altona, Hamburg, and Wandsbek. Authored *Urim VeTumim, Kreisi U'Pleisi* and *Ya'aros Devash.*

RABBI CHAIM ELFANDRY (d. 1733) — Distinguished Kabbalist and Rabbi in Istanbul.

RABBI MOSHE YECHIEL EPSTEIN [Ozrov Rebbe] (1890-1971) — Established a *beis midrash* in New York and later in Tel Aviv. Authored *Aish Da'as* and *Be'er Moshe.*

RABBI BARUCH MORDECHAI EZRACHI — Rosh Yeshivah of Ateres Yisrael (Yerushalayim) and author of *Birkas Mordechai.*

RABBI YISRAEL FEINHANDLER — Educator and author of several volumes, including *Priority in Prayer.*

RABBI YISSACHER FRAND — *Maggid shiur* in Ner Israel (Baltimore) and creator of a library of audio cassettes on *parashas hashavua.*

RABBI ALEXANDER ZUSHA FRIEDMAN (d. 1943) — Compiled *Ma'ayanah Shel Torah,* which includes his own insights labeled *Avnei Ezel.*

RABBI LEIB GURWICZ (d. 1983) — Rosh Yeshivah of the Bais Yosef Yeshivah (Gateshead). Author of *Rashei She'arim* and *Arza d'Vei Rav.*

RABBI YISRAEL MEIR HAKOHEN [Chafetz Chaim] (1838-1933) — Established the Radun Yeshivah and was known throughout Europe as a saintly scholar. Prolific writer on any subject that demanded greater public awareness, his works include *Chafetz Chaim* and *Mishnah Berurah.*

RABBI SHIMSHON REFAEL HIRSCH (1808-1888) — The father of modern German Orthodoxy, who revitalized the many Germanic Jewish communities such as Frankfort-am-Main. Authored Torah commentary and *Horeb.*

RABBI YOISEF YOIZEL HOROWITZ [Alter of Novardhok] (1848-1920) — Founder of the Novardhok Mussar Yeshivah Network and author of *Madreigas HaAdam.*

RABBI MORDECHAI ILAN (1917-1981) — *Dayan* in Tel Aviv and author of *Mikdash Mordechai.*

RABBI YAAKOV YISRAEL KANIEVSKY [the Steipler] (d. 1985) — Preeminent rabbinic authority of his time. Author of *Kehilas Yaakov, Birkas Peretz,* and *Chayei Olam.*

RABBI MORDECHAI KATZ (d. 1965) — Co-founded Telz Yeshivah in America and authored *Be'er Mechokeik.*

RABBI CHAIM YITZCHAK KORB (1874-1957) — Rav in Europe and later Rosh Yeshivah of Beis Midrash L'Torah (Chicago). Author of *Nesivos Chaim* and *Tal Shechakim.*

RABBI YAAKOV KRANZ [Dubno Maggid] (1741-1804) — Preacher from Dubno famous for his parables. Author of *Kol Yaakov, Mishlei Yaakov, et al.*

RABBI YECHEZKAEL LANDAU [Noda BiYehudah] (1713-1793) — Known by the name of his volume of responsa, which established him as one of the most outstanding Halachic authorities of his time.

RABBI ZEV LEFF — Rav of Moshav Mattisyahu, former rabbi of North Miami Beach, and author of *Outlooks and Insights.*

RABBI HENOCH LEIBOWITZ — Rosh Yeshivah of Yeshivas Chafetz Chaim (Queens) and branch divisions since 1941. Author of *Chiddushei HaLev.*

RABBI YECHEZKEL LEVENSTEIN (1884-1974) — Disciple of Reb Yeruchem Levovitz and his successor as *mashgiach* of the Mirrer Yeshivah. Upon arriving in Israel became *mashgiach* of the Ponevezh Yeshivah in Bnei Brak.

RABBI YERUCHEM LEVOVITZ (1876-1936) — *Mashgiach* of the Mirrer Yeshivah. His talks are collected in *Da'as Chochmah U'Mussar.*

RABBI YOSEF LIPOVITZ (1889-1962) — Student of the Alter of Slabodka and author of *Nachalas Yosef.*

RABBI YEHUDAH LOEWE BEN BEZALEL [Maharal] (1512-1609) — Chief rabbi of Prague and one of the most outstanding thinkers and wonder workers of his time. Author of *Gur Aryeh* and *Sifrei Maharal.*

RABBI ELIYAHU LOPIAN (1872-1970) — Taught in yeshivah in London before becoming *mashgiach* of K'far Chasidim, in northern Israel. Authored *Lev Eliyahu.*

RABBI AARON LOPIANSKY — *Rosh Beis Midrash* of the Yeshivah of Greater Washington and author of *Timepieces.*

RABBI MOSHE CHAIM LUZZATO (1707-1746) — Kabbalist and author of the premier ethical treatise *Mesillas Yesharim, Derech Hashem,* and other works.

RABBI MORDECHAI MILLER — Vice-principal of the seminary of Gateshead, and author of *Sabbath Shiurim.*

RABBI MENACHEM MENDEL MORGENSTERN [Kotzker Rebbe] (1787-1859) — Dynamic Chasidic leader whose thoughts were collected in *Emmes MiKotzk Titzmach.*

RABBI SHLOMO MORGENSTERN — Rosh Yeshivah of Hebrew Theological College (Skokie).

RABBI ELIYAHU MUNK (1900-1978) — Founder of the Munk Synagogue (London) and author of *The Six Days of Creation.*

RABBI AVIGDOR NEBANZAHL — Primary disciple of Rabbi Shlomo Zalman Auerbach *zt"l, maggid shiur* in Yeshivat HaKotel, and rabbi of the Old City of Yerushalayim. Authored *BeYitzchak Yikarei* and *Sichos.*

RABBI YAAKOV NEIMAN (1895-1983) — Founder of Yeshivas Ohr Yisrael (Petach Tikvah).

RABBI SHLOMO OSTROK — Student of the Rashba.

RABBI ZELIG PLISKIN — Educator and consultant in Yerushalyim. Author of *Love Your Neighbor, Guard Your Tongue, Gateway to Happiness, et al.*

RABBI MEIR OF PREMISHLAN (1783-1870) — Prominent Chasidic Rebbe noted for his incisive insights.

ROSH (1250-1327) [Acronym for Rav Asher] — Towering Halachic authority in Spain and author of a famous commentary on the Talmud.

RABBI MEIR SHAPIRO (1887-1934) — Rav of Lublin, builder of the Chachmei Lublin Yeshivah, and innovator of the "*Daf Yomi*" learning program.

RABBI ISAAC SHER (1875-1952) — Son-in-law of Rabbi Nosson Tzvi Finkel. Founded the Slabodka Yeshivah in Bnei Brak and contributed to *Leket Sichos Mussar.*

RABBI CHAIM SHMUELEVITZ (1902-1979) — Rosh Yeshivah of the Mirrer Yeshivah and author of *Sichos Mussar.*

RABBI AVRAHAM BINYAMIN SOFER [Kesav Sofer] (1815-1871) — Succeeded his father, the Chasam Sofer, as the Rav and Rosh Yeshivah of Pressburg.

RABBI ELCHANAN SOROTZKIN (1906-1944) — Chairman of the *Vaad Hayeshivos.*

RABBI AVRAHAM TWERSKI — Psychiatrist and lecturer. Author of *Generation to Generation, Let Us Make Man, Living Each Day, et al.* Creator of the audio cassette series *Parashah Perspectives*, featuring psychological insights into the weekly Torah portion.

RABBI SHLOMO WOLBE — Preeminent Mussar thinker and *mashgiach* of this generation. Author of *Alei Shur, Bein Sheishes Le'Asor,* and *Zeriah U'Vinyan BeChinuch.*

RABBI ZVI HIRSH WOLK (1855-1907) — Rav in Pinsk and author of *Kesser Kehunah.*

Glossary

The following glossary provides a partial explanation of some of the foreign words and phrases used in this book. The spelling, tense, and explanations reflect the way the specific word is used in *A Midrash and a Maaseh*. Often, there are alternate spellings and meanings for the words. Foreign words and phrases which are immediately followed by a translation in the text are not included in this section. Furthermore, those foreign words and phrases which have become a part of contemporary English usage are neither italicized within the text, nor included in this glossary, but can be found in Websters' and other dictionaries.

voice is heard again, but this time it is an octave or so higher, and it is singing. It is singing that tune so familiar to anyone who has studied in yeshivah and so unknown to the rest of the world [illegible] the time that non-religious Jews hear, perhaps once a year — when the Four Questions are asked at the Seder. This time, this yeshivah sing-song has just one word: "Menashe[illegible]." And then, after a shorter pause, still in the song: "Menashe[illegible], [illegible] Menasheleh."

And the song continues: "[illegible] *ve-rabboisai*, you think this *kugel* is genuine? Have I got news for you! [illegible] tasted *kugel* [illegible]. [illegible] *ve-rabboisai*, you think we are all here to celebrate [illegible] bar mitzvah? Well, I've got even bigger news [illegible]: we're here to celebrate Menasheleh's [illegible]."

[illegible]

[illegible] But by this time, almost half of Hungary's Jews were [illegible]. We didn't know this [illegible] on that train, very few of us thought we'd ever come [illegible].

"How many [illegible] on that train, *rabboisai*, don't ask. No one ever counted. How many lost their minds? Who knows? But when we got there — when we got there, the first thing they did was throw out the bodies. The doors to that freight car opened wide, *rabboisai*. And before our eyes had even recovered from the sudden flash of sunlight, we could hear the thud of bodies hitting the ground.

ABBA — father

ACHARONIM — talmudic scholars of the last five hundred years

ADAM GADOL — a great person

AGUNAH — lit., a "chained woman"; refers to a woman whose marriage has been terminated *de facto* but not *de jure*, and who is therefore incapable of remarrying because she is still technically married to her absent husband

AH CHUTZPAH — (Yid.) "What audacity!"

"AIN TORAH K'TORAS ERETZ YISRAEL" — No learning is comparable to the learning of Torah in the Land of Israel

ALEINU — the prayer at the conclusion of the prayer services

ALIYAH — going up; term used in connection with 1. being called up to the reading of the Torah; 2. immigration to Israel

ALMANAH — widow

ALTER — (Yid.) aged one; a title of respect

AMUD — lit., pillar; place from where the CHAZZAN leads the congregation in prayer

ARON KODESH — lit., holy ark; ark containing the Torah scrolls

ASHRECHA — lit., happy are you; you are blessed

ATARAH — silver adornment attached to a TALLIS

AVEIRAH — a transgression

AVINU — our father

AVODAH ZARAH — idol worship

AVRAHAM AVINU — our father Abraham

AVRECH(IM) — young married yeshivah student(s)

B'EZER HASHEM — (colloq. form of *b'ezras Hashem*) with God's help

BAALEI BATIM — lay individuals

BAKSHEESH — (Arab., colloq.) bribe

BAR MITZVAH — 1. thirteen-year-old Jewish boy who assumes the religious responsibilities of an adult; 2. the ceremony confirming a bar mitzvah

BARUCH HASHEM — lit., the Lord is blessed; thank God

BASHERT — (Yid.) destined

BAVA KAMMA — A tractate in *Seder Nezikin* of the Talmud

BAVA METZIA — (Aram.) lit., the middle gate; tractate in *Seder Nezikin* of the Talmud

BEHAIMES —(colloq. form of *behemos*) animals

BEIS MIDRASH — house of study used for both Torah study and prayer

BEKKASHEH — (Yid.) a long frock coat worn by men, often reserved for festive occasions

BENTCHING GOIMEL — (Yid., colloq.) reciting *Birkas Hagomel*; *Birkas Hagomel* is the blessing recited after being spared from harm

BEREISHIS — the first book of the Torah. Its name is derived from its first word — *bereishis*, lit., in the beginning

BÊTE NOIRE — (Fr.) something unpleasant which one systematically avoids

BIKUR CHOLIM — visiting the sick

BITTE — (Ger.) please

BLATT SHIUR — see DAF SHIUR

BLI AYIN HARA — lit., without the evil eye; expression invoking Divine protection for children, good health, good fortune, etc.

BACHUR(IM) — unmarried yeshivah student

BRIS (BRIS MILAH) — the Jewish rite of circumcision

BUREAUCRATZIA — (Rus., colloq.) bureaucracy

CHABURAH — a topical discourse prepared for group discussion by a member of the group

CHABUSHA — (Arab.) apple

CHACHAM — wise man; "rabbi" in Sephardic circles

CHACHMEI HAKABBALAH — Kabbalists

CHALILAH — God forbid (idiom)

CHARGILLA — (Arab.) waterpipe; also nargileh

CHAS VE'CHALILAH — God forbid

CHAS VE'SHALOM — God forbid

CHASDEI HASHEM KI LO SAMNU — through God's grace were we not annihilated

CHASSUNAH — a wedding

CHASSAN — groom

CHASID(IM) — follower(s) of the teaching of the Baal Shem Tov

CHAZZAN — cantor; the leader of public worship

CHEDER (CHADARIM) — elementary school for religious studies

CHESSED — deeds of loving kindness

CHEVRA KADISHA — lit., holy society; a group which provides for the religious needs of the community, particularly in the area of the care and rites of the dead

CHEVRUSA (CHEVRUSOS) — study partner(s)

CHIDDUSH(IM) — novellae; new insights in Torah interpretation

CHIDDUSHEI HARIM — novellae of the Rim

CHULLIN — tractate in *Seder Kodashim* of the Talmud

CHUTZPAH — nerve, audacity

COUP DE GRACE — (Fr.) a death blow or finishing stroke

DAF SHIUR — GEMARA lesson focused on the page being studied

DAN L'CHAF ZECHUS — judge favorably, positively; give the benefit of the doubt

DANKE SCHÖN — (Ger.) thank you

DAVEN — (Yid.) pray

DERECH ERETZ KADMAH LATORAH — proper manners precede spiritual matters

DERASHAH — learned discourse

DU VAIST DOCH — (Yid.) you certainly know

DIN TORAH — case brought for adjudication according to Torah law

DUMMKOPF — (Ger.) dumbbell

EMMES — absolute truth

ERETZ YISRAEL — the Land of Israel

EREV — eve

ESROG(IM) — citron; one of the "four species" used on SUKKOS

FLEISHIG — (Yid.) containing or comprised of meat

FRAULEIN — (Ger.) Miss; an unmarried woman

FRUM — (Yid.) religious

GABBAI — warden of the synagogue who collects and dispenses charity

GADOL HADOR — greatest Torah scholar of the generation

GAN EDEN — lit., the Garden of Eden; Paradise

GEMACH — contraction of GEMILUS CHASSADIM; interest-free loan society

GEMARA — 1. commentary on the Mishnah (together they comprise the Talmud); 2. a volume of the Talmud

GEMILUS CHASSADIM — performance of acts of CHESSED

GEZEIRAH — decree

GET (GITTEN) — writ(s) of divorce

GLATT TRIEF — (Yid.) strictly unkosher

GLUZ TAY — (Yid.) glass of tea

GOTT IN HIMMEL — (Ger.) God in Heaven

GUTT SHABBOS — (Yid.) a good Sabbath

GUTT YONTIFF — (Yid.) a good holdiay

GVIR — man of substantial means

HACHNASAS ORCHIM — hospitality

HAISE VANT — (Yid.) hot wall

HAKADOSH BARUCH HU — the Holy One, blessed be He

HAKARAS HATOV — gratitude; recognition of the good

HALACHAH — Jewish law

HALEVAI — it should only be so

HAMOTZI — the blessing made over bread

HAREI AT — opening words of wedding formula said by the groom to his bride

HASHAVAS AVEIDAH — returning a lost object

HASHEM — lit., The Name; respectful reference to God

HATAFAS DAM — drawing of the blood during circumcision

HASHGACHAH — Kashruth supervision

HECHSHER — Rabbinic certification of Kashruth

HERR BARON — (Ger.) honored sir (honorific for nobility)

HESDER — combined program of yeshivah study and military service in the Israeli army

HETER — halachic dispensation

HEVAI DAN ES KOL HA'ADAM L'CHAF ZECHUS — judge all your fellow men favorably

HOSHANAH RABBAH — the seventh day of Sukkos

ICH HAB A NIESS — (Yid.) I have a novel idea

ILLUI — genius; towering Torah scholar

JIRNE — (Arab.) flute

KADDISH — prayer in praise of God recited by mourners

KALLAH — bride

KAMEAH — (Aram.) handwritten blessing in the form of an amulet, pendant or wall hanging

KAPITL(ACH) — (Yid.) small section(s)

KAPOTA — elegant caftan

KASHRUS — conforming to Jewish dietary regulations

KAVANAH — devotion, intent, concentration, purpose

KAVOD — glory, honor

KEHILLAH — organized community; congregation

KESUBAH — the Jewish marriage contract

KIDDUSH — sanctification; prayer recited over wine to usher in the Sabbath and festivals

KIDDUSH HASHEM — sanctification of God's name; martyrdom

K'NA HARA — (Yid.) see BLI AYIN HARA

KIPAH (KIPOS) — skullcap; head-covering worn by religious Jews

KITTEL — white cloak donned by the CHAZZAN on High Holy Days and other festivals and by married men on various festivals and occasions according to custom

KLAL YISRAEL — community of Israel; all of Jewry

KOHANIM — male decendants from the priestly family of Aaron

KOLLEL — post-graduate YESHIVAH in which student body is usually comprised of young married students who receive stipends

KRAITZ — (Yid.) lower part of the back

KRECHTZ — (Yid.) mournful sigh

KVELL(ED) — (Yid.) to beam with pride

LESHEV BASUKKAH — blessing recited upon sitting in a Sukkah

LAMDAN(IM) — scholar(s)

LASHON HARA — slander; a derogatory or damaging statement about someone

LIMUD HATORAH — learning Torah

LITVAK — (Yid.) a Lithuanian

LULAV — palm branch, one of the ARBA'AH MINIM

MA'ARIV — evening prayer

MAGEN DAVID — star of David

MAHN — manna which sustained the Children of Israel in the wilderness

MA'ASIM TOVIM — good deeds

MASHGIACH (MASHGIACH RUCHANI) — dean of students in a yeshivah who acts as a spritual guide and adviser

MASMID — a diligent student

MAYAIN OLAM HABA — like the World to Come

MECHADESH/ MECHADESH TORAH — someone who produces novel Torah interpretations

MECHITZAH — partition separating the men from the women in a synagogue

MEGILLAH — the scroll of Esther read in the synagogue on Purim

MEIN HERR — (Ger.) my master; sir

MEINE KARTOFFELN — (Ger.) my potatoes

MAZAL — luck; fortune

MISA MESHUNEHDIGGE — (Yid., colloq.) lit., like a macabre death; a vile color

MIN HASHAMAYIM — lit., from Heaven; Divinely inspired

MUSSAF — the additional prayer said on Sabbath and festivals

MELAMED — teacher

MENAHEL — yeshivah dean

MENORAH — eight-branched candelabrum kindled on CHANUKAH

MESADER KIDDUSHIN — the one who officiates at a wedding

MESECHTA — (Aram.) talmudic volume

MESHUGENAH — (Yid.) crazy person

MESHULACH — lit., messenger; itinerent fundraiser for a charitable institution

MESIVTA — (Aram.) academy of Jewish study for high school-age students

MESIRUS NEFESH — self-sacrifice

MIKDASH ME'AT — lit., a small Sanctuary; synagogue

MIKVEH (MIKVAOS) — a ritual bath used for the purpose of ritual purification

MINCHAH — the afternoon prayer service

MINYAN(IM) — quorum of ten adult Jewish males; the basic unit of community for certain religious purposes, including prayer

MISHNAH (MISHNAYOS) — the earliest codification of Jewish oral law by Rabbi Yehudah Hanassi; portions thereof

MISPALLELIM — worshippers

METZITZAH — suctioning of the blood during BRIS MILAH

MITZVAH (MITZVOS) — lit., commandments; applied to good deeds

MIZRACH — East

MOHEL — one who performs the religious ceremony of circumcision

MORAH — teacher

MORAI VE-RABBOSAI — my teachers and rabbis

MOTEK — (colloq.) sweetie

MOTZAI SHABBOS — Saturday night

MUSSAR — 1. school of thought emphasizing ethical perfection; 2. moral teachings; 3. ethical lecture

NACHAS — joy; fulfillment

NEBACH — (Yid.) unfortunately

NEDARIM — a tractate in *Seder Nashim* of the Talmud

NEIN — (Yid.; Ger.) no

NICHT WAHR — (Ger.) is that not so?

NEFESH — soul; spirit

NIFTAR — deceased

NISAYON — trial of faith

NESHAMAH — soul

NU, NU — (Yid.) "Oh well."

OBERLEUTNANT — (Ger.) first lieutenant

OY VEY'S MIR — (Yid.) oh, agony!

OLAM HABA — the world to come

OLAM HAZEH — this world

ONEG — lit., delight; gathering held in honor of the Sabbath

OY MEIN GOTT — (Yid.) Oh my God!

PAPERLACH — (Yid., colloq.) snippets of paper

PAYOS — sidelocks

PERUSH(IM) — commentary(ies)

PIRKEI AVOS — Chapters of the Fathers

PIRKEI TEHILLIM — chapters of Psalms

PISKEI HALACHAH — halachic rulings

PLAITZES — (Yid.) shoulders

PORETZ — sinister non-Jewish landowner

PSAK — halachic decision

P'SHAT — simple interpretation; meaning

PURIM — joyous festival commemorating salvation from genocide

RABBOSAI — gentleman

RACHMANA LITZLAN — (Aram.) may the Merciful One spare us [such sorrow]

RASHA — an evil person

RAV — Rabbi

REB YID — polite form of address for fellow Jew

REBBE MUVHAK — (Yid.) primary teacher

REBBE(IM) — (Yid.) 1. rabbi, usually a Talmud teacher; 2.instructor; 3. chassidic leader

REBBETZIN — rabbi's wife

REFUAH SHELEIMAH — a complete recovery

RIBONO SHEL OLAM — lit., Master of the Universe; God

RISHON (IM) — lit., first one; European scholars of the eleventh through the fifteenth century

ROSH CHODESH — beginning of the month

ROSH YESHIVAH (RASHEI YESHIVAH) — yeshiva dean

SANDAK — individual who holds the baby during the circumcision

SCHWEINHUND — (Ger.) swine hound

SECHEL — mind; intelligence

SEDER — 1. the order of the Pesach night ceremony recalling the Exodus from Egypt and the liberation from bondage; 2. a learning session

SEFER (SEFARIM) — book of religious content

SEFER TEHILLIM — the Book of Psalms

SEUDAH — festive meal

SHACHARIS — the morning prayer service

SHADCHAN(IM) — matchmaker(s)

SHADCHANTE — (Yid., fem.) a marriage broker

SHAILA (SHAILOS) — (Yid.) lit., question; halachic query

SHALIACH TZIBUR — leader of the congregation in prayer

SHALOM ALEICHEM — "Peace be upon you"; traditional greeting

SHALOM BAYIS — domestic tranquility

SHAS — [acronym for] the six orders of the MISHNAH; the Talmud

SHA'ATNES — mixture of wool and linen prohibited by the Torah

SHE'ELAH — a question; a halachic question

SHEITEL — (Yid.) wig

SHEMA — prayer recited daily proclaiming the oneness of God and affirming faith in HIm and His Torah

SHEMINI ATZERES — the eighth day of Sukkos

SHEVA BERACHOS — 1. the seven benedictions recited at a wedding and in the presence of the newlyweds during the first week of their marriage; 2. the seven days after a wedding during which festive meals are made in honor of the newlyweds

SHIDUCH(IM) — marital match(es)

SHIUR(IM) — Torah lecture

SHIUR KLALI — lit., general lecture; advanced lecture usually delivered by the senior ROSH YESHIVAH

SHIVAH — lit., seven; the seven-day period of mourning following a death

SHMUEZ(IM) — (Yid.) ethical discourse

SHNORER — (Yid.) beggar

SHOICHET — (Yid.) a ritual slaughterer

SHOMER SHABBOS — a Sabbath-observer

SHOMREI MITZVOS — lit., observers of the commandments; religious Jews

SHTADLANIM — (Yid.) activists

SHTEIT — (Yid.) says

SHTENDER — (Yid.) lectern, used in place of desks in many yeshivos

SHTIKL — (Yid.) a small piece

SHTIBL(ACH) — (Yid.) small, informal intimate room for prayer or study

SHTREIML(ACH) — (Yid.) decorative fur or fur-trimmed hat worn by male Chasidim on Sabbath and festivals

SHUL — (Yid.) synagogue

SIMCHAH — lit., joy; celebration

SIMCHAS TORAH — the holiday of the rejoicing of the Torah

SOFER — scribe

SUKKAH — temporary dwelling which is a central requirement of the holiday of SUKKOS

SUKKOS — autumn holiday held five days after Yom Kippur, during which time one dwells in a SUKKAH

TAKKEH — (Yid.) veritably

TALLIS — four-cornered prayer shawl with fringes at each corner worn by men during morning prayers

TALMID — student

TALMID(EI) CHACHAM(IM) — Torah scholar(s)

TASHMISHEI KEDUSHAH — religious articles

TEFILLAH (TEFILLOS) — prayer(s)

TEFILLAS HADERECH — a traveler's prayer for safety

TEFILLIN — black leather boxes containing numerous verses from the Bible bound to the arm and front of a man's head during morning prayers

TEHILLIM — Psalms

TISCH — (Yid.) lit., table; a chasidic meal presided over by a REBBE

TREIF (TEREIFAH) — lit., torn; non-kosher; unacceptable

TREIF(E) MEDINAH — lit., unkosher state; nickname for America prior to the immigration of Orthodox Jews after WWII

TZADDIK(IM) — righteous person(s)

TZEIDAH LADERECH — provisions for a journey

TZEDDAKAH — charity

TZIDKUS — righteousness

TZIPPALEH — (Yid., colloq.) little one

TZITZIS — the fringes worn by males on a four-cornered garment

TSUK — (Yid.) draft; strong breeze

VAYS-ALLES — (Yid.) "Mr. Know-it-all"

VERTL — (Yid.) a brief Torah insight

VEY IZ MIR — (Yid.) "Woe is me!"

VERZEIHUNG — (Ger.) pardon

VORT — (Yid.) lit., word; a short, novel explanation

VU DER FEFFER VAKST — (Yid. idiom) lit., where the pepper grows; far away

WUNDERBAR — (Ger.) wonderful

YA SADDAM! — (colloq.) "Down with Saddam!"

YAHRZEIT — (Yid.) anniversay of a death

YAMIM NORA'IM — Days of Awe; Rosh Hashanah and Yom Kippur

YEHAREG VE'AL YA'AVOR — refers to one of the three cardinal sins where the Torah mandates that a Jew must lay down his life rather than violate the commandment

YERUSHALMI — a Jerusalemite

YEVAMOS — tractate in *Seder Nashim* of the Talmud

YIBANEH HAMIKDASH — may the Holy Temple be [re]built

YICHUS — lineage

YID — (Yid.) Jew

YIDDISHEH KOP — (Yid.) a clever Jewish mind

YIDDISHEH NESHAMAH — (Yid.) Jewish soul

YINGELEH — (Yid.) little boy

YIRAS SHAMAIM — fear of Heaven

YISGADEL V'YISKADESH — lit., exalted and sanctified; the first words of the KADDISH

YISHUV — lit., settlement; refers to early settlement of Jews in ERETZ YISRAEL

YIZKOR — prayer said on the three festivals in memory of deceased relatives

YOM TOV — holiday

YUNTIFDIKKEH — (Yid., colloq.) festive; appropriate for a Yom Tov, or holiday

ZAIDENEH KAPOTA — (Yid.) elegant silk caftan

ZECHUS (ZECHUYOS) — merit(s)

ZETZ — (Yid.) slam

ZEMIROS — songs traditionally sung at the Sabbath table

ZMAN — yeshivah semester

ZOCHAH — (fem.) privileged

ZOLLEN OISGERISSEN VEHREN — (Yid.) "May they be ripped apart!"; a Yiddish curse

Z"L — abbreviation for "Of blessed memory"

ZT"L — abbreviation for "May the memory of this righteous person be for a blessing"

ZUGGER — (Yid.) speaker

will add to your detriment by harden-ing your heart."

Rabbi Elyah Lopian explains that sinners rationalize their inferior [illegible] [illegible] defend Pharaoh — by insisting, "I cannot overcome my nature." Such a claim borders on heresy. God's hardening of Pharaoh's heart gives heretics no excuse for [illegible] not have the ability to repent, but clearly the [illegible] [illegible] warning and ample opportunity [illegible].

Rabbi Shimon ben Lakish [illegible]. Like Pharaoh, every man is given fair warning, and ultimately must pay for his transgressions. Man certainly is able to change — if only he heeds the warnings.

H[illegible] [illegible] had been "Hey, Graybeard," but it was the second that made him pause in midstride. The Rebbe, as was well known, was a very modest man. He was also a venerable Torah authority and chassidic leader [illegible] unused to being addressed by that title — and certainly not in that tone.

He turned toward the source of the shouting, to see two of New York's Finest frisking a hirsute youth in bleached-out jeans and a stained T-shirt diagonally across the street. The Rebbe crossed over to investigate.

The youth, in his late teens, lolled languidly against a brick wall, with apparent disdain for the uniformed men examining the contents of his pockets.

The Sound of Soul

In a dozen different titles **Hanoch Teller** has delighted the Anglo-Jewish reader with inspiring tales of ordinary people who do extraordinary things. With a cast of fascinating characters and modern spiritual heroes and heroines, these true, contemporary stories touch the soul of readers everywhere and strike a responsive chord in their heart. Joy and drama, laughter and pathos combine to create a new genre of Jewish literature: "soul stories."

Each one of Teller's cherished tales of Jewish souls from all across the globe, skillfully written with powerful, image-evoking prose, conveys the timeless precepts of Judaism to young and old alike.

Now, in response to requests from countless educators, commuters, housewives, students, and program directors, these masterpieces have been reproduced on audio cassettes, fully dramatized with musical accompaniment and vivid sound effects.

The **Sound of Soul** volumes I & II provide over two hours of listening enjoyment for the entire family. The most heartwarming, enlightening, hilarious and poignant of Teller's tales have been transformed into an audio classic. Each cassette also contains new enchanting stories not featured in any of Hanoch Teller's books.

These high-quality tapes are not available in book stores. Please direct all orders and inquiries to:

Israel Media Group
c/o New York City Publishing Company
1 Crosswood Road
Great Neck, New York 11023

It did not matter. The Bostoner Rebbe had every intention of showing Mark the sights on a "trip" the boy clearly preferred not to travel. An unappreciative Goldberg was to have greater exposure to the Rebbe than some of the Bostoner's closest chasidim.

After supper, the Bostoner Rebbe showed his ward — so recently detained by the police on suspicion of robbery — to a bedroom containing several valuable items. "This will be your room," he said, as if welcoming an honored guest. Mark was overwhelmed, not by the Rebbe's gracious hospitality and generosity, but by his naiveté. And the test proved too great for him.

His first night at the Rebbe's residence, he began to "case the joint," prowling out of his room when he was sure that everyone in the household was asleep. He had already emptied his bedroom of valuables and stashed them in a pillowcase under the bureau. But just when his gaze fell on some silver ornaments which he thought might bring him a tidy sum, he heard a sound that made his heart pound loudly in his chest. Mark peered into the room from which the sound emanated and discovered his host reading aloud in a foreign language from an oversized book. The would-be thief could not have known that the Rebbe was merely engaged in talmudic research, but the fear of being caught [illegible] felony swiftly sent him tiptoeing back to bed to await a better opportunity.

Over the next few days Mark learned that this "Rabbi" whom he had stopped on the street was no ordinary cleric. His host was none other than "The Bostoner Rebbe," whatever that meant.

One thing it did mean, was that an incredible number of men in chasidic garb constantly swarmed all over Mark's newly-staked turf. There was always someone and his brother-in-law who wished to visit, consult, or seek the blessing of the Rebbe. All this interference placed a definite crimp in

A lot of things were "missing" from the house, but the Rebbe refrained from leveling any accusations. Mark felt certain that, no matter how much time the Rebbe spent studying his old books, he had to know about the pilfering, if not through the comments of others then by empirical evidence. The Rebbe was "cool" all right, frustratingly cool. Is this some psychological ploy, Mark wondered, or is he just giving me enough rope to hang myself? Mark vowed not to underestimate the Rebbe or be taken in by his unassuming [illegible].

When the Rebbe received a cassette in the mail of a well-received lecture which he had delivered, all the members of the household were anxious to hear it. But the tape recorder could not be found. This time, the family felt, the situation had gone too far. They brought their grievance to the Rebbe, but all he had to say was: "There really isn't time now to listen to the tape. We can wait until later."

Mark began to get nervous. The Rebbe's absolute confidence made Mark suspect that a trap had been set for him and he'd walked right into it. He surreptitiously replaced the tape recorder and some of his more valuable "loot."

The Rebbe, for his part, had no such trap set. He simply intended to wait for Mark to turn around. He held more discussions with him and continued to cater to his needs — physical and spiritual — and to try and kindle the dormant spark within Mark's [illegible] soul.

And that spark, like the sparks of so many other Jews, was eventually kindled by the warmth and affection and infinite patience of the Bostoner Rebbe.